Essential Statistics for Researchers

Tadhg L. O'Shea B.Comm M.Econ.Sc.

PUBLISHED BY:
Tadhg L. O'Shea
Institute of Technology Tralee
Dromtacker,
Tralee,
Co. Kerry,
Ireland

www.essentialstatistics.com

REVIEWER:
Dr. Sean Lacey
Cork Institute of Technology

PRODUCTION EDITOR:
Roisín McGuigan

COVER DESIGN:
Stephen & Elaine Scanlon

PRINTED AND BOUND BY:
Walsh Colour Print, Castleisland

ISBN: 978-0-9575059-0-2 (PB)

CONTENTS

ACKNOWLEDGEMENTS

The author would like to thank the following for their contributions and assistance in bringing this book to fruition:

Dr Joan Cleary
Marie Clifford
Dr Sean Connelly
Anne Corkery
Rosie Dempsey
Dr Pat Doody
Máiréad Enright
Martha Farrell
Dr Tom Farrelly
Margaret Finch
ITT computing staff
Carmel Kenny
Connie McHugh
Norma O'Brien
Martin O'Grady
Sheila O'Mahony
Dr Carol O'Shea
Jacqueline O'Neill
Marguerite O'Mahony
Aisling Sharkey
Derval Spring
Grainne Stack

All Institute of Technology Tralee

Stephen Burke	*Graphic Artist*
Prof. Christine Dancey	*University of East London*
Pat Dicker	*Royal College of Surgeons, Ireland*
Majella Forde	*Research Student, University of Limerick*
Prof. Paddy Hillyard	*Queens University Belfast*
Dr Sean Lacey	*Cork Institute of Technology*
Lynda M Mulcahy	*ITT Student*
Gregor Pituch	*Artist*
Donal O'Shea	*Primary school principal*
Eugene O'Sullivan	*Artist*
Stephen Scanlon	*Artist*
Elaine Scanlon	*Artist*
Carol Shanahan	*Tralee Regional Hospital*
Prof. David P. Doane	*Oakland University, USA*
Prof. Lori E. Seward	*University of Colorado*

The author wishes to thank Prof. David P. Doane and Prof. Lori E. Seward for their generosity of time and assistance, without which this guide would be materially diminished. The author is deeply indebted to Anne Corkery, Jacqueline O' Neill, Grainne Stack, Dr. Tom Farrelly, and Carol Shanahan for sharing their expertise and invaluable comments. A special thanks is offered to Majella Forde for designing the Marketing Plan for this project.

For my sons Robert and Ciarán

FOREWORD

Essential Statistics for Researchers is the ideal textbook for researchers and students taking statistics classes, as it emphasizes the rigour of statistical logic and critical thinking. This text is most suitable for a one or two semester course. Many people find statistics confusing, intimidating and even overwhelming, however this book will greatly simplify the essentials of statistical reasoning and analysis. Whether you're new to statistics or need to revise for an upcoming college exam, this book facilitates learning statistics in an efficient and friendly manner.

As you work your way through the book, you'll be able to tackle such concepts as graphical displays and numerical measures, sampling, principles of testing, and univariate, bivariate and multivariate inferential tests. The book is loaded with clear, practical advice illustrated by numerous invaluable examples. In total, it provides everything you need to analyse and interpret statistical data for improved classroom or on-the-job performance.

Dr Sean Connolly, Senior Lecturer in Statistics, IT Tralee

PREFACE

'If we knew what it was we were doing, it would not be called research, would it?'

Albert Einstein (1879–1955)

Welcome to ***Essential Statistics for Researchers***. I wrote this book with a variety of clients in mind, namely students, tutors and those brave souls who are in the midst of, or about to embark on, a piece of research. If you are a student or tutor then this text is ideal for a structured course of study. If you are pondering, or already engaged with a research topic, then I recommend you cherry pick in accordance with your essential needs.

Essential Statistics for Researchers was written to mimic the approach of a private tutor, who has the capacity to extract the *essential knowledge* from a discipline and deliver it to eager disciples with relative ease. I would caution the reader to dwell on the first two pages of the very first chapter. At the outset, the reader is alerted to the folly of proceeding along a path of research without an awareness of the challenges further down the road and the quality of information gathered, both of which will determine the value of the researcher's eventual analysis.

Essential Statistics for Researchers aims to protect those with a passion for research from the perils of adopting inappropriate research techniques and practices. The challenge for the researcher is to avoid the temptation to compromise on standards for the lure of preferred or desired outcomes. With this in mind, I bid you farewell on your journey and hope this guide will enlighten you along the way.

Tadhg L. O Shea

Chapter 1 – Foundations for Statistical Techniques

'Why are our days numbered and not, say, lettered?'

Woody Allen (1935 -)

1.1 Scope of Statistics

Each human being is unique. Yet each individual behaves like a sophisticated statistical instrument. We are each capable of receiving and processing sensory information and intuitively applying a spectrum of probabilities to help us decide on an array of alternative courses of actions. Consider the night before your Statistics exam; you are aware of the multiple competing topics that require your attention, and the diminishing amount of time available for revision along with the pressures you feel in the event of a failed attempt. These multiple thoughts force you to weigh up the likelihood of each topic appearing, followed by your decision to allocate the available time to the selected topics. Human beings are constantly applying statistical techniques to the daily challenges that life inevitably presents. A research project will also, amongst other things, involve collecting, processing and analysing information in an attempt to address a set of research questions. The focus in this book is to provide the researcher with the essential techniques for analysing data. Undertaking a research project generally involves a number of stages *(Figure 1.1)*.

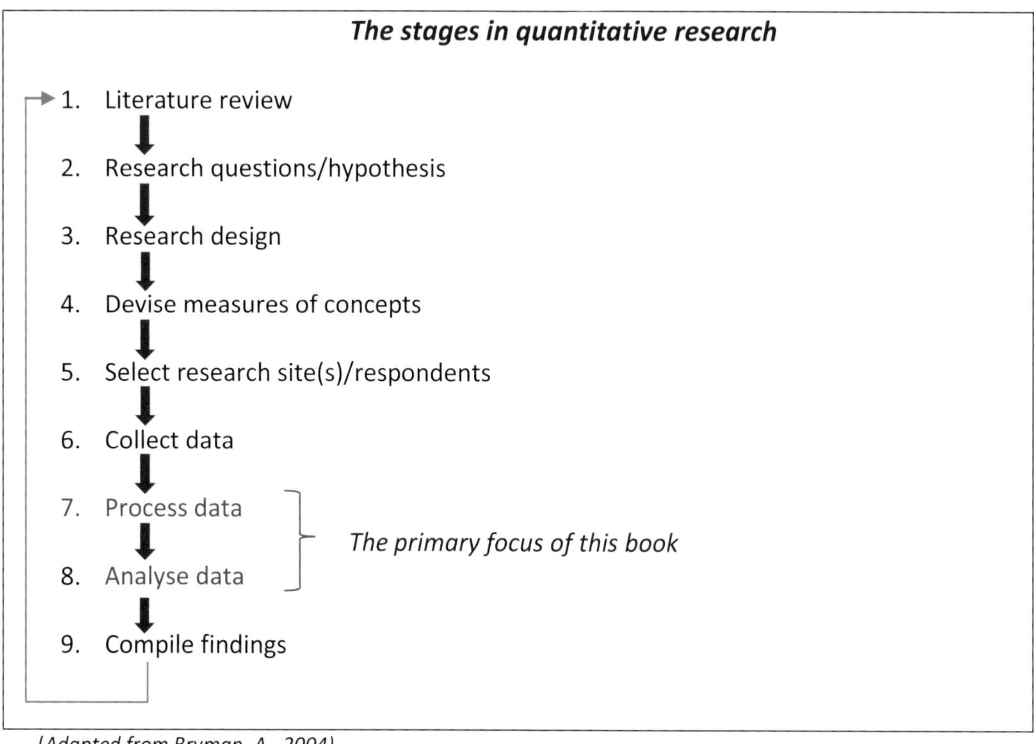

Figure 1.1 The stages in quantitative research

The stages of a research project appear as a logical linear sequence. However, whilst this sequence provides a useful order to a research project, stage eight must be considered in parallel with the early stages. Decisions made in the early stages of a research project impact on the sorts of analysis that can be conducted later on.

Whilst these stages are presented in a linear format, an appreciation of what is involved in the later stages will influence your approach in earlier stages. A common error made during the research process is to avoid all consideration of stage eight until the previous stages have been completed. An appreciation of stage eight implies an awareness of:

1. *The variety of statistical techniques available.*
2. *The steps that must be followed to allow proper application of these statistical techniques.*

Insufficient consideration of stage eight will severely restrict the type and quality of analysis carried out at the latter stage of the research project. The quality of analysis is also very dependent on the quality of the data or information collected. This point is not lost in the following extract from 'How to lie with Statistics' *(Huff, 1973)*;

> *'When you are a bit older,' a judge in India once told an eager young British civil servant 'you will not quote Indian statistics with that assurance. The government are very keen on amassing statistics – they collect them, add them, raise them to the nth power, take the cube root and prepare wonderful diagrams. But what you must never forget is that every one of those figures comes in the first instance from the chowty dar (village watchman), who just puts down what he damn pleases'*

Statistics, or the statistical method, may be regarded as a method of dealing with data. This definition embraces three key elements of the statistical method: Collecting, Summarising/Describing, and Making inferences from data. The subject matter of this book concerns the latter two elements of the statistical method *(Figure 1.2)*.

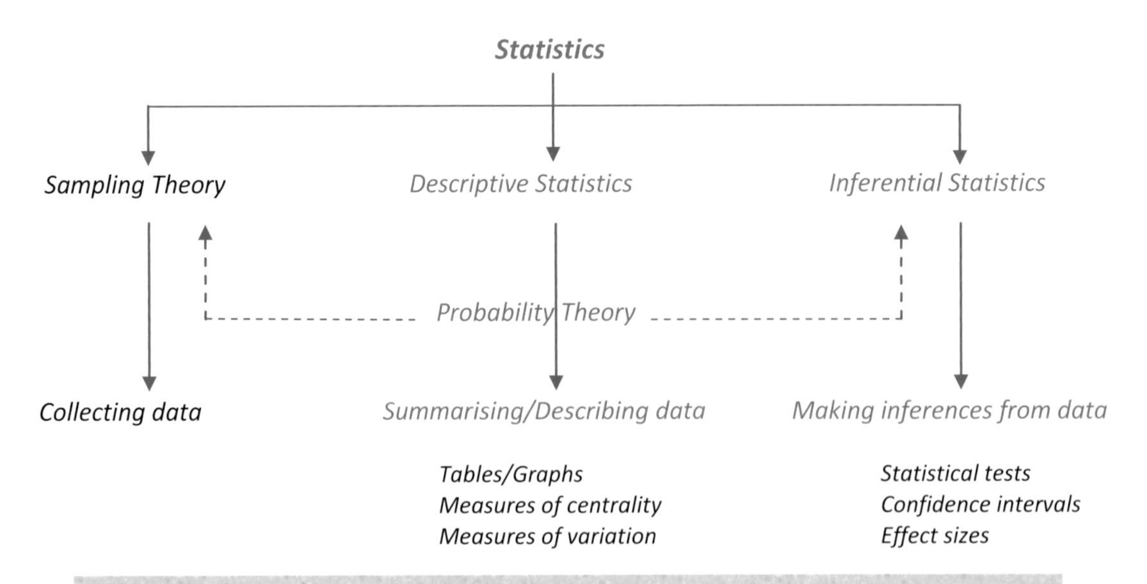

Figure 1.2 The scope of statistics

Statistics involves collecting sample data, summarising sample data and making inferences from sample data. Each of these three elements embraces the subject matter of probability.

1.2 Population versus Sample

One of the main aims of research is to generalise from a sample to the wider population. Therefore, we must know what the relevant population under investigation is. In statistical terms, a population may mean something quite different from the population of a country. In statistical research, the population refers to the *total number of units per time period* that we wish to focus on. The following populations may be of interest to us:

i. All flights out of Kerry airport in 2011
ii. All the current players in the English Premiership
iii. All the winners of the Champions League Cup (irrespective of competition names)
iv. All third level students currently studying Statistics

A sample is a slice taken from our population of interest. Our capacity to generalise from samples to populations is strengthened when the selected sample is truly representative of the population of interest *(Figure 1.3)*. As previously stated, the subject matter of this book concerns the latter two elements of the statistical method *(Figure 1.2)*. Descriptive statistical techniques will be used to summarise *(measures of centrality and variation)* and present *(graphical and tabular representations)* the collected sample data, whilst inferential statistical techniques will be used to make inferences or generalisations from the sample to the population under investigation.

In an ideal research study, we would like to survey the entire population, but it is more likely that we will be confined to using a sample. Therefore, we will frequently use a sample to gain an impression of the population under investigation. We can achieve this impression by calculating *sample statistics (sample mean, sample standard deviation, etc.)*, which we hope will closely mirror the corresponding *unknown population parameters (population mean, population standard deviation, etc.)*. These calculable *sample statistics* capture the essence of a sample, but our hope is that they mirror the essence of the population under study. *Sample statistics* are point estimates of their respective *population parameters.*

There will always be some doubt as to how well our sample represents the population of interest. Since we are working with a sample, it is very unlikely that the calculated sample mean *(sample average)* will exactly equal the *(possibly)* unknown population mean. The distance between the sample mean and population mean will often remain unknown and can be explained and referred to as *sampling error.* In statistical research, we will have to accept that some degree of *sampling error* will always be present since we are working with a sample. However, as the sample size gets closer to the population size, the degree of *sampling error* will fall. One of the primary functions of statistical testing *(the subject matter of later chapters)* is to ascertain whether or not *observed differences or observed associations* are too large to be solely attributed to *sampling error.*

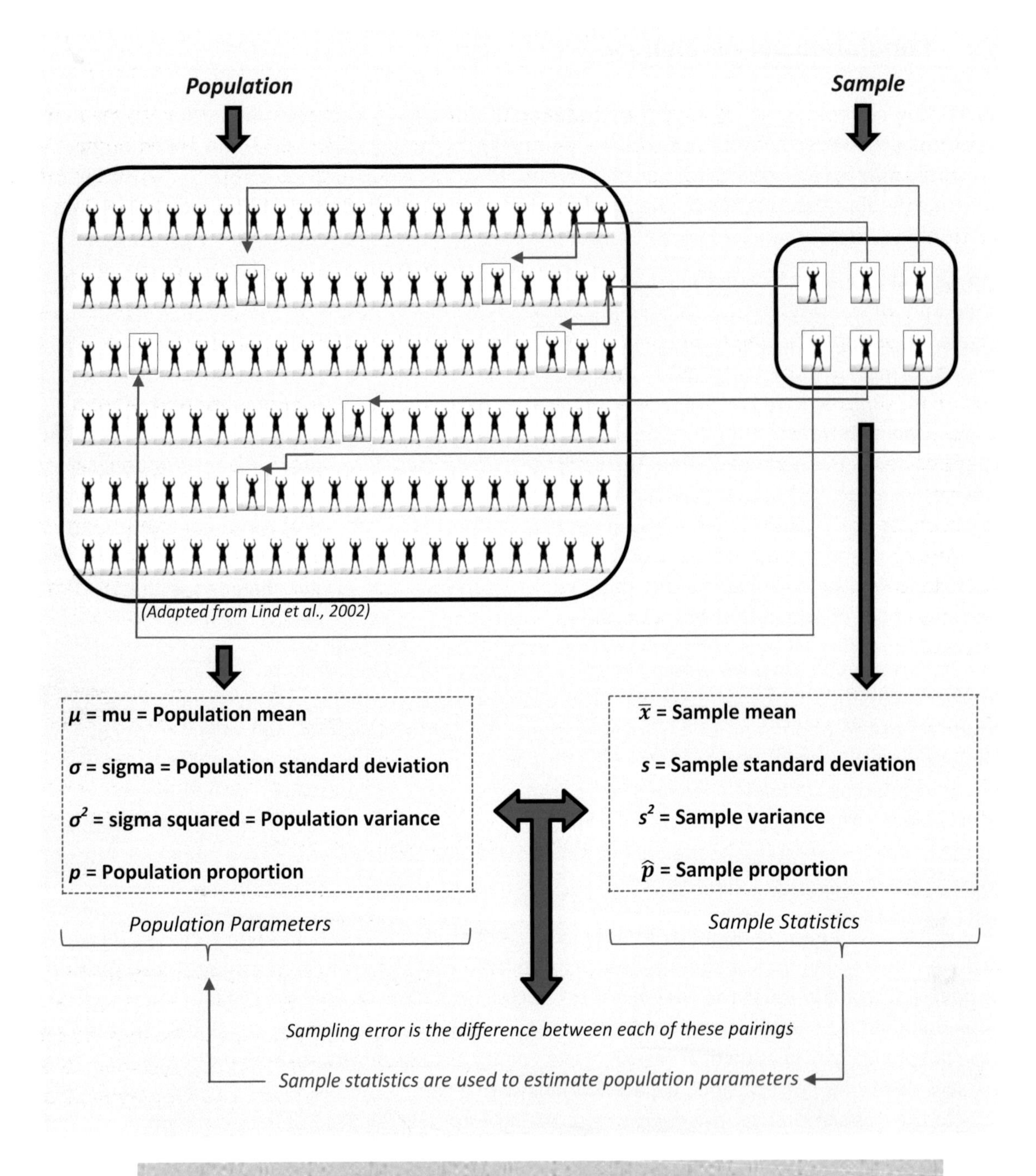

Figure 1.3 Population versus Sample

A sample is selected from the population. The mean (i.e. sample statistic) of the sample group is calculated. This sample statistic is an estimate of the population mean (i.e. population parameter). The difference between the sample estimate and the possibly unknown population parameter is the sampling error. As the sample size approaches the population size the degree of sampling error is likely to decrease.

1.3 Classification of variables/data types

Undertaking a research project may ultimately involve gathering *real* numbers/data or transforming gathered information into *coded* numerals/data. *Real* numbers and *coded* numerals constitute different types of data. Real numbers are a consequence of a measurement instrument/scale and coded numerals are tags or labels purposely assigned to facilitate quantitative analysis.

Suppose the research interest is to measure the earnings of Premiership football players. One component of earnings is the salary of players *(measured in euro)*. The salary *(in euro)* is one variable *(a variable is simply anything that can assume more than one value measurement)* selected to measure the earnings of players. A variable can be defined as a *universally accepted measure* for observing *(measuring)* some characteristic *(earnings of Premiership football players)* of a population of interest. A variable can take on any one of a set of different values. These values can either be ordinary numbers *(real numbers)* or categories *(coded numerals)*. The variable salary *(in euros)* will yield ordinary numbers *(real numbers)*. The salary of one player is often referred to as a *datum* or *observed value or measurement*. The salaries of a sample of players is often referred to as *data* or *observed values or measurements or data type*. Any reference to the term *data* in the remainder of this text will imply a collection of *observed values or measurements or data type* from a particular variable. Any reference to the term *dataset* will imply the collection of *observed values or measurements* from each of the several variables under investigation.

The researcher must begin research with, amongst other things, some consideration of the types of data that is to be collected. A naïve researcher, one who has not given due consideration to his data gathering requirements, may find himself 'shopping around' in the dark after the data has been collected. This shopping expedition amidst the plentiful descriptive and inferential statistical techniques will leave his task of analysis bewildering and fraught with serious potential errors. An understanding of alternative *classifications of variables/data types* will enable him to:

1. *Match variables/data types with appropriate descriptive statistical techniques.*
2. *Match variables/data types with appropriate inferential statistical techniques.*

Therefore, the researcher must ensure that he collects data types which are appropriate to those statistical techniques that will enable him to address the research questions chosen at the beginning of the project. A decision to employ particular statistical techniques will also depend on other necessary conditions being satisfied *(the subject matter of later chapters)*. Consider the following questionnaire which yields both *coded* numerals *(Q1, Q2 yield the 'coded' numerals 1 & 3)* and *real* numbers *(Q3, Q4 yield the 'real' numbers 19 & 190)*.

Questionnaire		*Coded Numerals & Real Numbers*
1. Are you male or female (please tick)		
Male __✓__ Female _____		~~1~~ 2
2. In which height category do you belong? (Please tick)		
Tall _____ Middle _____ Short __✓__		1 2 ~~3~~
3. What ambient indoor temperature do you prefer *(°C)*	_19°C__	19
4. What weight are you *(kg)*	_90kg_	90

Let's assume that this questionnaire is administered to a sample of people. Each question represents a variable type *(Q1 – Gender, Q2 – Categories of height, Q3 – Temp °C, Q4 – Weight in kg)* and each variable type will yield *data* or *a data type.* The researcher must be able to pigeonhole these different variables/data types using the following classification charts:

1. *General classification of variables/data types (Figure 1.4)*
2. *Stevens' classification of variables/data types (Figure 1.5)*

Using the *General classification* of variables/data types

1. *The variable Gender is classified under Qualitative/Categorical variables*
2. *The variable Categories of Height is classified under Qualitative/Categorical variables*
3. *The variable Temp °C is classified under Quantitative/Numerical variables – Continuous variables*
4. *The variable* Weight *(kg) is classified under Quantitative/Numerical variables - Continuous variables*

Using the *Stevens' classification* of variables/data types

1. *The variable Gender is classified under Qualitative/Categorical variables – Nominal variables*
2. *The variable Categories of Height is classified under Qualitative/Categorical variables – Ordinal variables*
3. *The variable Temp °C is classified under Quantitative/Numerical variables – Interval variables/Continuous*
4. *The* variable Weight *(kg) is classified under Quantitative/Numerical variables – Ratio variables/Continuous*

There is much debate about the merits of alternative classification of variables/data types; no one classification system is perfect. Whilst *Stevens' classification of variables/data types* is widely adopted, it does not enjoy universal acceptance. The *General classification of variables/data types* chart differentiates between qualitative *categorical* variables and quantitative *numerical* variables. The *Stevens' classification of variables/data types* chart subdivides qualitative *categorical* variables into nominal and ordinal scaled variables, and subdivides quantitative *numerical* variables into interval and ratio scaled variables.

Both classification charts enable the researcher to pigeonhole each question or variable type identified at the outset of their research project. Each chart classifies the variable *Gender* as a qualitative *categorical* variable but Stevens' typology further classifies *Gender* as a nominal scaled variable. *Gender* is a dichotomous/alternative variable *(a qualitative variable with only two values).* An important criticism of classification systems/charts is their failure to classify or accommodate certain variable/data types. In practice, researchers may decide to assume/debate that some data types they collect achieves a 'higher level' classification. This liberty allows them to employ more powerful statistical test procedures. The *Stevens' classification chart* will be adopted in this text.

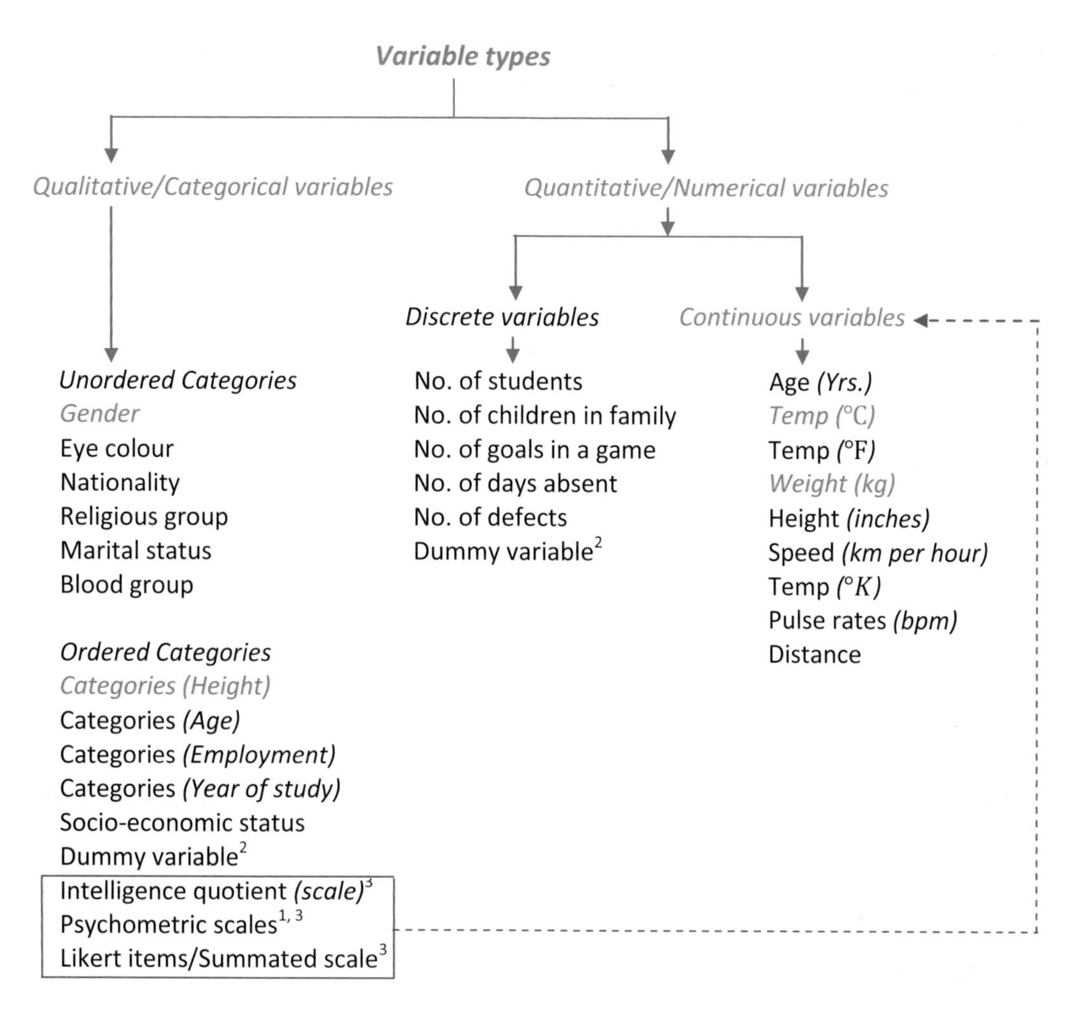

---- *Many researchers assume/debate that data derived from these scales is continuous. They work with the assumption that the underlying variable is conceptually continuous (Dancey & Reidy, 2004)*

Figure 1.4 General classification of variables/data types

This classification chart enables the researcher to pigeonhole each question or variable type identified at the outset of a research project.

1. *Psychometrics is a branch of psychology which deals with the measurement of mental traits, capacities, and processes.*
2. *A dummy variable is classified as qualitative when we assign 1 to a positive outcome category (yes) and 0 to a negative outcome category (no). A dummy variable is classified as quantitative when we count the number of positive and negative outcomes to an experiment or question. In this context, if we subject the two possible values (0 and 1) to the 'subtraction test' (see section 1.4) the answer has a quantitative meaning i.e. one more positive outcome (Nieuwenhuis 2009).*
3. *A scale (designed to measure some underlying variable which is not directly measurable e.g. a self-confidence), consists of a number of items/questions (each item has multiple response options). An individual is assigned a score from the summation of his responses to these scale items.*

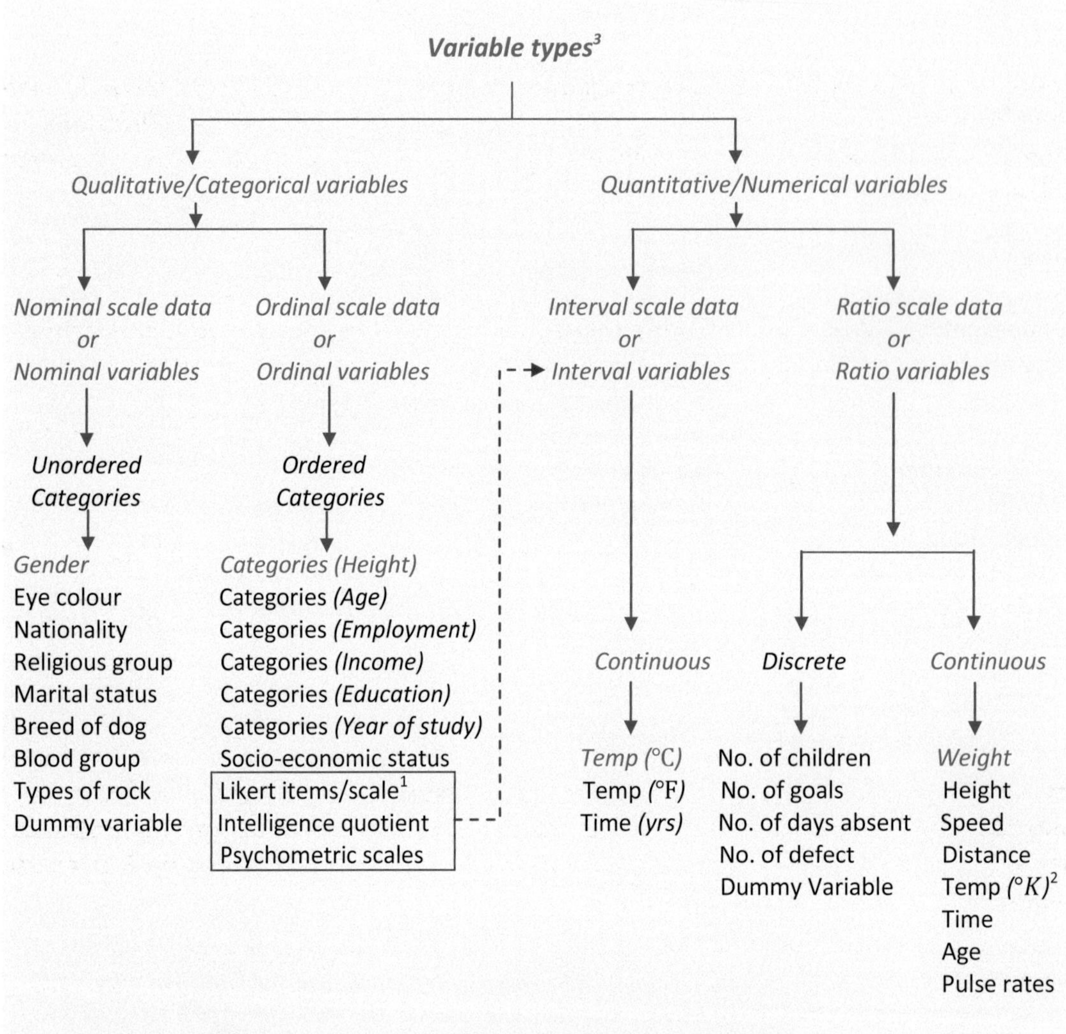

Figure 1.5 Stevens' classification of variables/data types

This classification chart enables the researcher to pigeonhole each question or variable type identified at the outset of a research project.

1. *Intervals between the data points cannot be presumed equal even though researchers frequently assume that they are.*
2. *Kelvin temperature scale has a non-arbitrary point of absolute zero. Both the Centigrade and Fahrenheit scales of temperature employ an arbitrary zero point*
3. *SPSS (Statistical Package for the Social Sciences) simply uses the following three levels of measurement/classification (Nominal data, Ordinal data and Scale data). SPSS does not distinguish Interval data and Ratio data (Kinnear & Gray, 2011).*

1.4 Distinguishing variables/data types

The researcher must be able to classify all variables/data types in order to correctly match variables/data types with appropriate statistical techniques at a later stage. Therefore, it is essential to understand the difference between the different types of variables/data. This section should be read with reference to the classification charts *(Figures 1.4, 1.5)*.

1. Qualitative Variable Versus Quantitative Variable

To decide whether a variable/data type/question should be classified as qualitative or quantitative, consider the following check.

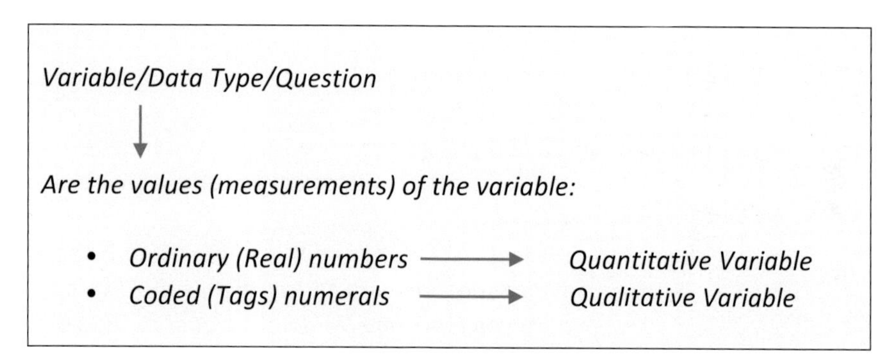

Whilst it is appropriate to calculate the *average or mean* value for values derived from a quantitative variable, this practice should be resisted with data values derived from qualitative variables. The difference between qualitative and quantitative variables can also be decided using the *subtraction test* and/or the *interval test.*

Subtraction Test

a. A variable can be classified as qualitative if the difference *(subtraction)* between its values makes no sense. The variable *Gender* has two values *(coded numerals)* and if these values are subtracted from each other, the result has no meaningful interpretation. The variable *Height (kg)* has three values *(coded numerals)* and if these values are subtracted from each other, the result is meaningless. *Coded numerals* are simply conveniently assigned tags which are used to describe the categories.

Gender	*Values*	*Subtraction doesn't make sense*
Male	*1*	*2 minus 1 = 1 (cannot be meaningfully interpreted)*
Female	*2*	

Height	*Values*	*Subtraction doesn't make sense*
Tall	*1*	*3 minus 2 = 1 (cannot be meaningfully interpreted)*
Middle	*2*	*2 minus 1 = 1 (cannot be meaningfully interpreted)*
Short	*3*	

b. A variable can be classified as quantitative if the difference between its values makes sense. The variables *Weight (kg)* and *Temp* °C will result in ordinary numbers *(real numbers)*. Subtracting values for each of these variables makes sense.

Weight	*Values*	*Subtraction does make sense*
John	*80 kg*	*80 kg minus 75 kg = 5 kg*
Jim	*75 kg*	

Temp °C	*Values*	*Subtraction does make sense*
Paris	*36.8 °C*	*36.8 °C minus 20.8 °C = 16.0 °C*
Dublin	*20.8 °C*	

Interval Test

a. A variable can be classified as qualitative if we cannot say with certainty that the intervals along the response categories *(which are assigned coded numerals)* are of equal distance.

Height	*Values*	*Interval distances cannot be declared to be equal*
Tall	*1*	*We cannot say with certainty that the distance*
Middle	*2*	*between 'Tall' and 'Middle' is equal to the distance*
Short	*3*	*between 'Middle' and 'Short'*

Opinion	*Values*	*Interval distances cannot be declared to be equal*
Very Satisfied	*1*	
Satisfied	*2*	*We cannot say with certainty that the distance*
Neutral	*3*	*between 'Very Satisfied' and 'Satisfied' is equal to the*
Dissatisfied	*4*	*distance between 'Dissatisfied' and 'Very Dissatisfied'*
Very Dissatis...	*5*	

b. A variable can be classified as quantitative if we can say with certainty that the intervals along the response categories *(which are assigned real numerals)* are of equal distance.

Weight	*Values*	*Interval distances can be declared to be equal*
Tom	*80 kg*	*We can say with certainty that the distance between*
Tim	*75 kg*	*80 kg and 75 kg is equal to the distance between 75 kg*
Terry	*70 kg*	*and 70 kg*

Temp °C	*Values*	*Interval distances can be declared to be equal*
Dubai	*40 °C*	*We can say with certainty that the distance between*
Rome	*30 °C*	*40 °C and 30 °C is equal to the distance between 30 °C*
Dublin	*20 °C*	*and 20 °C*

2. Nominal, Ordinal, Interval and Ratio scaled variables

To decide whether a variable/data type/question should be classified as Nominal, Ordinal, Interval or Ratio, consider the following check.

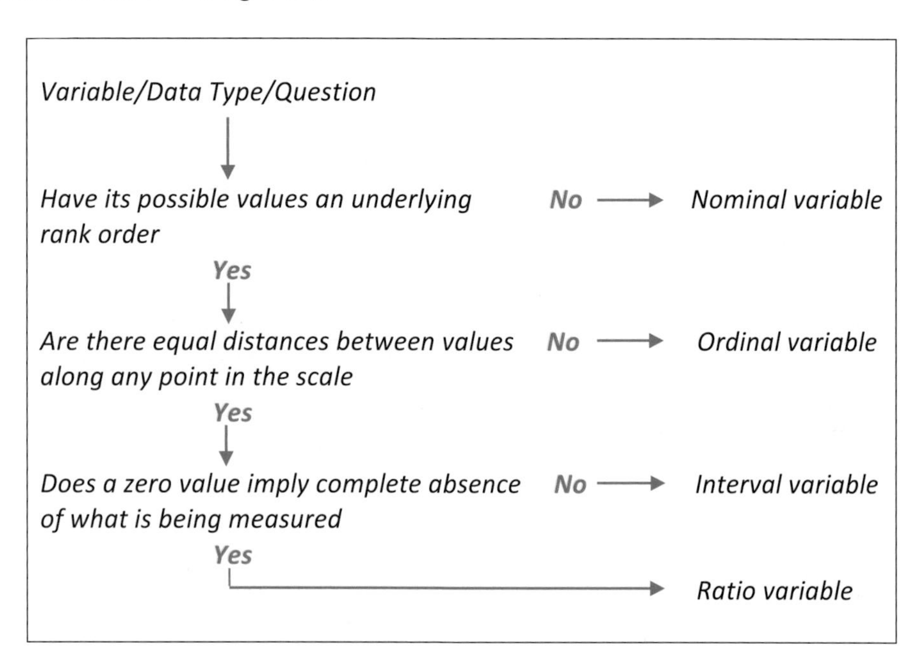

Nominal Variable Versus Ordinal Variable – The difference between nominal variable and ordinal variable can be decided using the *Order Test*.

Order Test

A variable can be classified as a nominal or nominal scaled if there is no underlying natural order to its possible values *(coded numerals)*. The variable *Gender* has two possible values *(coded numerals)* but it would be incorrect to suggest that they could be placed in some order. A variable can be classified as ordinal or ordinal scaled if there is an underlying natural order to its possible values *(coded numerals)*. The variable *Height* which has three possible values *(1 = Tall, 2 = Middle, 3 = Short)* has an underlying natural order.

Interval Variable Versus Ratio Variable – The difference between an interval variable and a ratio variable can be decided using the *Ratio Test*.

Ratio Test

It is incorrect to state that the temperature in Dubai *(40* °C) is twice the temperature in Dublin *(20* °C) because 0 °C is not an absolute zero temperature *(a value of 0* °C *does not mean the complete absence of heat and is merely the point at which water freezes at sea level)*. Therefore the variable *Temperature* °C fails the *Ratio Test* and will consequently be classified as interval or interval scaled.

The zero in an interval scale is artificially positioned rather than being an absolute zero. It does make sense to state that Peter *(72'')* is twice as tall as Wayne *(36'')* because a height of 0'' is an absolute zero height *(a height of 0'' does mean an absolute zero height)*. Therefore *Height (inches)* passes the *Ratio Test* and will consequently be classified as ratio or ratio scaled. Whilst values below zero can be assigned for interval scaled variable, this is not so for ratio scaled variables.

	Height (inches)	*Temperature* °C	
	60	60	
	50	50	
	40	40	
	30	30	
	20	20	
	10	10	
Absolutely no height ←	0	0	→ *Some heat is present at 0*
This is the true zero point		- 10	
		- 20	
		- 30	
		.	
		.	
		.	
		- 273.15	→ *Absolutely no heat*
			This is the true zero point

A height of 60'' is twice the height of 30'' since *Height (Inches)* has a true zero point *(absolute zero)*. However, a temperature of 60 °C is not twice as warm as a temperature of 30 °C since *Temperature* °C has an artificially positioned zero point. What we can say is that 60 °C is 1.1 times warmer than 30°C:

Height (Inches)
60'': 30''
2: 1

Temperature °C
60 °C: 30 °C
60 + 273.15: 30 + 273.15
333.15: 303.15
1.1: 1

With a ratio variable or ratio scaled data it would be correct to state that the ratio of 40 inches to 20 inches *(2:1)* is equal to the ratio of 20 inches to 10 inches *(2:1)*. However, with an Interval variable or interval scaled data it would be incorrect to state that the ratio of 40 °C to 20 °C is equal to 20 °C to 10 °C. If we convert these temperatures using the true zero point of temperature, the ratios would read 313:293 and 293:283. These ratios are not equal.

3. Discrete Variable Versus Continuous Variable

If you have declared a variable to be *ratio scaled* then the next task is *to* decide whether the *ratio scaled* variable should be classified as discrete or continuous, consider the following check.

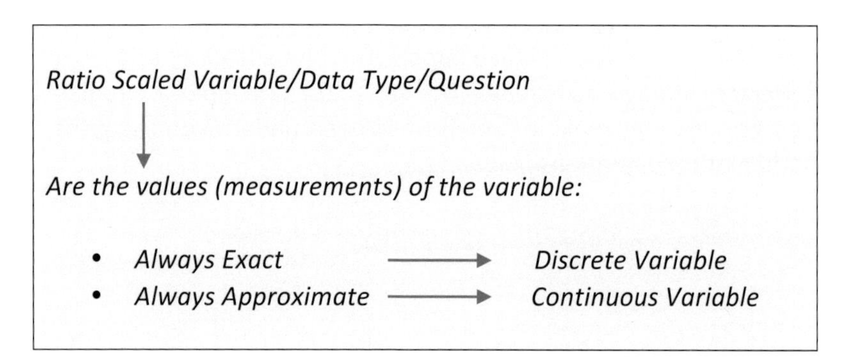

Ratio scaled variables can be classified as either discrete or continuous. A variable can be classified as *Continuous* if it can take on any value *(i.e. an infinite number of values or real numbers)* in any selected interval. This is a conceptual definition that sets aside the restrictions of measurement precision. The term *continuous* implies a seamless continuum *(of values or real numbers)* in which there are no gaps or incremental steps between values. The reality is that we live in a world where all variables are, strictly speaking, *discrete (there are gaps/incremental steps between values)* because of the limitations of measurement instruments. Therefore, to recognise and classify a variable as continuous we need to design a working definition of what constitutes both a continuous variable and a discrete variable.

a. A variable can be classified as continuous if its values *(measurements)* are always approximate *(Runyon and Haber, 1976)* and that it is conceivable that a more sensitive measurement instrument can further increase the accuracy of its measurements *(weight of a new-born baby in kilograms to two decimals).*

b. A variable can be classified as discrete if its values *(measurements)* are always exact *(Runyon and Haber, 1976)* and fully measured *(number of children in the family, the number of white blood cells in 1ml of blood, the number of bedrooms in the house, the number of symptoms of an illness a person has).*

1.5 Hierarchy of variables/data types

In the previous sections *(1.3, 1.4)* we learned how to classify variables/data types. Two classification charts *(Figures 1.4, 1.5)* were presented to facilitate the exercise. In addition to the skill of classifying variables/data types into their appropriate classifications, we can rank variables/data types in terms of their relative importance and usefulness. This section will focus on *Stevens' classification of variables/data types*. The variables/data types are ranked in terms of their importance and usefulness. This ranking exercise has been undertaken using the criteria 'number of permissible mathematical operations' *(Figure 1.6)*.

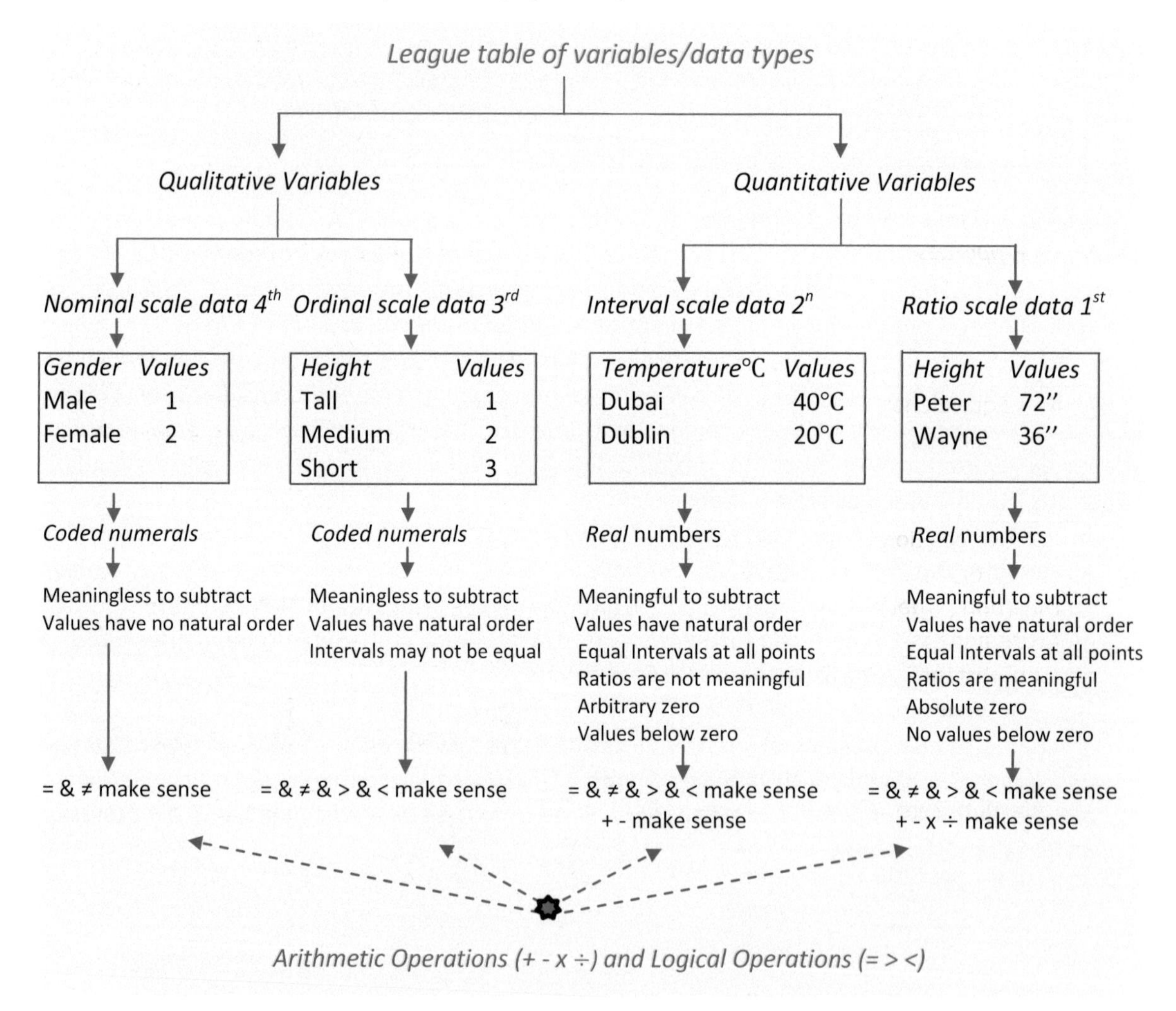

Figure 1.6 Hierarchy of data – Stevens' classification

This chart is a league table of data types. At the top of the table sits ratio scaled data. Ratio scaled data allows us to undertake more mathematical operations compared to the other data types. Nominal scaled data sits at the bottom of the table since the data is merely unordered coded numerals.

Qualitative variables/data types

If we collect data *(measurements)* for variables that are classified as *nominal variables* or *nominal scaled data* then this collected data *(measurements)* constitutes a very low level of measurement. *Nominal scaled data* is placed in 4th position in our league table of measurements. Whilst we can assign numerical values to represent the categories *(Male = 1, Female = 2)* of a nominal variable, the numbers are merely coded numerals *(solely indicating that the categories of this variable are different to each other)* and have no quantitative properties *(Figure 1.7)*. However, if we collect data for variables that are classified as *ordinal variables* then these measurements constitute a relatively higher level of measurement. This *ordinal scaled data* is placed in 3rd position by virtue of its additional permissible mathematical operations. Whilst we assign coded numerals to the categories of such variables, these codes reflect both a difference and an underlying natural order between the categories.

Properties	Nominal Scale *Gender* Male = 1 Female = 2	Ordinal Scale *Height* Tall = 1 Medium = 2 Short = 3	Interval Scale *Temperature (°C)*	Ratio Scale *Weight (kg)*
Non-Equivalence or Difference (≠)	2 ≠ 1	3 ≠ 2 ≠ 1	30°C ≠ 20°C	180 ≠ 170
Relative position or Direction (order) (< and >)	Nominal scale does not qualify	3 < 2 < 1 or 1 > 2 > 3	20°C < 30°C or 30°C > 20°C	170 < 180 or 180 > 170
Equi-Distant Intervals (+ and -)	Nominal scale does not qualify	Ordinal scale does not qualify	30°C - 20°C = 20°C - 10°C	180 - 170 = 170 - 160
Absolute Zero (+ - x ÷)	Nominal scale does not qualify	Ordinal scale does not qualify	Interval scale does not qualify	180 : 90 = 2 : 1

Figure 1.7 Hierarchy of data – Permissible mathematical operators

This chart looks at each of Stevens' categories and distinguishes them with respect to permissible mathematical properties. The data values derived from the variable Gender are merely coded numerals - there is a difference between a male and a female but male is not greater than or lower than female.

Quantitative variables/data types

If we collect data for variables that are classified as *Interval* and/or *Ratio variables,* then these measurements achieve 2nd and/or 1st place respectively in our league table *(Figure 1.6)*. The measurements we gather associated with these variables are *real* numbers and allow the researcher to employ a wider variety of statistical techniques compared to studies that restrict data collection to lower order levels of measurement. The only difference between i*nterval and ratio variables* relates to the appointment of an arbitrary zero point to the interval scale of measurement.

Once you have mastered the art of classifying variables, then you can match different variable/data types with appropriate statistical techniques

1.6 Distinguishing data types – *A note on the debate*

In practice, many researchers assume/debate that variables/data types which ought to be classified as qualitative achieve the classification *continuous* in the context of the general classification *(Figure 1.4)* or achieve the classification *interval scale* in the context of Stevens' classification *(Figure 1.5)*.

General classification of variables/data types (Figure 1.4)

Research studies which focus on the measurement of *attitudes, mental states [anxiety, stress, and self-esteem, intelligence etc.]* involve variables which are conceptually *continuous*, but which cannot be measured directly. Consider the following scenarios:

Scenario 1 – A variable measured using a single Likert item which ought to be classified as qualitative

Consider a conceptually *continuous* variable *(opinion of students)* which is measured using a *single Likert item* with 5 response categories *(the number of response categories used can vary)*.

'The lecturer explains things very clearly'

Strongly Disagree	*Disagree*	*Neutral*	*Agree*	*Strongly Agree*
1	*2*	*3*	*4*	*5*

Each respondent is asked to select one of the ordered response categories. The collection of measurements or data derived from this Likert item is classified as continuous by many researchers. This assumption leads those researchers to entertain the possible usage of higher order statistical test procedures *(parametric in preference to non-parametric test procedures)*. It is difficult to see how normally distributed data can arise in a single Likert-type item. According to *Clason and Dormody (1994, pp. 31-35) 'The data will frequently be skewed, and often these items do not capture the true limits of the attitude/opinion. Statistical procedures that meaningfully answer the research questions and maintain the richness of the data, and are not subject to scaling debates, should be the methods of choice in analysing Likert-type items'.*

Scenario 2 – A variable which is measured using a summated scale (Likert scale) ought to be classified as Qualitative or at best Quantitative-Discrete

There are numerous validated scales *(summated scales)* available which attempt to measure conceptually *continuous* variables that cannot be measured directly. Consider a conceptually *continuous* variable *(perceived stress)* which is measured using the *20 item Perceived Stress Scale (Cohen et al., 1983)*. Each respondent is asked to select one of the 5 ordered response categories for each of the 20 items. The respondent's total score is derived by summing all the responses to the 20 *items*. The collection of scores *(measurements or data)* derived from this *Perceived Stress Scale* is classified as *continuous* by many researchers. Whilst the individual items ought to be classified as qualitative/categorical *(assigned coded numerals to the 5 response categories)*, the summated scale takes on the appearance of a quantitative-discrete variable. The range of possible total scores on this *Perceived Stress Scale* is from 20 to 100 and total scores can only increase in increments of whole units, for example 20, 21, 22 etc.

Scenario 3 – A variable which ought to be classified as Quantitative-Discrete

In practice, many researchers assume/debate that variables/data types which ought to be classified as *quantitative-discrete,* achieve the classification *continuous*. They argue that if the *quantitative-discrete variable* can assume any one of a large number of values within a specified range, then they are willing to declare the variable *continuous*. Examples might include: *number of internet hits per hour, number of visitors to cultural and recreational sites per day.*

Stevens' classification of variables/data types (Figure 1.5)

Consider the following scenarios:

Scenario 1 – A variable which is measured using a single Likert item ought to be classified as Ordinal

Consider the variable *(opinion or evaluations of students)* which is measured using a *single Likert item* with 5 response categories *(the number of response categories used can vary).*

'The lecturer explains things very clearly'

Strongly Disagree	*Disagree*	*Neutral*	*Agree*	*Strongly Agree*
1	*2*	*3*	*4*	*5*

Each respondent is asked to select one of the ordered response categories. The collection of *measurements or data* derived from this *Likert item* is classified as *interval-scaled* by many researchers *(Blaikie, 2003)*. However, *Cohen et al. (2000)* contend that it is *'illegitimate to infer that the intensity of feeling between 'strongly disagree' and 'disagree' is equivalent to the intensity of feeling between other categories on the Likert scale'.*

Scenario 2 – A variable which is measured using a summated scale (Likert scale) ought to be classified as Ordinal

In practice, many researchers are willing to assume that the data derived from summated scales *(Likert scale)* achieve interval measurement. If the conceptually *continuous* variable could be measured directly then the measurement level that the variable could reach would be, at best, Interval *(Clason and Dormody, 1994)*. According to *Goldstein and Hersen (1984) 'The level of scaling obtained from the Likert procedure is rather difficult to determine. The scale is clearly at least ordinal. Those persons with the higher level properties in the natural variable are expected to get higher scores than those persons from lower properties. . . In order to achieve an Interval scale, the properties on the scale variable have to correspond to differences in the trait on the natural variable. Since it seems unlikely that the categories formed by the misalignment of the five responses will all be equal, the Interval scale assumption seems unlikely'.*

1.7 MCQs and Solutions

1. The area of statistics which involves Summarising/Describing sample data is referred to as:

   (a) Sampling theory
   (b) Descriptive statistics
   (c) Inferential statistics
   (d) Probability theory

2. The area of statistics which involves using a sample to make inferences about a population*(s)* is referred to as:

   (a) Sampling theory
   (b) Descriptive statistics
   (c) Inferential statistics
   (d) Probability theory

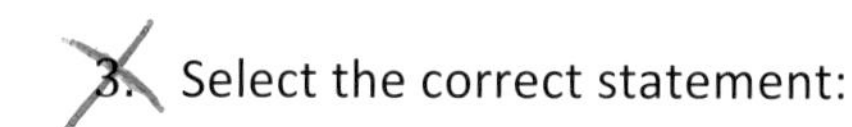

3. Select the correct statement:

   (a) The distance/difference between the sample mean and the population mean is referred to as sampling error
   (b) The distance/difference between the sample mean and the population mean is always known
   (c) Population parameters are used to estimate sample statistics
   (d) As the sample size increases then the sampling error also increases

4. Which of the following constitutes a qualitative variable:

   (a) Gender
   (b) Number of children per family
   (c) Temperature (°C)
   (d) Weight *(kg)*

5. Which of the following constitutes a quantitative variable:

   (a) Gender
   (b) Colour of eyes
   (c) Marital Status
   (d) Weight *(kg)*

6. Which level of measurement is associated with Height *(inches)*:

   (a) Nominal
   (b) Ordinal
   (c) Ratio
   (d) Interval

7. 'Kingdom Air' claims that $< 1\%$ of its scheduled flights out of Knock airport depart late. From a random sample of 250 flights, 1.5% were found to depart late. The population of interest is:

   (a) All flights from 'Kingdom Air' out of Knock airport
   (b) All flights from 'Kingdom Air' out of all Irish airports
   (c) The 250 flights that have been recorded for the study
   (d) All flights from all airlines out of Knock airport

8. In exercise 7, how would you describe the finding '1.5%':

   (a) It is a population parameter
   (b) It is a sample statistic
   (c) It is a stated target set by 'Kingdom Air'
   (d) None of the above

9. I am interested in examining earnings dissimilarities in the English Premiership. I wish to include wages, sponsorship deals, etc. in my assessment of total earnings per player. Assuming such detail is unavailable. I will therefore select a sample of players and record their total earnings. The population of interest is:

   (a) All players in the English Premiership
   (b) All players in English football *(i.e. English Premiership + 1st & 2nd & 3rd & 4th Leagues)*
   (c) The sample of players that I select
   (d) All players in UK football *(i.e. including England + Scotland + Wales)*

10. When a researcher asks one person a question, to elicit their attitude to corporal punishment for school children, this produces a response. If the researcher asks 500 people then he/she will get a set of responses. This set of responses is referred to as:

   (a) A datum
   (b) A measurement
   (c) An observed value
   (d) Measurements or observed values

11. The Champions League cup *(formerly The European Cup)*, is restricted to European football. I wish to present an overview of the success (number of times the cup was won by all individual countries) of all countries in this competition. The population of interest is:

(a) All winners of the cup *(irrespective of what the competition was called)*
(b) All winners of the Champions League Cup
(c) All winners of the European Cup
(d) None of the above

12. Academic staff at an Institute of Higher Learning were asked the following questions. How might you classify the data collected from these questions? Select the correct option below:

i. Did you attend the President's Annual Address?
ii. How many exam scripts did you correct last Semester?
iii. How satisfied are you with the new staff photocopying service?
iv. How long does it take you to prepare a lecture (in minutes)?

(a) Numerical, Categorical, Numerical, Categorical
(b) Categorical, Numerical, Categorical, Numerical
(c) Categorical, Numerical, Numerical, Categorical
(d) Numerical, Categorical, Categorical, Numerical

13. Academic staff at an Institute of Higher Learning were asked the following questions. How might you classify the data collected from these questions? Select the correct option below:

i. Did you attend the President's Annual Address?
ii. How many exam scripts did you correct last Semester?
iii. How satisfied are you with the new staff photocopying service?
iv. How long does it take you to prepare a lecture?

(a) Qualitative, Quantitative, Qualitative, Quantitative
(b) Quantitative, Qualitative, Quantitative, Qualitative
(c) Qualitative, Quantitative, Quantitative, Qualitative
(d) Quantitative, Qualitative, Qualitative, Quantitative

14. Academic staff at an Institute of Higher Learning were asked the following questions. How might you classify the data collected from these questions? Select the correct option below:

    i. Did you attend the President's Annual Address?
    ii. How many exam scripts did you correct last Semester?
    iii. How satisfied are you with the new staff photocopying service?
    iv. How long does it take you to prepare a lecture?

    (a) Nominal, Ratio (Discrete), Ordinal, Ratio (Continuous)
    (b) Nominal, Ratio (Continuous), Ordinal, Ratio (Discrete)
    (c) Ordinal, Ratio (Continuous), Nominal, Ratio (Discrete)
    (d) Ratio (Discrete), Nominal, Ratio (Continuous), Ordinal

15. Which of the following is incorrect:

    (a) Gender is a dichotomous variable
    (b) The centigrade temperature scale employs an arbitrary zero point
    (c) Ratio scale data are measured on scales that have an non-arbitrary point of absolute zero
    (d) The values collected for a continuous variable are exact measurements

16. Which of the following is incorrect:

    (a) The *Subtraction Test* helps to explain the difference between quantitative and qualitative variables
    (b) The *Ratio Test* helps to explain the difference between Ratio and Interval level data
    (c) Levels of data follow the following hierarchy: 1st = Ratio, 2nd = Interval, 3rd = Ordinal, 4th = Nominal
    (d) The ordinal scale of measurement has the property of equidistant intervals

17. Which of the following is incorrect:

    (a) The values of a continuous variable are always approximate
    (b) The values of a discrete variable are always exact
    (c) ~~A Likert scale definitely reached the Interval scale of measurement~~
    (d) ~~The absolute zero point is also the true zero point~~

18. Which of the following is incorrect:

    (a) μ = mu = Population Mean
    (b) σ = sigma = Population Standard Deviation
    (c) σ^2 = sigma squared = Population Variance
    (d) s^2 = Sample Standard Deviation

19. Which of the following is incorrect:

(a) Qualitative variable = Categorical variable
(b) Quantitative variable = Numerical variable
(c) Ratio variable can be either discrete or continuous
(d) ~~Nominal and ordinal variables are distinguished by subjecting their values to the *Ratio Test*~~

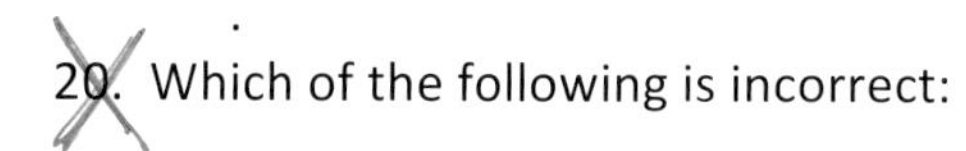

20. Which of the following is incorrect:

(a) A primary function of statistical testing is to ascertain whether or not observed differences of observed associations are too large to be solely attributed to sampling error
(b) The researcher must be able to classify all variables/data types in order to correctly match variables/data types with appropriate statistical techniques
(c) A dichotomous variable is also called a dummy variable
(d) If one of the two values of a dichotomous variable is coded as 1 and the other as 0, the variable is called a dummy variable

MCQ Solutions

1. (b)	6. (c)	11. (a)	16. (d)
2. (c)	7. (a)	12. (b)	17. (c)
3. (a)	8. (b)	13. (a)	18. (d)
4. (a)	9. (a)	14. (a)	19. (d)
5. (d)	10. (d)	15. (d)	20. (c)

1.8 IBM SPSS Statistics 20 – *Creating your data file*

Consider the following questionnaire which contains a selection of questions that represent a variety of variable types. Assume this questionnaire has been administered to a random sample of 100 people. The researcher must input the completed questionnaires into SPSS.

Sample Questionnaire **Coded Numerals & Real Numbers**

Qualitative – Categorical nominal variable (unordered categories)

1. Are you

   1. Male _____
   2. Female _____ 1 2

Qualitative – Categorical nominal variable (unordered categories)

2. Do you

   1. Smoke _____
   2. Not smoke _____ 1 2

Qualitative – Categorical ordinal variable (ordered categories)

3. In which age category do you belong?

   1. < 20 _____
   2. 20 - 35 _____
   3. > 35 _____ 1 2 3

Qualitative – Categorical ordinal variable (ordered categories)

4. *'The airline company were a pleasure to travel with' (Strike off your preferred choice)*

Strongly Disagree	*Disagree*	*Neutral*	*Agree*	*Strongly Agree*
1	2	3	4	5

1 2 3 4 5

Quantitative – Numerical Interval variable (continuous)

5. What ambient indoor temperature do you prefer _____

Quantitative – Numerical Interval variable (continuous)

6. What ambient outdoor temperature do you prefer on holiday _____

Quantitative – Numerical Ratio variable (continuous)

7. What weight are you _____

Quantitative – Numerical Ratio variable (continuous)

8. What height are you _____

Quantitative – Numerical Ratio variable (discrete)

9. How many children do you have _____

The following is an example of a fully completed questionnaire. This questionnaire was filled in by the first male in the sample. He is a non-smoker and falls into the over 35 age category.

Questionnaire **Coded Numerals & Real Numbers**

Qualitative – Categorical nominal variable (unordered categories)

1. Are you

    1. Male __✓__
    2. Female ______ ~~1~~ 2

Qualitative – Categorical nominal variable (unordered categories)

2. Do you

    1. Smoke ______
    2. Not smoke __✓__ 1 ~~2~~

Qualitative – Categorical ordinal variable (ordered categories)

3. In which age category do you belong?

    1. < 20 ______
    2. 20 - 35 ______
    3. > 35 __✓__ 1 2 ~~3~~

Qualitative – Categorical ordinal variable (ordered categories)

4. *'The airline company were a pleasure to travel with' (Strike off your preferred choice)*

Strongly Disagree	*Disagree*	*Neutral*	*Agree*	*Strongly Agree*	
1	2	3	4	~~5~~	1 2 3 4 ~~5~~

Quantitative – Numerical Interval variable (continuous)

5. What ambient indoor temperature do you prefer _21°C_ 21

Quantitative – Numerical Interval variable (continuous)

6. What ambient outdoor temperature do you prefer on holiday _28°C_ 28

Quantitative – Numerical Ratio variable (continuous)

7. What weight are you _82kg_ 82

Quantitative – Numerical Ratio variable (continuous)

8. What height are you _72"__ 72

Quantitative – Numerical Ratio variable (discrete)

9. How many children do you have __4___ 4

IBM SPSS Statistics 20 – Creating your data file

Step 1 – When you start up *IBM SPSS Statistics 20* select *Type in data* and click *OK*.

Data View Editor

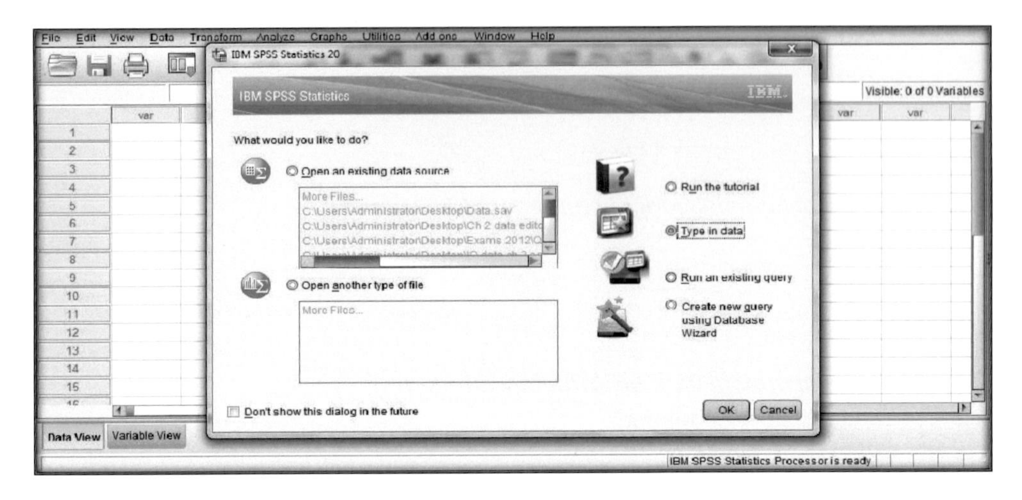

Step 2 – Click *Variable View* at the bottom left corner of the data editor to reveal a new screen where each row will represent a variable. The first question in the questionnaire represents the variable *Gender*. The variable *Gender* will feature in the first row of *Variable View*. Fill in each cell in the first row as shown by clicking on each cell. The cell *Name* will not allow a space between letters or words and variable names can be abbreviated. The variable name entered into the cell *Gender* will appear in the statistical output, therefore, it is preferable that the full variable name is entered in this cell. The cell *Type* defaults to numeric. The cell *decimals* can be set at zero unless there are decimals in the data collected. The cell *Missing* allows you to accommodate missing data *(no response to a question)*. To accommodate for missing data, click the rightward segment of *Missing* and select *Discrete missing values* and type 999 into the first of the three cells shown and click *OK (missing data will be entered as 999 in the Data View Editor)*.

Variable View Editor

File Edit View Data Transform Analyze Graphs Utilities Add-ons Window Help

	Name	Type	Width	Decimals	Label	Values	Missing	Columns	Align	Measure	Role
1	Gender	Numeric	8	0	Gender	None	None	8	Right	Nominal	Input
2											
3											
4											
5											
6											
7											
8											
9											
10											
11											
12											
13											
14											
15											
16											
17											

Data View | Variable View

IBM SPSS Statistics Processor is ready

Step 3 – Click the cell directly under the column *Values* and click the rightward segment of that cell until the *Value Labels* box appears. Enter the coded numeral 1 *(which represents male)* into the *Value* cell and enter *Male* into the *label* cell and then click *Add*. Then enter the coded numeral 2 *(which represents female)* into the *Value* cell and enter *Female* into the *Label* cell and then click *Add*. Then click *OK*.

Variable View Editor

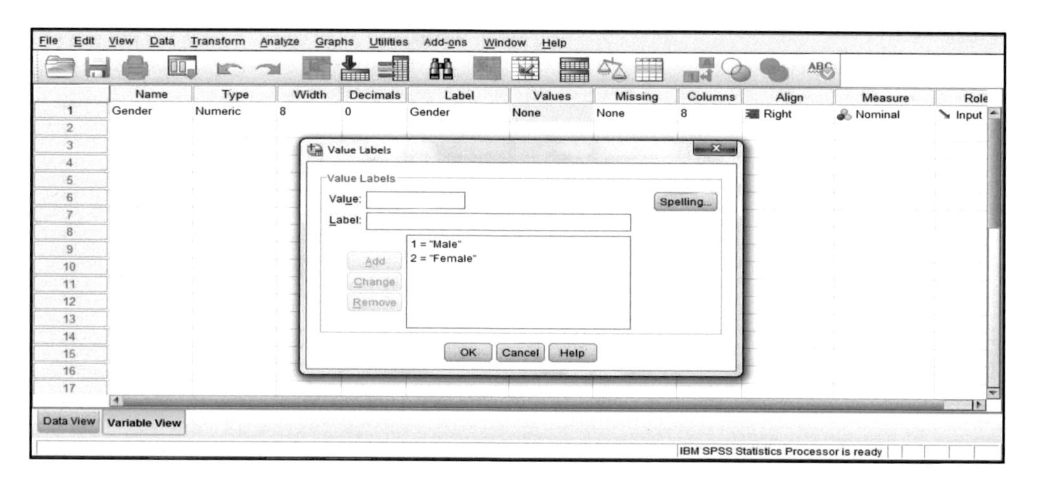

Step 4 – Enter the remaining variables *(each new question in the questionnaire represents a new variable)* as per step 2 *(Question 2 through to question 9 will be represented by variable 2 through to variable 9).*

Notes:

a. The column *Values* is only relevant for both nominal and ordinal scaled variables *(these variable types require you to enter coded numerals into a Value Labels box to represent the categories of these variables)*. This column can be avoided when you are entering Quantitative variables *(i.e. Interval and Ratio scaled variables)*
b. The column *Measure* requires you to describe the variable type i.e. *Nominal or Ordinal or Scale*, where appropriate. Both Interval and Ratio scaled variables can be described using *Scale* under the column *Measure*.

Variable View Editor

File Edit View Data Transform Analyze Graphs Utilities Add-ons Window Help

	Name	Type	Width	Decimals	Label	Values	Missing	Columns	Align	Measure	Rol
1	Gender	Numeric	8	0	Gender	{1, Male}...	None	8	Right	Nominal	Input
2	SmokeBeh	Numeric	8	0	Smoking Behave	{1, Smoke}...	None	8	Right	Nominal	Input
3	AgeCat	Numeric	8	0	Age Category	{1, < 20}...	None	8	Right	Ordinal	Input
4	Opinion	Numeric	8	0	The airline ...	{1, Strongly ...	None	8	Right	Ordinal	Input
5	TempIndoor	Numeric	8	0	Temperature Ind...	None	None	8	Right	Scale	Input
6	TempOutdoor	Numeric	8	0	Temperature Out...	None	None	8	Right	Scale	Input
7	Weight	Numeric	8	0	Weight (kgs)	None	None	8	Right	Scale	Input
8	Height	Numeric	8	0	Height	None	None	8	Right	Scale	Input
9	Children	Numeric	8	0	Number of Childr...	None	None	8	Right	Scale	Input
10											
11											
12											
13											
14											
15											
16											
17											

Data View | Variable View

IBM SPSS Statistics Processor is ready

Step 5 – Once each question in the questionnaire has been represented in *Variable View* click *Data View* at the bottom left corner and enter the data from the first completed questionnaire in the first row of *Data View* as shown.

Data View Editor

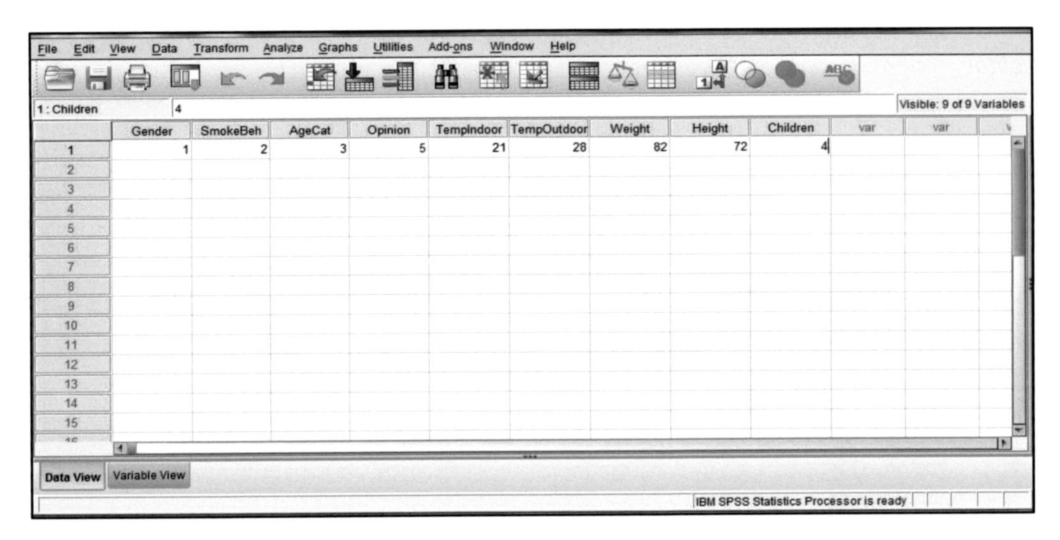

The first row contains the responses of the first male in our sample. The coded numeral 1 in the column *Gender* indicates that the person is a male. The coded numeral 2 in the column *SmokeBeh* indicates that the male is a non-smoker and so on.

Step 6 – Repeat Step 5 for each completed questionnaire. As an exercise, enter data for several fictional questionnaires *(this exercise will enhance your knowledge of SPSS data entry).*

Data View Editor

File Edit View Data Transform Analyze Graphs Utilities Add-ons Window Help

17 : Children — Visible: 9 of 9 Variables

	Gender	SmokeBeh	AgeCat	Opinion	TempIndoor	TempOutdoor	Weight	Height	Children	var	var
1	1	2	3	5	21	28	82	72	4		
2	1	2	3	3	23	28	90	70	2		
3	2	1	2	4	21	30	80	65	3		
4	2	1	2	2	20	26	75	64	2		
5	2	1	1	2	20	25	65	63	1		
6	1	2	1	3	23	30	80	70	1		
7	1	2	1	3	21	26	80	70	2		
8	1	1	3	4	20	25	85	72	2		
9	2	1	3	4	19	24	70	66	3		
10	2	1	2	4	19	22	65	65	3		
11	1	2	2	4	19	24	90	69	2		
12	1	2	3	5	18	20	92	71	2		
13	1	2	3	5	18	21	87	73	3		
14	2	2	1	4	22	24	65	60	3		
15	2	1	1	4	22	23	70	61	4		

Data View Variable View

IBM SPSS Statistics Processor is ready

The Lady with the Lamp

She is a 'ministering angel' without any exaggeration in these hospitals and as her slender form glides quietly along each corridor every poor fellow's face softens with gratitude at the sight of her. When all the medical officers have retired for the night and silence and darkness have settled down upon those miles of prostrate sick she may be observed alone with a little lamp in her hand making her solitary rounds. (Cited in Cook, E. T. The Life of Florence Nightingale. (1913), p. 237.)

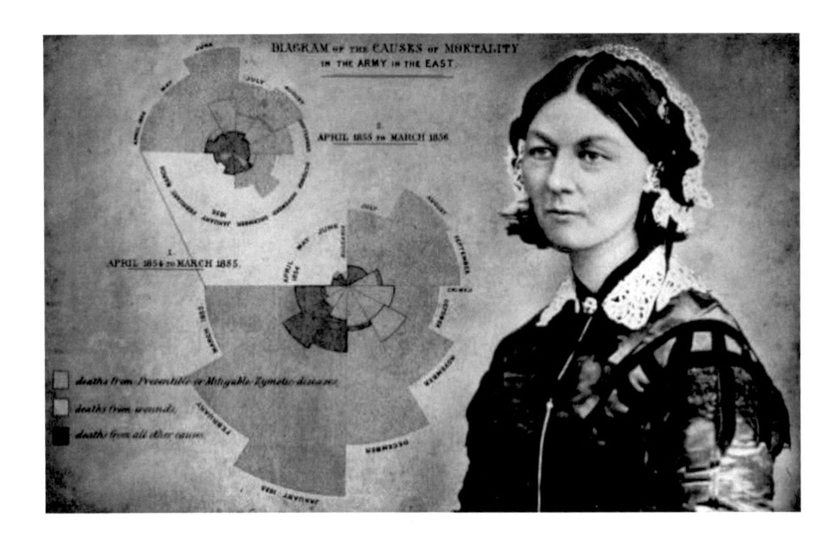

"When Nightingale returned from the Crimean war, she was obsessed with a sense of failure. Despite her efforts, thousands of men had died needlessly during the war from illnesses they acquired in the hospital. Without widespread changes in Army procedures, the same disaster could occur again, she worried. So she began a campaign for reform. She persuaded Queen Victoria to appoint a Royal Commission on the Army medical department. Nightingale compiled vast tables of statistics about how many people had died, where and why. Many of her findings shocked her. [...]

For example, she discovered that in *peacetime*, soldiers in England died at twice the rate of civilians — even though they were young men in their primes. The problem with the military health service, she realized, extended far beyond a few terrible hospitals during a war. As impressive as her statistics were, Nightingale worried that Queen Victoria's eyes would glaze over as she scanned the tables. So Nightingale devised clever ways of presenting the information in charts. Statistics had been presented using graphics only a few times previously and perhaps never to persuade people of the need for social change. [...]

Nightingale's best-known graphic has come to be known as a "coxcomb." It is a variation on the familiar modern pie graph, showing the number of deaths each month and their causes. Her report and commission had an enormous impact, leading to systematic changes in the design and practices of hospitals. By the end of the century, Army mortality was lower than civilian mortality. Furthermore, statistics has become a powerful tool for reform. And powerful graphics like Nightingale's have spared the eyes of many more than just Queen Victoria's from glazing over." *(Rehmeyer, 2008).*

Chapter 2 – Descriptive Statistical Techniques 1

Overview

Applications

'Everything should be made as simple as possible, but not simpler.'

Albert Einstein (1879 – 1955)

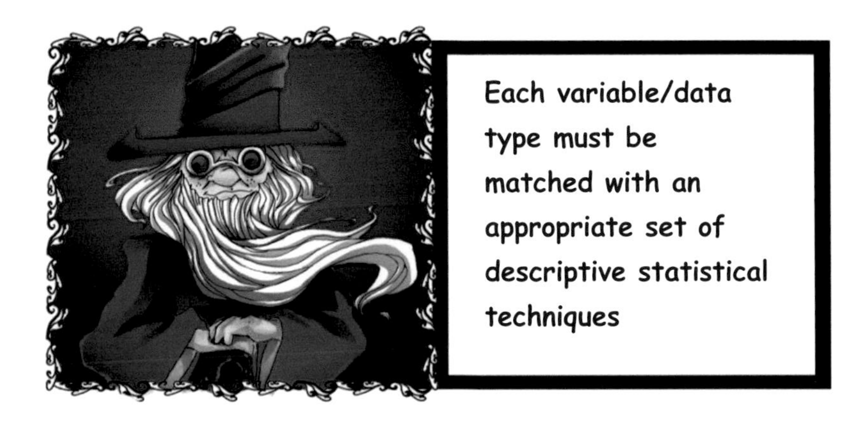

2.1 Schematic Chart – *Appropriate Tables/Graphs/Statistics*

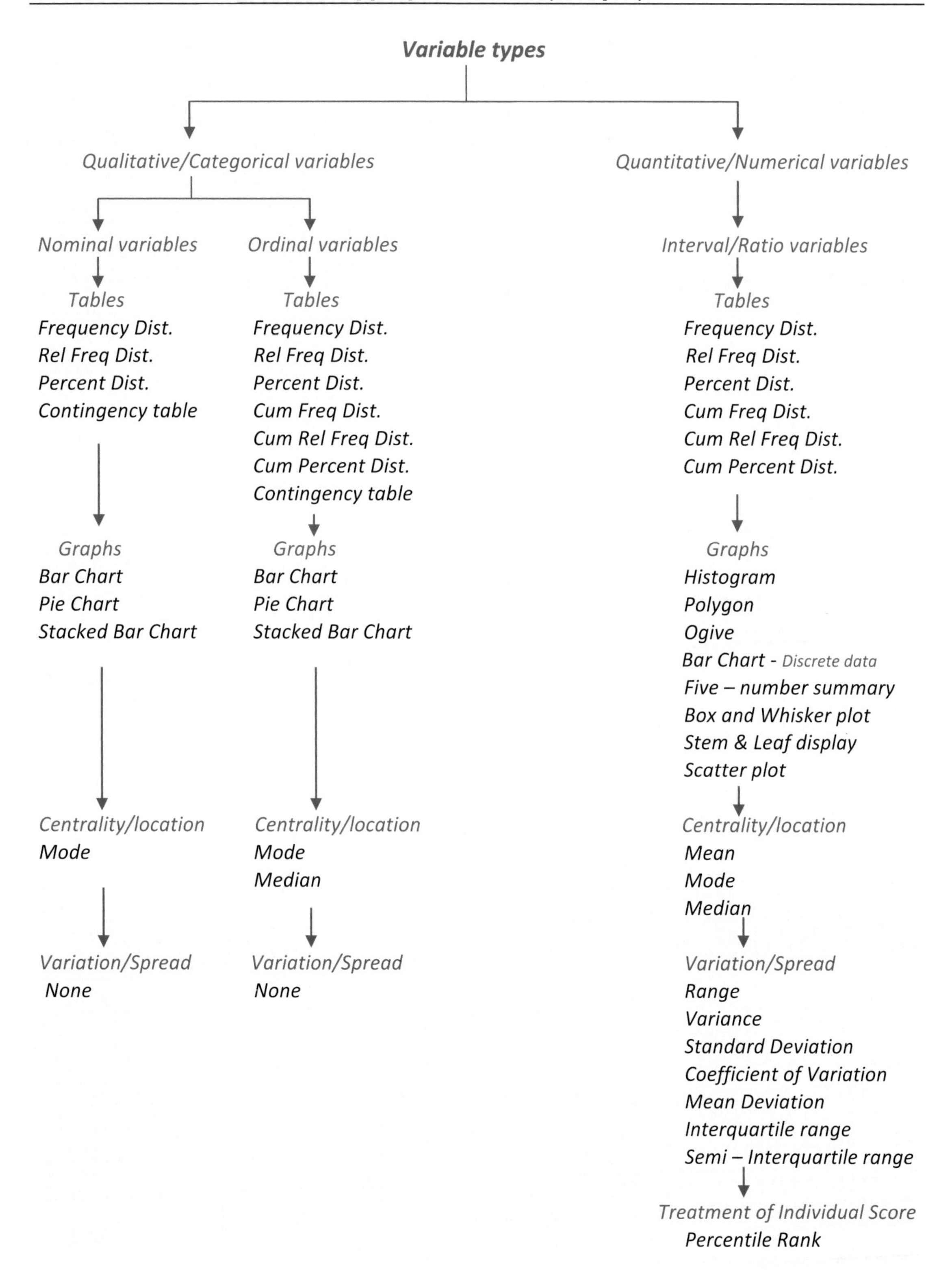

2.2 Introductory Comments

In this chapter descriptive statistical techniques will be used to summarise *(measures of centrality and variation)* and present *(graphical and tabular representations)* the collected sample data. In later chapters inferential statistical techniques will be used to make inferences or generalisations from the sample to the population under investigation. The researcher must select appropriate graphs/measures of centrality/measures of variation for each variable/data type *(see the schematic chart on the previous page)*.

The application of descriptive statistical techniques to the sample data or dataset *(the collection of observed values or measurements from each of the several variables under investigation)* achieves the following aims:

1. *The dataset is made accessible to the end-user in the form of tables, charts and summary measures. This will enable the end-user to discover the concealed information that an unprocessed dataset will inevitably disguise.*

2. *Enable the researcher to address basic research questions (non-inferential type research questions).*

3. *Enable the researcher to decide which inferential statistical techniques (parametric test procedures versus distribution-free test procedures) to use when addressing more advanced research questions (inferential type research questions).*

We will examine each variable/data type in turn and recommend appropriate tables, charts and summary measures. In addition, the chapter will examine appropriate descriptive techniques for both a single variable as well two variables combined. Both ungrouped *(raw data)* and grouped data *(raw data which has been converted into distribution tables)* will be examined.

This chapter will focus on constructions and calculations whilst Chapter 3 will focus on interpreting the tables, charts and summary measures from Chapter 2. The process of summarising the dataset using summary measures *(measures of centrality and measures of variation)* will inevitably result in a loss of information. Therefore, the challenge for the researcher is to compile a combination of measures that adequately captures the essence of the dataset.

2.3 Constructing Distribution Tables

Raw data was collected from a sample of 65 college students who were asked to estimate the time it takes to apply their make-up. We will classify the variable *Make-up time (minutes)* as a quantitative *(continuous)* variable.

22	**29**	16	15	18	17	12	13	17	16	15
19	17	**10**	21	15	14	17	18	12	20	14
16	15	16	20	22	14	25	19	23	15	19
18	23	22	16	16	19	13	18	24	24	26
13	18	17	15	24	15	17	14	18	17	21
16	21	25	19	20	27	16	17	16	21	

This raw data can be converted into the following distribution tables using the 5 step procedure below:

a. *Frequency distribution table*
b. *Relative frequency distribution table*
c. *Percentage distribution table*

} *Table 2.2 incorporates tables a, b and c*

d. *Cumulative frequency distribution table*
e. *Cumulative relative frequency distribution table*
f. *Cumulative percentage distribution table*

} *Table 2.3 incorporates tables d, e and f*

STEP 1 - Calculate the range of the raw data on Make-up time (minutes)

Range = highest value – lowest value = 29 - 10 = 19

If there are outliers or extreme value in the raw dataset, one can opt to avoid these values when calculating the range.

STEP 2 - Decide on the number of classes or class intervals for the distribution tables – Two alternative approaches are available for Step 2

Approach 1: Scientific Approach – useful when you are constructing distribution tables for the first time (Groebner & Shannon, 1985)

Given that the sample size in the current example is 65 students, a glance at table 2.1 suggests that we choose 7 classes or class intervals. The number of classes selected is k, such that 2^K falls between 65 and 128 inclusive *(this sample size interval contains our sample size of 65)*. A calculation with 2^6 will result in 64, however, this does not fall between 65 and 128 inclusive. A calculation with 2^7 will result in 128 and this does fall between 65 and 128 inclusive. Therefore, the number of classes is $k = 7$.

Table 2.1

Scientific Approach		
If we have a sample of:	2^K	*Recommended no. of classes k*
9 – 16	2^6	4
17 – 32	2^5	5
33 – 64	2^6	6
65 – 128	2^7	7
129 – 256	2^8	8
257 – 512	2^9	9
513 – 1,024	2^{10}	10

Approach 2: Judgement Approach – useful if you have previously constructed distribution tables

This approach is useful when you have previously constructed distribution tables. The number of classes selected will usually be in the range ≥ 5 and ≤ 15. Experience will guide the researcher in this approach. *(The shape of some the charts derived from constructed distribution tables will vary according to the number of classes or class intervals chosen).*

STEP 3 - Calculate the class interval width

The calculation of the class interval width makes use of the range derived from Step 1.

Class interval width = $\frac{\text{Range}}{\text{Number of classes}} = \frac{19}{7}$ = 2.71 *(round up to 3)*

Custom and practise would suggest that you always adjust this answer as appropriate. In this example the answer is adjusted upwards to a class width of 1, 2, 3 etc. *(or multiples, such as 10, 20, 30 etc.)* whichever is appropriate.

STEP 4 - Identify the class boundaries and class midpoints

The distribution tables will therefore have 7 classes or class intervals, each with a class width of 3. The first class interval should contain the lowest value in your raw data *(10 in this example)* and the last class interval should contain the highest value in your raw data *(29 in this example).* At this point you have 2 acceptable class interval designs available to you.

Design 1: You can design the first class interval beginning with the lowest value in the raw data and count upwards three values *(class width = 3)*: 10 11 12 giving a class interval design of [10 – 12]. The value 10 represents the lower class limit and the value 12 is the upper class limit.

Classes or Class Intervals
10 – 12
13 – 15
16 – 18

Design 2: You can design the first class interval beginning with the lowest value in the raw data and count upwards three values *(class width = 3)*: 10 11 12 giving a class interval design of [10 but < 13]. The value 10 represents the lower class limit and the value 13 is the upper class limit. However, a raw data value of 13 will not be assigned to the first class interval.

Classes or Class Intervals
10 but < 13
13 but < 16
16 but < 19

It is important to identify class boundaries *(lower boundary and upper boundary)* as we shall see later in this chapter. A class boundary is that value which is common to or overlaps adjacent classes. Assuming that we adopt design 1 above, then the first two classes will be:

10 – **12**
13 – 15

There appears to be no value that is common to or overlaps these two classes. In fact there is a gap between 12 and 13. Therefore, the boundary will be located half way along the gap (12.5). This value (12.5) represents the upper boundary for the first class and the lower boundary for the second class: Runyon and Haber said in 1976 (p. 41) 'the "true" value of a number is equal to its apparent value plus and minus one-half of the unit of measurement'.

Class widths are the numerical differences between lower and upper class boundaries *(not the class limits)*. Class midpoints are mid-way between lower and upper boundaries *(alternatively, calculation of the mid-points can be made using the class limits)*. Consider the following two acceptable class interval designs available to you:

Option 1

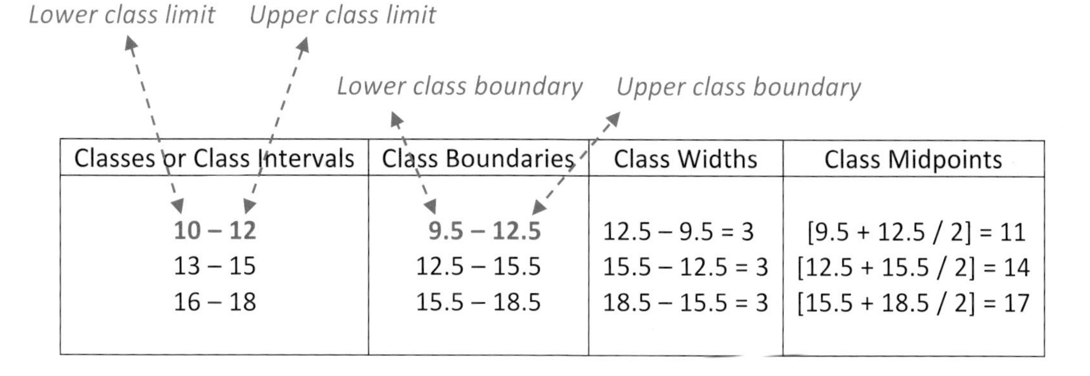

Classes or Class Intervals	Class Boundaries	Class Widths	Class Midpoints
10 – 12	**9.5 – 12.5**	12.5 – 9.5 = 3	[9.5 + 12.5 / 2] = 11
13 – 15	12.5 – 15.5	15.5 – 12.5 = 3	[12.5 + 15.5 / 2] = 14
16 – 18	15.5 – 18.5	18.5 – 15.5 = 3	[15.5 + 18.5 / 2] = 17

Option 2

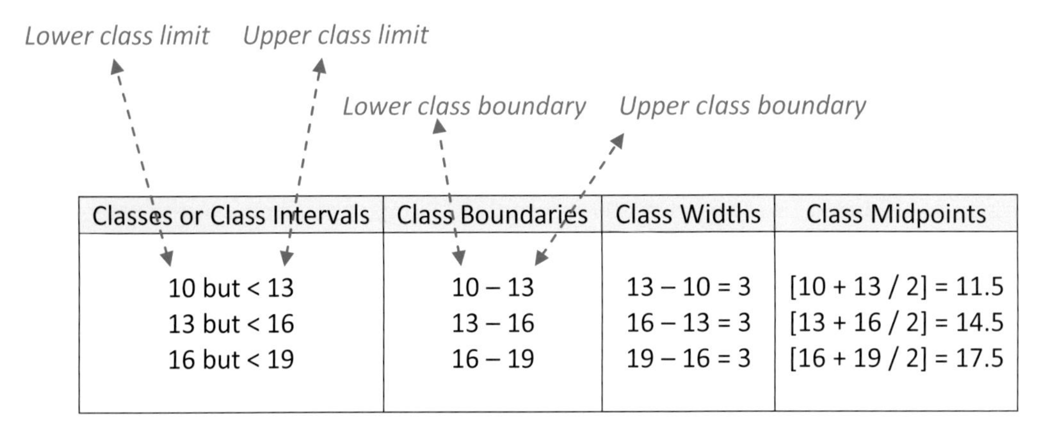

Classes or Class Intervals	Class Boundaries	Class Widths	Class Midpoints
10 but < 13	10 – 13	13 – 10 = 3	[10 + 13 / 2] = 11.5
13 but < 16	13 – 16	16 – 13 = 3	[13 + 16 / 2] = 14.5
16 but < 19	16 – 19	19 – 16 = 3	[16 + 19 / 2] = 17.5

STEP 5 - Use a tally sheet to assist your construction of distribution tables

A tally sheet can be of assistance at this point *(particularly if the data is not ordered)*. Once we have determined the number of class intervals/class interval widths/class interval boundaries, we can assign each value of the raw data to a class interval *(using one stroke per raw data value)*.

Tally sheet

Classes or Class Intervals 1	Tally 2	Frequency 3
10 – 12	///	3
13 – 15	~~////~~ ~~////~~ ////	14
16 – 18	~~////~~ ~~////~~ ~~////~~ ~~////~~ ///	23
19 – 21	~~////~~ ~~////~~ //	12
22 – 24	~~////~~ ///	8
25 – 27	////	4
28 – 30	/	1

Following completion of these steps, the tally sheet will form the basis for the construction of the following tables which are amalgamated into table 2.2:

a. *Frequency distribution table - column 1 & column 3*
b. *Relative frequency distribution table - column 1 & column 4*
c. *Percentage distribution table - column 1 & column 5*

} *Amalgamated into table 2.2*

The frequency distribution table is constructed directly from the tally sheet. This table is represented by column 1 and column 2 in table 2.2. The relative frequency distribution table adapts the frequency distribution table by converting the frequency column into a relative frequency column $\left[\frac{Frequency}{Total\ Frequency}\right]$. This table is represented by column 1 and column 4 in table 2.2.

The percentage distribution table adapts the relative frequency distribution table by converting the relative frequency column into a percentage column [Relative Frequency x 100]. This table is represented by column 1 and column 5 in table 2.2.

Table 2.2 - Distribution Tables

Classes 1	Midpoint 2	Frequency 3	Relative Frequency 4	Percentage 5
10 – 12	11	3	3/65 = .05 *(approx.)*	.05 x 100 = 5%
13 – 15	14	14	14/65 = .22	22%
16 – 18	17	23	23/65 = .35	35%
19 – 21	20	12	12/65 = .18	18%
22 – 24	23	8	8/65 = .12	12%
25 – 27	26	4	4/65 = .06	6%
28 – 30	29	1	1/65 = .02	2%
		Total Frequency = 65	1.0	

Once we have constructed table 2.2, we can proceed to construct the following three tables which are amalgamated into table 2.3:

a. Cumulative frequency distribution table - column 4
b. Cumulative relative frequency distribution table - column 5
c. Cumulative percentage distribution table - column 6

} *Amalgamated into Table 2.3*

The cumulative frequency distribution table is represented by column 4 in table 2.3. Column 4 is subdivided into two columns. This table focuses on the upper class limit of each class interval. For example the first class interval is 10 – 12 inclusive, to which we attach ≤ to its upper class limit. The cumulative frequency is derived by adding to each frequency the frequency of a preceding class.

The cumulative relative frequency distribution table is represented by column 5 in table 2.3. This table adapts the cumulative frequency distribution table by converting the cumulative frequency column into a cumulative relative frequency column $\left[\frac{Cumulative\ Frequency}{Total\ Frequency}\right]$.

The cumulative percentage distribution table is represented by column 6 in table 2.3. This table adapts the cumulative relative frequency table by converting each cumulative relative frequency column into a cumulative percentage column [Cumulative relative frequency x 100].

Table 2.3 - Cumulative Distribution Tables

Classes 1	Midpoint 2	Frequency 3	Cum. Freq. 4		Cum. Rel. Freq. 5		Cum. Percent 6	
			UCL*	Cum. Freq.	UCL*	Cum. Rel. Freq.	UCL*	Cum. %
10 – 12	11	3	≤ 12	3	≤ 12	.05 *(approx.)*	≤ 12	5%
13 – 15	14	14	≤ 15	17 (3 + 14)	≤ 15	.27 (.05 + .22)	≤ 15	27%
16 – 18	17	23	≤ 18	40 (17 + 23)	≤ 18	.62 (.27 +. 35)	≤ 18	62%
19 – 21	20	12	≤ 21	52 (40 + 12)	≤ 21	.80 (.62 + .18)	≤ 21	80%
22 – 24	23	8	≤ 24	60 (52 + 8)	≤ 24	.92 (.80 + .12)	≤ 24	92%
25 – 27	26	4	≤ 27	64 (60 + 4)	≤ 27	.98 (.92 + .06)	≤ 27	98%
28 – 30	29	1	≤ 30	65 (64 + 1)	≤ 30	1.00 (.98 + .02)	≤ 30	100%
		65	*UCL = Upper class limit					

The histogram may reveal to the researcher how the data collected for a quantitative continuous variable is distributed

2.4 **Summarising data** – *Nominal scaled variables (Grouped)*

In this section we consider how we might appropriately treat one or two qualitative *(nominal scaled)* variable*(s)*. The data values or observations we derive from a nominal variable are merely coded values. There is no natural underlying order to these categories/coded values and subtraction between these coded values is meaningless. The variable *Blood Group* has 4 categories which we assume has no underlying order.

		Coded Values
	Group O	1
Blood Group	Group A	2
	Group B	3
	Group AB	4

Tables for one Nominal variable (Blood Group)

The appropriate tables for one nominal scaled variable include:

1. *Frequency distribution table*
2. *Relative frequency distribution table*
3. *Percentage distribution table*

A researcher selected a random sample of 2,000 students from the population of 20,000 third level students. He converted the raw data into the following distribution tables. Since the variable *Blood Group* has four categories, these categories represent the classes or class intervals. The researcher was able to go directly to Step 5 of the 5 step procedure for constructing distribution tables. A tally sheet was used to assign each value of the raw data to a class interval and the distribution tables were constructed as follows:

Distribution tables

Blood Group 1	Frequency 2	Relative Frequency 3	Percentage 4
Group O = 1	880	0.44	44%
Group A = 2	840	0.42	42%
Group B = 3	200	0.10	10%
Group AB = 4	80	0.04	4%
	2000		

(Adapted from Kinnear and Gray, 2011)

Table for two Qualitative Nominal Scaled variables (Gender and Survival)

An appropriate table for two qualitative nominal scaled variables is the *contingency table*. A contingency table allows us to combine two qualitative nominal scaled variables. Consider the following contingency table *(data derived from the British Board of trade report on the sinking of the Titanic in the North Atlantic Ocean on 15 April 1912)*. The data related to adult male and female passengers of all classes. A contingency table enables us to explore presence or absence of association between the two nominal variables *(is survival associated more with one gender over another).*

Contingency Table - Survival by Gender

		Lost	*Survived*	Total
Men	Count	**659**	**146**	805
	% within gender	81.9%	18.1%	
Women	Count	**106**	**296**	402
	% within gender	26.4%	73.6%	
Total	Count	765	442	1207

(Compiled from British Board of Trade Report, 1912)

Graphs for one Nominal Scaled variable (Blood Group)

The appropriate graphs for one nominal scaled variable include:

1. *Bar Chart*
2. *Pie Chart*

The bar chart can be presented with vertical or horizontal bars. The length and area of each bar can be represented by frequency, relative frequency or percentage. The width of each bar is identical, and the bars are separated by an equal distance *(e.g. a single or half bar width)*. The scaling *(frequency/relative frequency/percentage)* should be selected according to the intended needs of the eventual user *(see section 2.10 for Excel instructions to derive charts).*

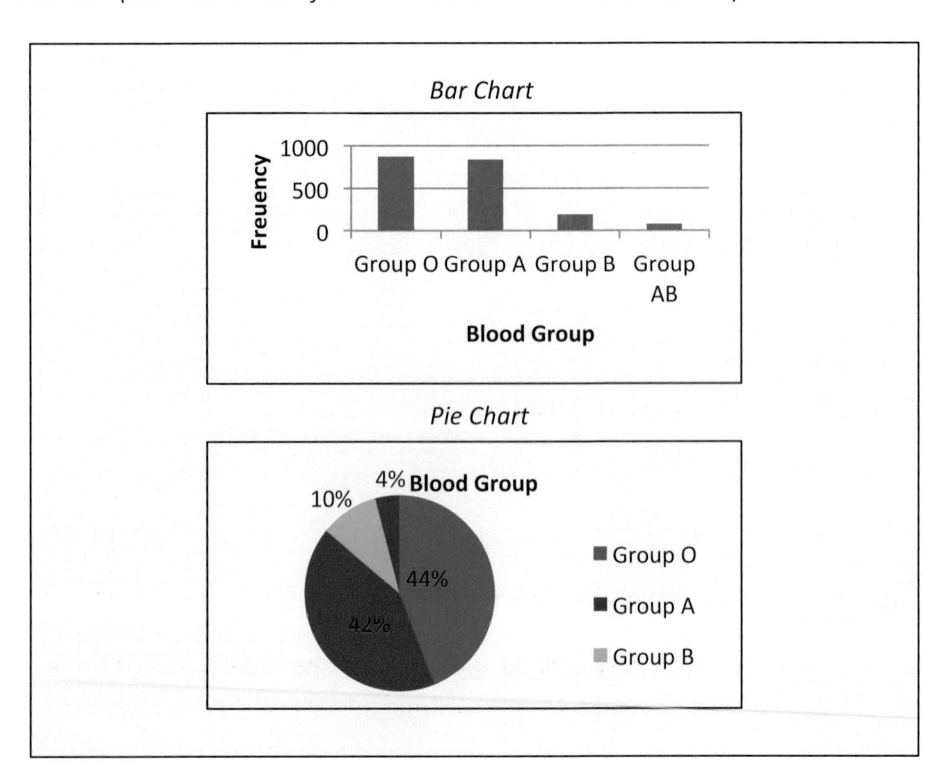

The pie chart can also be used to represent relative differences between the categories. The area of the pie represents 100% of the variable of interest and a slice of pie reveals what any one category contributes to the total. The angle for a slice of pie can be derived by multiplying 360° by the relative frequency of a selected category *(360°x 0.10 = an angle of 36° for the Group B).*

Graphs for two Qualitative Nominal Scaled variables (Gender and Survival)

The appropriate graphs for two qualitative nominal scaled variables include:

1. *Bar Chart*
2. *Stacked Bar Chart*

The bar chart allows us to chart two qualitative nominal scaled variables. The following bar chart is a graphical representation of the contingency table *(Survival by Gender):*

The stacked bar chart, a version of the bar chart, also enables us to chart two nominal variables. The following stacked bar chart is an alternative graphical representation of the contingency table *(Survival by Gender).*

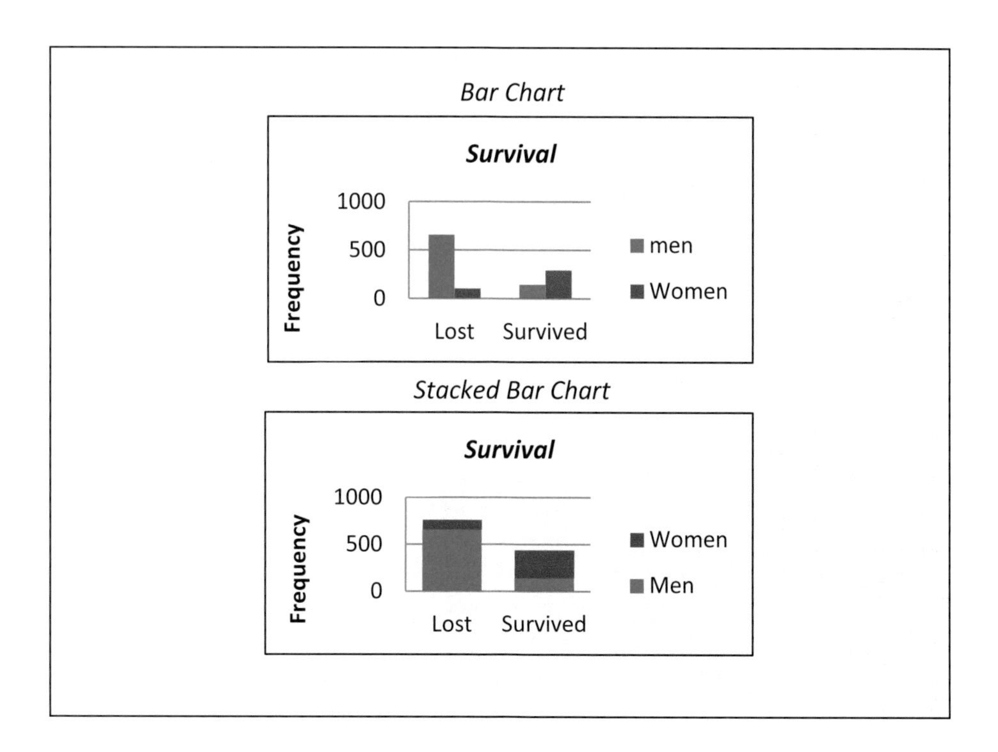

Centrality

The mode or modal value *(the category with the most data values/observations)* for the variable *blood group* is Group O *(880 observations).*

2.5 **Summarising data** – *Ordinal Scaled variables (Grouped)*

In this section we consider how we might appropriately treat one or two qualitative *(one nominal and one ordinal)* variable*(s)*. The data values or observations we derive from an ordinal variable are merely coded values. There is a natural underlying order to these categories/coded values but subtraction between these coded values is meaningless. The variable *Lecturer explains things clearly* has 5 categories which we assume does have an underlying order.

		Coded Values
	Strongly Disagree	1
	Disagree	2
Lecturer explains things clearly	Neutral	3
	Agree	4
	Strongly Agree	5

Tables for one Ordinal Scaled variable (Lecturer explains things clearly)

The appropriate tables for one Ordinal Scaled variable include:

1. *Frequency distribution table*
2. *Relative frequency distribution table*
3. *Percentage distribution table*
4. *Cumulative frequency distribution table*
5. *Cumulative relative frequency distribution table*
6. *Cumulative percentage distribution table*

A sample of 131 students was selected from a population of 13,100 students. The students were asked to indicate their views about the communication skills of their lecturer. The raw data was converted into the following distribution tables. Since the variable *Lecturer explains things clearly* has five categories, these categories represent the classes or class intervals. The researcher was able to go directly to Step 5 of the 5 step procedure for constructing distribution tables. A tally sheet was used to assign each value of the raw data to a class interval and the distribution tables were constructed as follows:

Distribution Tables

'Lecturer explains things clearly'	Freq.	Rel. Freq.	Percent	Cum. Freq.	Cum. Rel. Freq.	Cum. Percent
Strongly Disagree = 1	8	0.06	6%	8	0.06	6%
Disagree = 2	13	0.10	10%	21	0.16	16%
Neutral = 3	21	0.16	16%	42	0.32	32%
Agree = 4	52	0.40	40%	94	0.72	72%
Strongly Agree = 5	37	0.28	28%	131	1.00	100%
	131	1.00				

Table for two Qualitative variables (one nominal and one ordinal variable)

The appropriate table for two qualitative variables is the *contingency table*. A contingency table allows us to combine two qualitative variables.

Contingency Table - Opinion by Gender

	Lecturer explains things clearly					
	Strongly Disagree	Disagree	Neutral	Agree	Strongly Agree	Total
Male students	8	12	8	30	17	75
Female students	6	8	8	40	18	80
Total	14	20	16	70	35	155

Graphs for one Ordinal Scaled variable (Lecturer explains things clearly)

The appropriate graphs for one ordinal scaled variable include:

1. *Bar Chart*
2. *Pie Chart*

Once again the scaling *(frequency/relative frequency/percentage)* for the bar chart should be selected according to the intended needs of the eventual user.

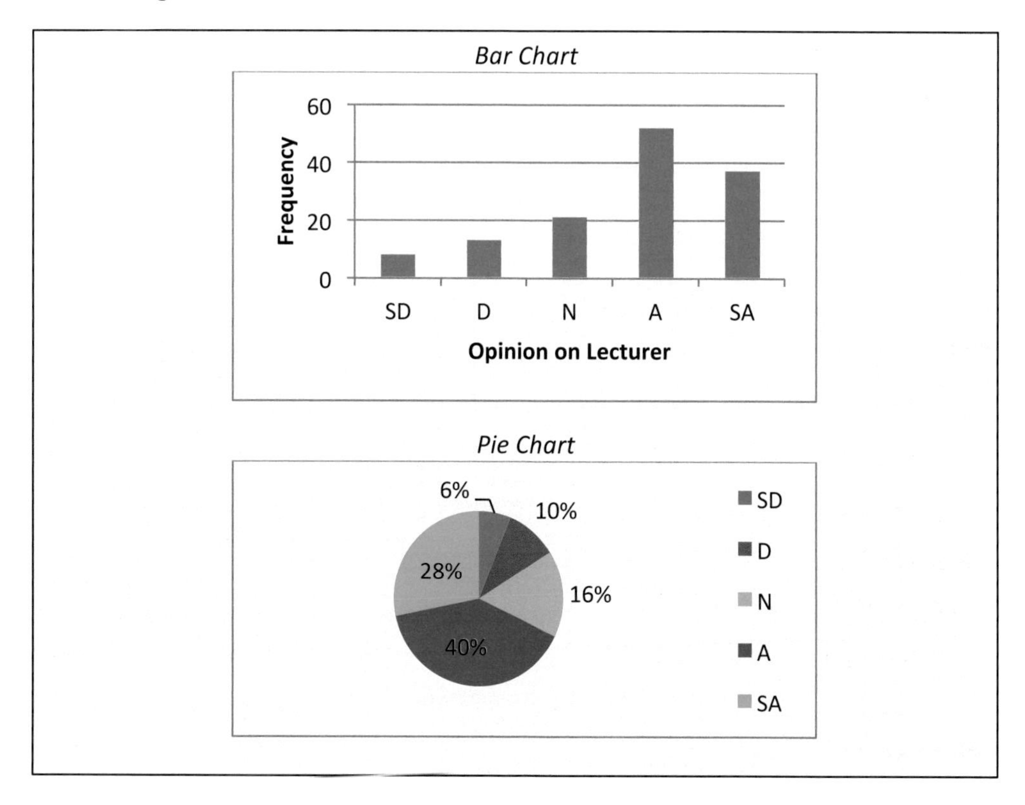

Graphs for two Qualitative variables (one ordinal and one nominal)

The appropriate graphs for two qualitative variables include:

1. *Bar Chart*
2. *Stacked Bar Chart*

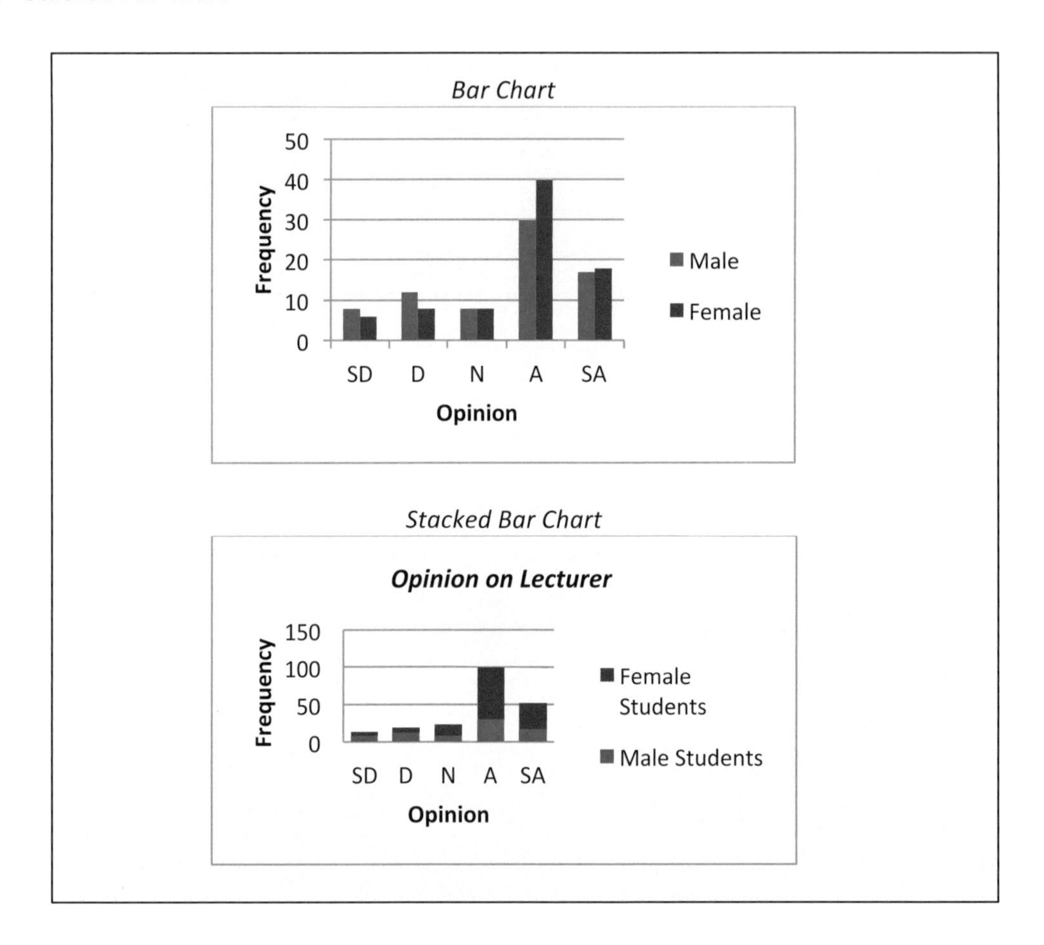

Centrality

The mode or modal value *(the category with the most data values/observations)* for the variable *Lecturer explains thing clearly* is 'Agree' *(52 observations)*.

The median value *(middlemost data value/observation of the ordered data)* for the variable *Lecturer explains things clearly* is 'Agree'.

From a dataset of size 131, the middlemost observation is the 66th approximately *(131/2)*. According to the distribution tables, the first 42 observations were matched to the coded values 1, 2 and 3 while the first 94 observations were matched with the codes 1, 2, 3 and 4. Consequently, the 66th observation must be matched with the code 4 *(Agree)*. Hence the median is the category 'Agree'.

2.6 Summarising data – *Quantitative variables (Grouped)*

In this section we consider how we might appropriately treat a quantitative variable. The data values or observations we derive from a quantitative variable are ordinary 'real' numbers *(uncoded values)*. The data values or observations derived from a quantitative variable may be *discrete* or *continuous*. The variable *IQ of first year college students* can be assumed to be a quantitative *continuous* variable.

	Ordinary 'real' Values
	80
IQ of First year college students	90
	110
	105
	100
	110

Tables

The appropriate distribution tables for a quantitative *continuous* variable include:

1. *Frequency distribution table*
2. *Relative frequency distribution table*
3. *Percentage distribution table*
4. *Cumulative frequency distribution table*
5. *Cumulative relative frequency distribution table*
6. *Cumulative percentage distribution table*

A sample of 140 students was selected from a population of 1,400 students. The data was converted into the following distribution tables using the 5 step procedure from section 2.3. On this occasion, the researcher opted to choose 9 classes or class intervals based on his own judgement rather than apply the scientific approach to selecting the number of classes.

Raw Data – Ungrouped data

80 80 81 81 81 82 82 82 82 83 83 83 84 85 85 86 86 86 87 87 87 88
88 89 89 89 89 90 90 90 91 91 92 92 92 93 93 93 93 94 94 94 94 95
95 96 96 96 97 97 97 97 98 98 98 98 98 99 99 99 99
100 100 100 100 101 101 101 101 102 102 102 103 103 103 103 104
104 104 104 104 105 105 105 105 106 106 106 107 107 108 108 108
109 109 109 109 109 110 110 111 111 111 111 111 112 112 112 113
113 114 114 114 114 114 115 115 115 115 116 116 117 117 118 118
119 119 119 119 120 120 120 120 121 121 121 122 122 123 123

Distribution Tables– Grouped data

IQ Score	Freq.	Rel. Freq.	Cum. Freq.		Cum. Rel. Freq.		Cum. Percent	
			UCL*	Cum. F	UCL*	Cum. RF	UCL*	Cum. %
80 – 84	12	0.09	≤ 84	12	≤ 84	0.09	≤ 84	9%
85 – 89	14	0.10	≤ 89	26	≤ 89	0.19	≤ 89	19%
90 – 94	16	0.11	≤ 94	42	≤ 94	0.30	≤ 94	30%
95 – 99	18	0.13	≤ 99	60	≤ 99	0.43	≤ 99	43%
100 – 104	20	0.14	≤ 104	80	≤ 104	0.57	≤ 104	57%
105 – 109	18	0.13	≤ 109	98	≤ 109	0.70	≤ 109	70%
110 – 114	16	0.11	≤ 114	114	≤ 114	0.81	≤ 114	81%
115 – 119	14	0.10	≤ 119	128	≤ 119	0.91	≤ 119	91%
120 – 124	12	0.09	≤ 124	140	≤ 124	1.00	≤ 124	100%
	140	1.00						

**UCL = Upper class limit*

Graphs

The appropriate graphs for a quantitative *continuous* variable include:

1. *Histogram* } *Grouped data*
2. *Polygon*
3. *Ogive*
4. *Five-Number Summary* } *Ungrouped data* (items 1–6)
5. *Stem & Leaf Display*
6. *Scatter Plot – to chart two quantitative continuous variables*
7. The appropriate graph for a quantitative discrete variable is the bar chart *(Grouped & ungrouped data)*

Grouped data – A Quantitative Continuous variable

A histogram resembles a bar chart with its bars connected *(since the class intervals have common boundaries)*. A histogram has connected bars to remind us of the seamless nature of a *continuous* variable. The following example demonstrates how a histogram can be constructed:

Class Intervals	Class Boundaries	Frequency
80 – 84	79.5 – 84.5	12
85 – 89	84.5 – 89.5	14
90 – 94	89.5 – 94.5	16

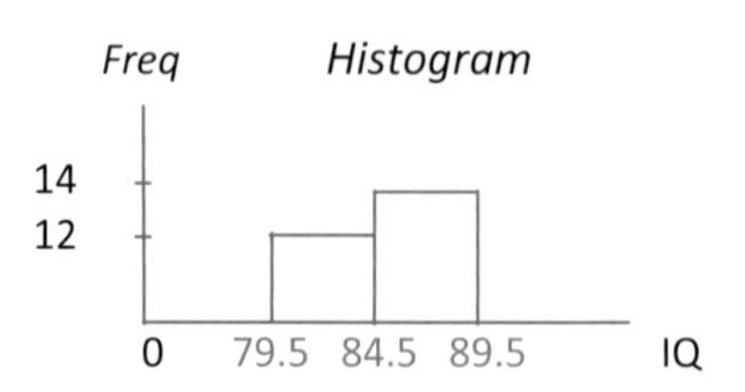

The vertical axis of the histogram/frequency polygon can be represented by *frequency, relative frequency or percent.*

Distribution Table

IQ Score	Class Boundaries	Freq.
80 – 84	79.5 – 84.5	12
85 – 89	84.5 – 89.5	14
90 – 94	89.5 – 94.5	16
95 – 99	94.5 – 99.5	18
100 – 104	99.5 – 104.5	20
105 – 109	104.5 – 109.5	18
110 – 114	109.5 – 114.5	16
115 – 119	114.5 – 119.5	14
120 – 124	119.5 – 124.5	12

To derive a frequency Polygon or frequency curve, a point is placed at the midpoint at the top of each bar in the histogram. The frequency polygon reflects the shape of the histogram. In Chapter 3 we will pay special attention to the shape of frequency polygons and compare a variety of frequency polygons to a standardised distribution *(normal 'bell shaped' distribution).* The leftmost and rightmost points of the frequency polygon represent zero frequency. The midpoints are joined to give us a frequency polygon.

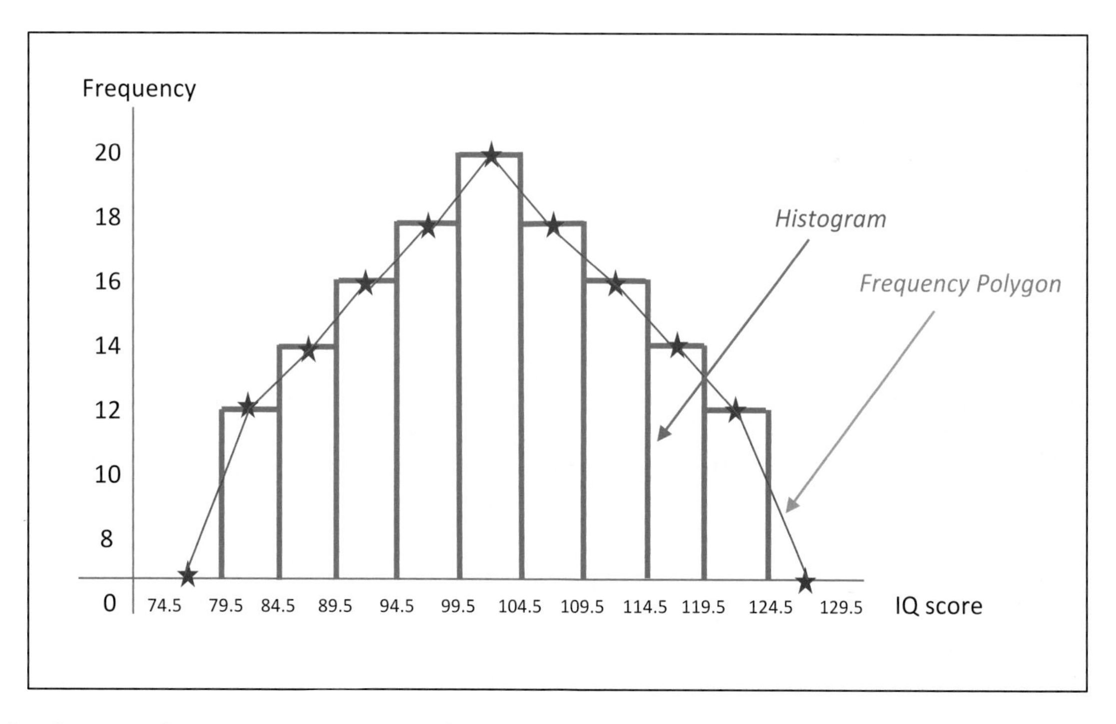

The charting of an ogive or cumulative *(relative)* frequency requires the inclusion of an additional class to which we assign a zero frequency. In the following distribution table, the interval 75 – 79 has been added to enable us to chart the ogive.

Distribution Tables

I Q	Frequency	Cumulative Frequency	
		UCL*	Cum. F
75 - 79	0	≤ 79	0
80 - 84	12	≤ 84	12
85 - 89	14	≤ 89	26
90 - 94	16	≤ 94	42
95 - 99	18	≤ 99	60
100 - 104	20	≤ 104	80
105 - 109	18	≤ 109	98
110 - 114	16	≤ 114	114
115 - 119	14	≤ 119	128
120 - 124	12	≤ 124	140
	140		

**UCL = Upper Class Limit*

The vertical axis for an ogive can be represented by *cumulative frequency or cumulative relative frequency or cumulative percent.*

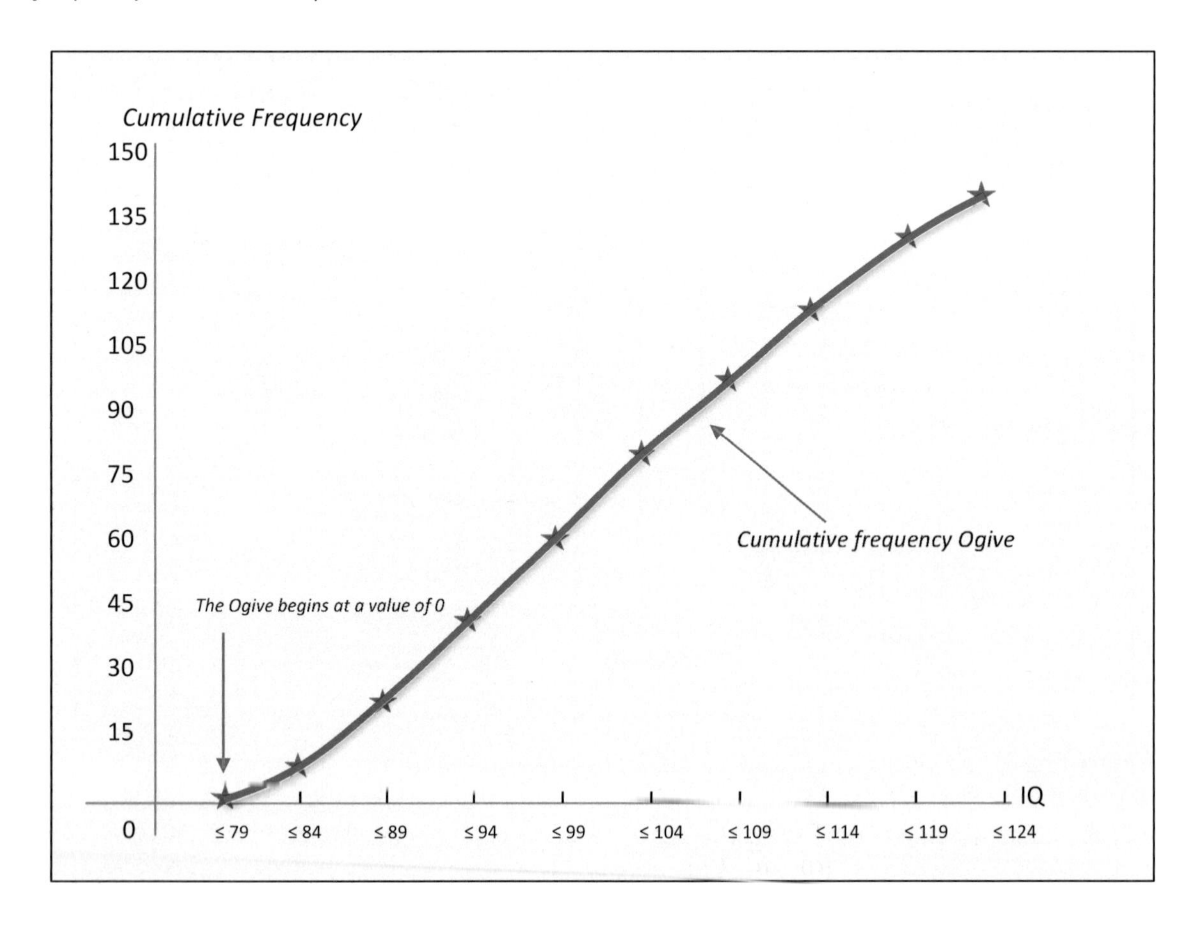

Ungrouped data – A Quantitative Continuous variable

In addition to the above charts, there are a variety of charts that can be derived directly from the raw data. These include:

1. *Five-Number Summary*
2. *Box and Whisker Plot*
3. *Stem & Leaf Display*

Consider the following raw data collected from a sample of 100 college students. The quantitative *continuous* variable of interest is *Walking Times (in minutes)* from town centre to the college.

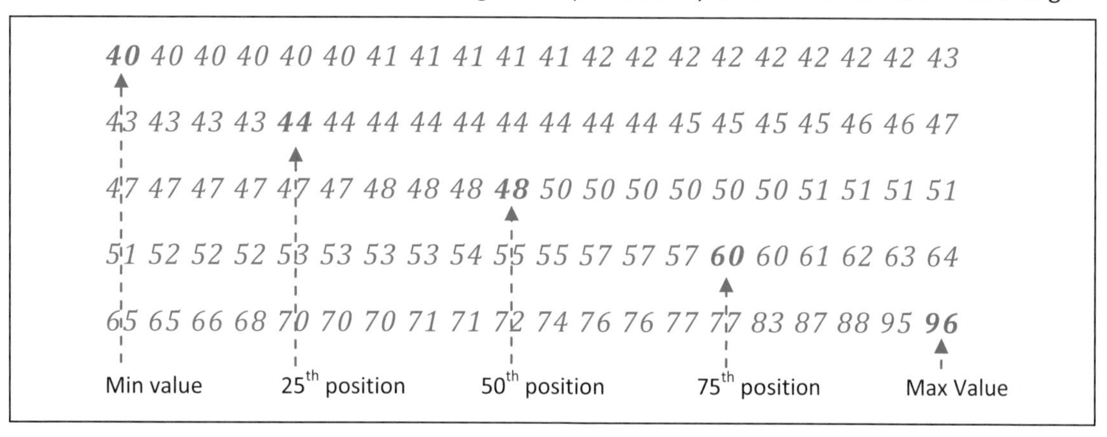

40 40 40 40 40 40 40 41 41 41 41 41 42 42 42 42 42 42 42 42 43

43 43 43 43 **44** 44 44 44 44 44 44 44 44 45 45 45 45 46 46 47

47 47 47 47 47 47 48 48 48 **48** 50 50 50 50 50 50 51 51 51 51

51 52 52 52 53 53 53 53 54 55 55 57 57 57 **60** 60 61 62 63 64

65 65 66 68 70 70 70 71 71 72 74 76 76 77 77 83 87 88 95 **96**

Min value | 25th position | 50th position | 75th position | Max Value

To derive the Five Number Summary, we must identify the following values:

1. Minimum number = **40** *[.25 times the difference from next data point]*
2. Maximum number = **96**
3. $Q_1 = \frac{1}{4}(n + 1) = \frac{1}{4}(100 + 1) = 25.25^{th}$ position i.e. Q_1 = **44** + .25 (44 - **44**) = 44
4. $Q_2 = \frac{1}{2}(n + 1) = \frac{1}{2}(100 + 1) = 50.50^{th}$ position i.e. Q_2 = **48** + .50 (50 - **48**) = 49
5. $Q_3 = \frac{3}{4}(n + 1) = \frac{3}{4}(100 + 1) = 75.75^{th}$ position i.e. Q_3 = **60** + .75 (60 - **60**) = 60

SPSS (Statistical Package for the Social Sciences) definitions for the calculation of the quartiles (Q_1 = first quartile, Q_2 = second quartile, Q_3 = third quartile)

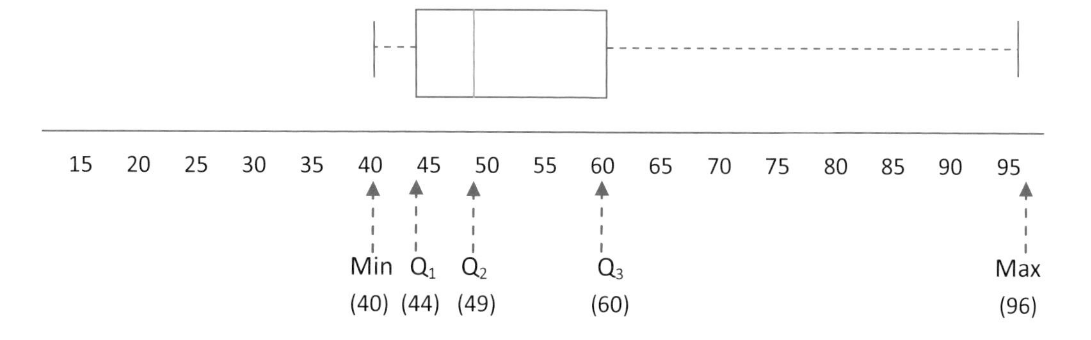

To derive the box and whisker plot, we must identify the following values:

[.25 times the difference from next data point]

1. $Q_1 = ¼ (n + 1) = ¼ (100 + 1) = 25.25^{th}$ position i.e. $Q_1 = 44 + .25 (44 - 44) = 44$
2. $Q_2 = ½ (n + 1) = ½ (100 + 1) = 50.50^{th}$ position i.e. $Q_2 = 48 + .50 (50 - 48) = 49$
3. $Q_3 = ¾ (n + 1) = ¾ (100 + 1) = 75.75^{th}$ position i.e. $Q_3 = 60 + .75 (60 - 60) = 60$
4. IQR *(Interquartile range)* = $Q_3 - Q_1 = 60 - 44 = 16$
5. Suspected Outliers are investigated if they are outside the lower and upper fences
   Lower fence = $Q_1 - 1.5$ (IQR) = 44 – 1.5 (16) = 20
   Upper fence = $Q_3 + 1.5$ (IQR) = 60 + 1.5 (16) = 84
6. Lower Adjacent Value LAV *(minimum value above the lower fence)* = 40 *(which is above 20)*
7. Upper Adjacent Value UAV *(maximum value below the upper fence)* = 83 *(which is below 84)*

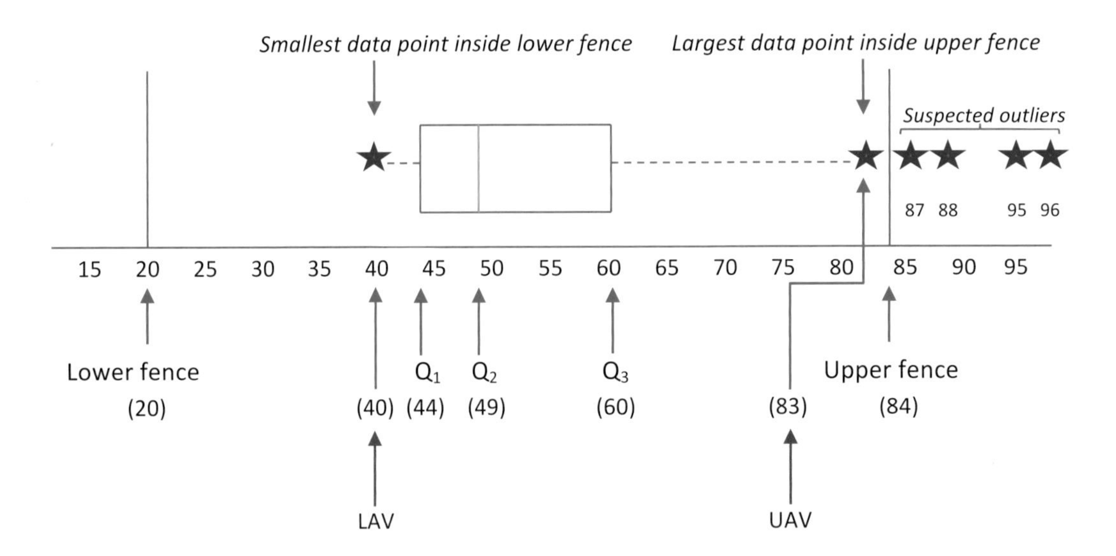

A stem and leaf plot contains some of the features of a histogram but avoids that loss of information which is a consequence of bundling data into class intervals. Consider the following example of a simple stem and leaf construction.

Stem and Leaf Display for the values 80 83 88

Stem	Leaf
8	0 3 8

The number '8' represents the stem and the numbers '0 3 8' represent the leaf. The following Stem and Leaf display is constructed for the variable *Walking Times (in minutes)*. Two options are presented.

Option 1

Each line in the chart is a block of ten *(e.g. Line 1 is a block ranging from 40 to 49).*

4 | 0 0 0 0 0 0 1 1 1 1 1 2 2 2 2 2 2 2 3 3 3 3 3 4 4 4 4 4 4 4 4 4 5 5 5 5 6 6 7 7 7 7 7 7 7 8 8 8 8

5 | 0 0 0 0 0 0 1 1 1 1 1 2 2 2 3 3 3 3 4 5 5 6 6 6

6 | 0 0 1 2 3 4 5 5 6 7

7 | 0 0 0 1 1 2 3 6 6 7 7

8 | 3 4 8

9 | 5 6

Option 2

Each line in the chart is a block of five *(e.g. Line 1 is a block ranging from 40 to 44).*
In this chart the *walking times* have been grouped in fives i.e. the first line will accommodate values ranging from 40 to 44.

4 | 0 0 0 0 0 0 1 1 1 1 1 2 2 2 2 2 2 2 3 3 3 3 3 4 4 4 4 4 4 4 4 4

4 | 5 5 5 5 6 6 7 7 7 7 7 7 7 8 8 8 8

5 | 0 0 0 0 0 0 1 1 1 1 1 2 2 2 3 3 3 3 4

5 | 5 5 7 7 7

6 | 0 0 1 2 3 4

6 | 5 5 6 8

7 | 0 0 0 1 1 2 4

7 | 6 6 7 7

8 | 3

Ungrouped data – Two quantitative continuous variables

A scatter plot allows us to visually explore the relationship between two quantitative variables. Suppose we wish to explore the relationship between self-esteem and levels of optimism. Two validated scales were administered to a sample of 10 people:

	1	2	3	4	5	6	7	8	9	10
Self-esteem scores (Score range 10 – 40)	22	26	13	16	25	19	17	25	26	27
Optimism scores (Score range 6 - 30)	35	40	18	23	34	18	21	38	36	34

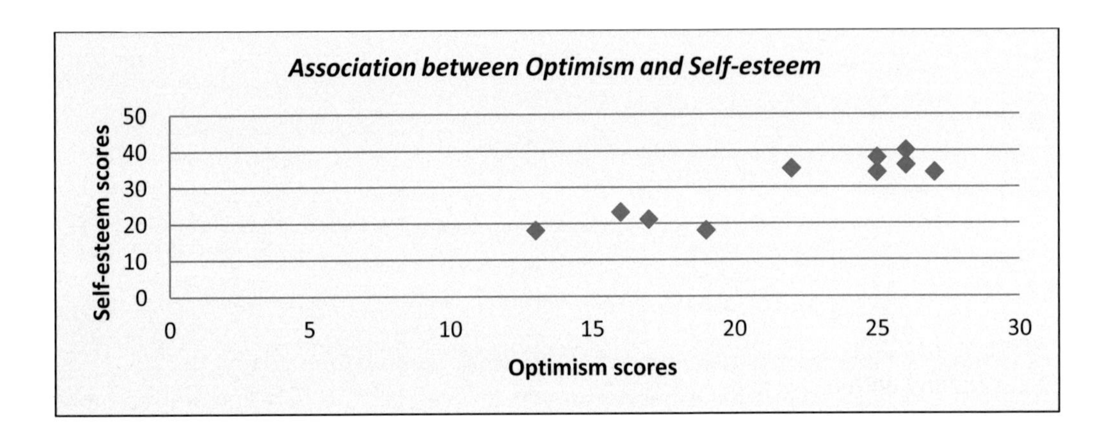

Grouped data – Quantitative Discrete Variable

Whilst a histogram is appropriate for a quantitative *continuous* variable, a bar chart will best represent a quantitative *discrete* variable. Consider the following quantitative *discrete* variable:

	Ordinary 'real' values
	0
	1
Number of children per family	2
	3
	> 3

Each of these values can represent a class in our construction of a bar chart. It may be necessary to limit the number of bars appearing in a bar chart by simply including a catch all category such as '> 3' above. Consider the following sample of 115 households from a population of 1,150 households. Since the variable *Number of children per family* has five values, these values can represent the classes or class intervals. The researcher was able to go directly to Step 5 of the 5 step procedure for constructing distribution tables. A tally sheet can be used to assign each value of the raw data to a class interval and the distribution tables can be constructed as follows:

Distribution Tables

Children per family	Freq.	Rel. Freq.	Cum. Rel. Freq.	Cum. Percent
0	35	0.30	0.30	30%
1	30	0.26	0.56	56%
2	25	0.22	0.78	78%
3	15	0.13	0.91	91%
> 3	10	0.09	1.00	100%
	115			

A bar chart will best represent this quantitative *discrete* variable.

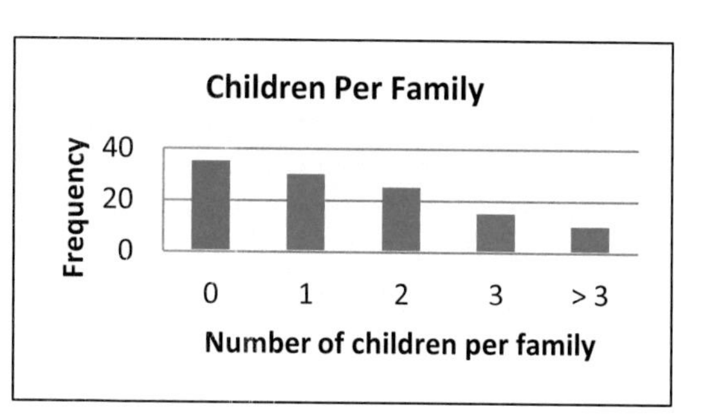

A bar chart can also be employed if we wish to combine a quantitative discrete variable *(Number of children per family)* with a categorical variable. Consider the following example where we compare the relative frequencies of three countries with respect to the quantitative *discrete* variable:

Distribution tables

Children per family	Ireland		China		Algeria	
	Rel. Freq.	Cum. Rel. Freq.	Rel. Freq.	Cum. Rel. Freq.	Rel. Freq.	Cum. Rel. Freq.
0	0.30	0.30	0.20	0.20	0.05	0.05
1	0.26	0.56	0.45	0.65	0.10	0.15
2	0.22	0.78	0.25	0.90	0.15	0.30
3	0.13	0.91	0.05	0.95	0.25	0.55
> 3	0.09	1.00	0.05	1.00	0.45	1.00
	1.00		1.00		1.00	

Bar Chart

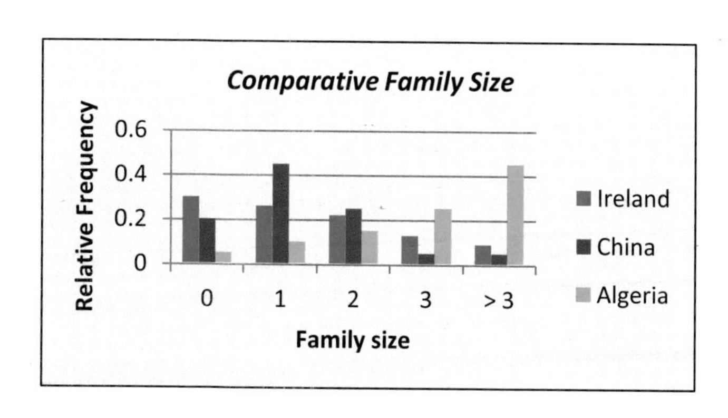

The appropriate measures of centrality for quantitative variables include:

1. *Mean*
2. *Mode* } *Grouped data and Ungrouped*
3. *Median*

Grouped data

The following measures of centrality are calculated for the *continuous* variable *IQ of First year college students.*

1. *Mean*
2. *Mode*
3. *Median*

The calculation of the mean begins with the calculation of the midpoint. Class midpoints are mid-way between lower and upper boundaries *(or class limits).* Therefore the midpoint for the first class is $\frac{80+84}{2}$ = 82. The key to calculating the mean is to allow the formula for the mean to guide your calculations.

Distribution Table

I Q	Freq = f	Midpoint = x	fx
80 - 84	12	82	984
85 - 89	14	87	1218
90 - 94	16	92	1472
95 - 99	18	97	1746
100 - 104	20	102	2040
105 - 109	18	107	1926
110 - 114	16	112	1792
115 - 119	14	117	1638
120 - 124	12	122	1464
	$\sum$f = 140		$\sum$fx = 14280

Mean = $\frac{\sum fx}{\sum f}$ *(where $\sum$ is the sum of)*

Mean = $\frac{\sum fx}{\sum f} = \frac{14280}{140}$ = 102

The calculation of the mode is a little more daunting. Once again the key is to allow the formula for the mode to guide the calculations.

Distribution Table

I Q	f = Frequency
80 - 84	12
85 - 89	14
90 - 94	16
95 - 99	18
100 - 104	20
105 - 109	18
110 - 114	16
115 - 119	14
120 - 124	12
	140

$$\text{Mode} = L + \left[\frac{D1}{D1+D2}\right].C$$

$$\text{Mode} = L + \left[\frac{D1}{D1+D2}\right].C = 100 + \left[\frac{2}{2+2}\right].5 = 102.5$$

L = Lower limit (100) of modal class
C = Modal class width (104.5 – 99.5 = 5)
D1 = Highest freq - freq immediately preceding it (20 – 18 = 2)
D2 = Highest freq - freq immediately following it (20 – 18 = 2)

Some authors prefer to regard the mode the midpoint of the class interval which has the highest frequency (in this case the midpoint of class interval 100 – 104 = 102).

The mode can be derived using a variety of alternative approaches:

a. *Using the formula approach above (102.5)*
b. *In accordance with the preference of other authors (102)*
c. *Graphically (102 approximately). Select 3 histogram bars (one on either side of the class with the highest frequency. The estimate of the mode is derived from the intersection of 2 lines as shown)*

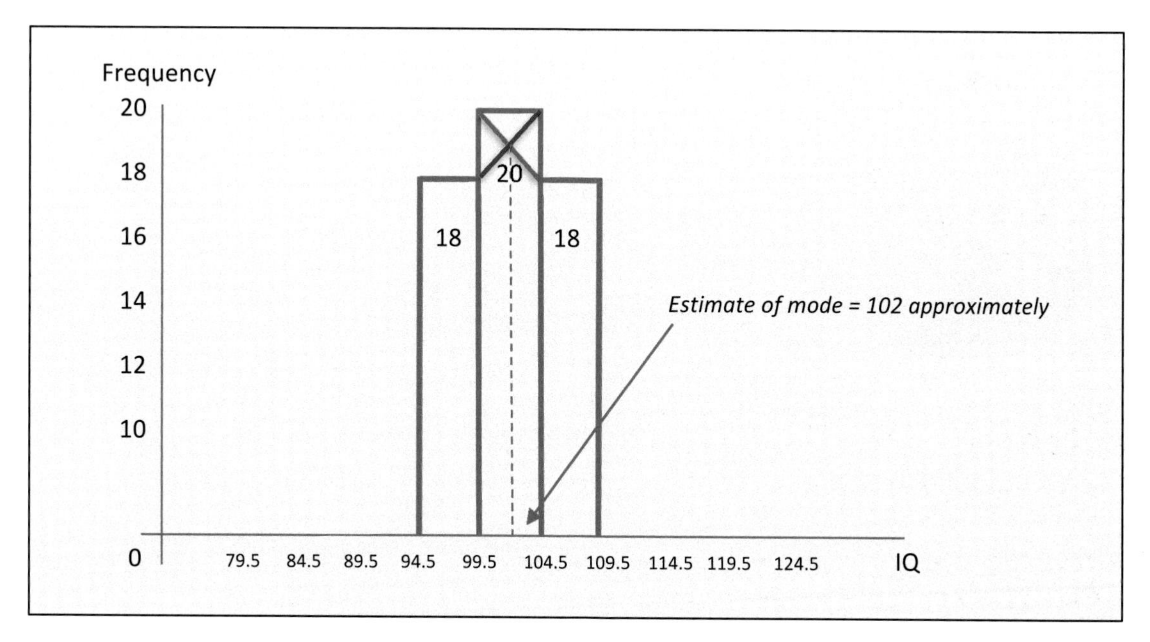

The calculation of the median demands a similar approach to the mode. Again the key is to allow the formula to guide the calculations.

Distribution Table

I Q	*f* = Frequency	F = Cum. Freq.
80 - 84	12	12
85 - 89	14	26
90 - 94	16	42
95 - 99	18	60
100 - 104	20	80
105 - 109	18	98
110 - 114	16	114
115 - 119	14	128
120 - 124	12	140
	140	

$$\text{Median} = L + \left[\frac{\frac{n}{2} - Fm{-}1}{\text{fm}}\right].cm$$

$$\text{Median} = L + \left[\frac{\frac{n}{2} - Fm{-}1}{\text{fm}}\right].cm = 100 + \left[\frac{\frac{140}{2} - 60}{20}\right].5 = 102.5$$

$\frac{n}{2} = \frac{140}{2}$ = 70 = median is in the 70th position
The Median Class contains the 70th position i.e. 100 to 104
L = Lower limit of the median class = 100
Fm-1 = Cum. Freq of the class just prior to the median class i.e. 60
Cm = Median class width = 5 (104.5 – 99.5 = 5)
f_m = frequency of median class = 20

Ungrouped data

The following measures of centrality can be calculated for ungrouped raw data.

1. *Mean*
2. *Mode*
3. *Median*

The anonymous Banksy is considered the most elusive artist in history. His trademark work is street art, graffiti and stenciled pictures. He produces alternative artworks that are often displayed in public areas around the world.

The most expensive Banksy piece sold for $1,870,000 in December 2008 at Sotheby's RED charity auction. The spotted background of the piece is originally an artwork by Damien Hirst who is also a controversial contemporary artist.

1. Keep It Spotless – $1,870,000m
2. Simple Intelligence Testing - $1,265,120m
3. The Rude Lord - $658,025
4. Vandalised Phone Box - $605,000
5. Space Girl and Bird - $575,813
6. Insane Clown - $481,000
7. Queen Victoria - $478,000
8. Laugh Now - $449,349
9. David - $416,742
10. Ruined Landscape - $385,000

Top ten most expensive pieces sold

Average or mean price = $718,405

The mean or average price of the top ten pieces is $718,405

Mean = $\frac{\sum_1^{10} Xi}{n} = \frac{x_1 + x_2 + x_3 + \cdots + x_{10}}{10} = \frac{1{,}870{,}000 + 1{,}265{,}120 + 658{,}025 + \cdots + 385{,}000}{10}$ = 718,405

David Blaine, the magician, has mystified audiences with his combination of intimate magic and death-defying stunts. His mesmerising card tricks are well rehearsed and reliant on the some of the tools of statistics. He has devised techniques for predicting the card that his unsuspecting volunteer is requested to visualise. Demonstrating the trick 'think of a card' does not just give a one in fifty-two chance of correctly guessing the card. His experience is that men will often choose the ace of spades and women will typically select the queen of hearts. These choices represent the most frequently occurring selections in his experience. The mode is the most frequently occurring value for a set of scores or data. Blaine can vary this trick by requesting a volunteer to think of a card that they wouldn't normally think of and men most typically go for the seven of spades whilst women will switch to the seven of diamonds. In fact men will tend to select the seven of spades, seven of clubs, six of spades, eight of spades, six of clubs, eight of clubs, three of spades, four of spades, or four of clubs, in that order. Women will tend to select the seven of diamonds, six of clubs, six of spades or the seven of any of those suits *(Blaine, 2003).* In essence, if you were to attempt each experiment on a sample of men and a sample of women and count the responses, then the mode is that selection that occurs most frequently.

Consider the following set of scores recorded for nine students who attempt the 1st hole at a local 'Crazy Golf' course:

1 2 2 3 3 3 4 4 5

The mean for this set of scores is $\left(\frac{27}{9}\right)$ = 3. The mode for this set of scores is also 3. It is the most frequently occurring value. The mode does not require any calculation or manipulation of the scores. The median is that score which is located exactly half way *(for arranged data)*. The median will have the same number of scores on either side of it. Consider the set of scores recorded for nine students who attempt the 1st hole at a local 'Crazy Golf' course:

Scores	4	5	3	3	2	3	1	4	2

The median is calculated by ordering and ranking these scores and selecting the one in the middle. In this example two students had a score of 2 and will share 2nd and 3rd place between them *(recorded as joint 2nd in this example)*:

Ordered Scores	1	2	2	3	**3**	3	4	4	5
Rank	1st	2nd	2nd	4th	4th	4th	7th	7th	9th
Rank position	1	2	3	4	5	6	7	8	9
					↑ Median				

The median is the score in the middle of the ranked scores *(4th)* or in the middle of the rank position *(5)*. If you have an odd number of scores *(as in this example)* the median is at rank position $\frac{n+1}{2} = \frac{9+1}{2} = 5$. If you have an even number of scores the median is the average of the two middle numbers as located at rank position $\frac{n+1}{2}$ as the following example demonstrates:

Scores	4	5	3	3	2	3	1	4	2	6
Ordered Scores	1	2	2	3	**3**	**3**	4	4	5	6
Rank	1st	2nd	2nd	4th	4th	4th	7th	7th	9th	10th
Rank position	1	2	3	4	5	6	7	8	9	10

↑ *Median*

The median is located at position $\frac{n+1}{2} = \frac{10+1}{2} = 5.5$ which will be the average of the two middle scores $\frac{3+3}{2} = 3$.

Variation

The following measures of variation or spread that can be calculated for the *continuous* variable *IQ of First Year college students* include:

1. *Standard deviation*
2. *Variance*
3. *Mean deviation*
4. *Interquartile range*
5. *Semi interquartile range*

} *Grouped and ungrouped data*

Grouped data

The standard deviation, variance and mean deviation can be calculated as follows:

Distribution Table

I Q	Freq = f	Mid-Point = x	fx	x^2	$f.x^2$
80 - 84	12	82	984	6724	80688
85 - 89	14	87	1218	7569	105966
90 - 94	16	92	1472	8464	135424
95 - 99	18	97	1746	9409	169362
100 - 104	20	102	2040	10404	208080
105 - 109	18	107	1926	11449	206082
110 - 114	16	112	1792	12544	200704
115 - 119	14	117	1638	13689	191646
120 - 124	12	122	1464	14884	178608
	$\sum f = 140$		$\sum fx = 14280$		$\sum f.x^2 = 1476560$

S = $\sqrt{\frac{\sum fx^2}{\sum f} - \left(\frac{\sum fx}{\sum f}\right)^2} = \sqrt{\frac{1476560}{140} - \left(\frac{14280}{140}\right)^2} = \sqrt{143}$ =11.96 = Standard deviation

The variance is the square of the standard deviation [$S^2 = (11.96)^2 = 143$ = Variance]

Mean Deviation

Distribution Table

I Q	Freq = f	Mid-Point = x	fx	$\lvert x - \bar{x}\rvert$	$f\lvert x - \bar{x}\rvert$
80 - 84	12	82	984	20	240
85 - 89	14	87	1218	15	210
90 - 94	16	92	1472	10	160
95 - 99	18	97	1746	5	90
100 - 104	20	102	2040	0	0
105 - 109	18	107	1926	5	90
110 - 114	16	112	1792	10	160
115 - 119	14	117	1638	15	210
120 - 124	12	122	1464	20	240
	$\sum f = 140$		$\sum fx = 14280$		$\sum f\lvert x - \bar{x}\rvert = 1400$

Mean deviation = $\frac{\sum f\,\lvert x-\bar{x}\rvert}{\sum f} = \frac{1400}{140} = 10$

Interquartile Range *(IQR)*

We can divide any data set into four equal parts. This can be done by identifying three quartiles:

1. *Q_1 = First quartile = That value below which 25% of the data lie*
2. *Q_2 = Second quartile =That value below which 50% of the data lie*
3. *Q_3 = Third quartile = That value below which 75% of the data lie*

A quartile can be calculated using the following formula:

$$Q = L_Q + \left[\frac{P_Q - F_{Q-1}}{f_Q}\right] . c_Q$$

Q = Quartile formula for grouped data
L_Q = Lower limit of the quartile class
P_Q = Position of quartile in the distribution
F_{Q-1} = Cumulative frequency of class just prior to the quartile class
f_Q = frequency of quartile class
c_Q = quartile class width

Consider the sample of 140 students selected from a population of 1,400 students. The raw data was converted into the following distribution tables and the quartiles Q_1 Q_2 Q_3 are calculated.

Distribution tables

I Q	f = Frequency	F = Cum. Freq.
80 - 84	12	12
85 - 89	14	26
90 - 94	16	42
95 - 99	18	60
100 - 104	20	80
105 - 109	18	98
110 - 114	16	114
115 - 119	14	128
120 - 124	12	140
	n =140 =$\sum f$	

1. Q_1 is that value below which 25% of the data lie

The first quartile is located at $\left(\frac{1}{4}\right)$. n = $\left(\frac{1}{4}\right)$. 140 = 35th position *(P_Q = 35)*. So Q_1 lies in the class 90 – 94 and L_Q = 90 F_{Q-1} = 26 f_Q = 16 c_Q = 5.

$$Q_1 = L_Q + \left[\frac{P_Q - F_{Q-1}}{f_Q}\right] . c_Q = 90 + \left[\frac{35 - 26}{16}\right] . 5 = \mathbf{92.81}$$

2. Q_2 is that value below which 50% of the data lie

The second quartile is located at $\left(\frac{1}{2}\right) . n = \left(\frac{1}{2}\right). 140 = 70^{th}$ position *($P_Q = 70$)*. So Q_2 lies in the class 100 - 104 and $L_Q = 100$ $F_{Q-1} = 60$ $f_Q = 20$ $c_Q = 5$.

$$Q_2 = L_Q + \left[\frac{P_Q - F_{Q-1}}{f_Q}\right]. c_Q = 100 + \left[\frac{70 - 60}{20}\right]. 5 = \mathbf{102.5}$$

3. Q_3 is that value below which 75% of the data lie

The third quartile is located at $\left(\frac{3}{4}\right) . n = \left(\frac{3}{4}\right). 140 = 105^{th}$ position *($P_Q = 105$)*. So Q_3 lies in the class 110 - 114 and $L_Q = 110$ $F_{Q-1} = 98$ $f_Q = 16$ $c_Q = 5$

$$Q_3 = L_Q + \left[\frac{P_Q - F_{Q-1}}{f_Q}\right]. c_Q = 110 + \left[\frac{105 - 98}{16}\right]. 5 = \mathbf{112.18}$$

Interquartile Range (IQR)

The Interquartile range can be calculated from the two quartiles Q_1 and Q_3

$IQR = Q_3 - Q_1 = 112.18 - 92.81 = 19.37$

Semi - Interquartile Range *(SIQR)* or Quartile Deviation

The Semi - Interquartile range is the interquartile range divided by 2

$SIQR = \frac{IQR}{2} = \frac{Q3 - Q1}{2} = \frac{112.18 - 92.81}{2} = \frac{19.37}{2} = 9.69$

Appropriate treatment of an individual score

Percentile Rank *(PR)* = If I scored 117 *(X = 117)* in this IQ test, what percentage of students scored lower?

Distribution Table

I Q	f = Frequency	F = Cum. Freq.
80 - 84	12	12
85 - 89	14	26
90 - 94	16	42
95 - 99	18	60
100 - 104	20	80
105 - 109	18	98
110 - 114	16	114
115 - 119	14	128
120 - 124	12	140
	n=140 = $\sum f$	

$$PR = \frac{Fx-1+\left[\frac{X-Xl}{Cx}\right].fx}{n} \; x\; 100$$

$$PR = \frac{114+\left[\frac{117-115}{5}\right].14}{140} \text{ x } 100 = 85.43$$

X = A given score in the question
F_{x-1} = Cum. Freq. of class just prior to the class containing X
Xl = Score at the lower limit of the class containing X
Cx = Width of class containing X
f_x = frequency of class containing X

If I scored 117 *(X = 117)* in this IQ test, 85.43% of students scored lower.

Ungrouped data

Consider the set of scores recorded for nine students who attempt the 1st hole at a local 'Crazy Golf' course:

Scores *1 2 2 3 3 3 4 4 5*

The range is the difference between the minimum and maximum scores *(5 – 1 = 4)*. The standard deviation can be calculated as follows:

Scores = x	Mean = $\bar{x} = \frac{27}{9} = 3$	Difference = x - $\bar{x}$	Difference squared = $(x - \bar{x})^2$
1	3	-2	4
2	3	-1	1
2	3	-1	1
3	3	0	0
3	3	0	0
3	3	0	0
4	3	1	1
4	3	1	1
5	3	2	4
n = 9 scores			$\sum(x - \bar{x})^2 = 12$

Standard Deviation = S = $\sqrt{\frac{\sum(x-\bar{x})^2}{n-1}} = \sqrt{\frac{12}{9-1}}$ = 1.225 Variance = $S^2 = (1.225)^2$ = 1.5

The mean deviation can be calculated as follows:

Scores = x	Mean = $\bar{x} = \frac{27}{9} = 3$	Absolute Difference = $\lvert x - \bar{x} \rvert$
1	3	2
2	3	1
2	3	1
3	3	0
3	3	0
3	3	0
4	3	1
4	3	1
5	3	2
n = 9 scores		$\sum \lvert x - \bar{x} \rvert = 8$

Mean deviation = $\frac{\sum \lvert x - \bar{x} \rvert}{n} = \frac{8}{9} = 0.89$

The Interquartile Range *(IQR)* can be calculated as follows:

Scores	1	2	2	3	3	3	4	4	5
Rank Position	1	2	3	4	5	6	7	8	9

↑ 2.5^{th} position (between ranks 2 and 3) ↑ 7.5^{th} position (between ranks 7 and 8)

[.5 times the difference from next data point]

Q_1 = ¼ (n + 1) = ¼ (9 + 1) = 2.5^{th} position = 2 + .5 (2 – 2) = 2

Q_3 = ¾ (n + 1) = ¾ (9 + 1) = 7.5^{th} position = 4 + .5 (4 – 4) = 4

IQR = $Q_3 - Q_1$ = 4 – 2 = 2

The semi – Interquartile range is calculated as follows = $\frac{Q3-Q1}{2} = \frac{4-2}{2} = 1$

Deriving Quartiles from an Ogive

The Ogive can also be used to get *approximate* values for Q_1 Q_2 and Q_3. These quartiles can then be used to estimate a number of measures *(e.g. median, interquartile range)*. Consider the sample of 140 students which were selected from a population of 1400 students. The ogive was charted as follows:

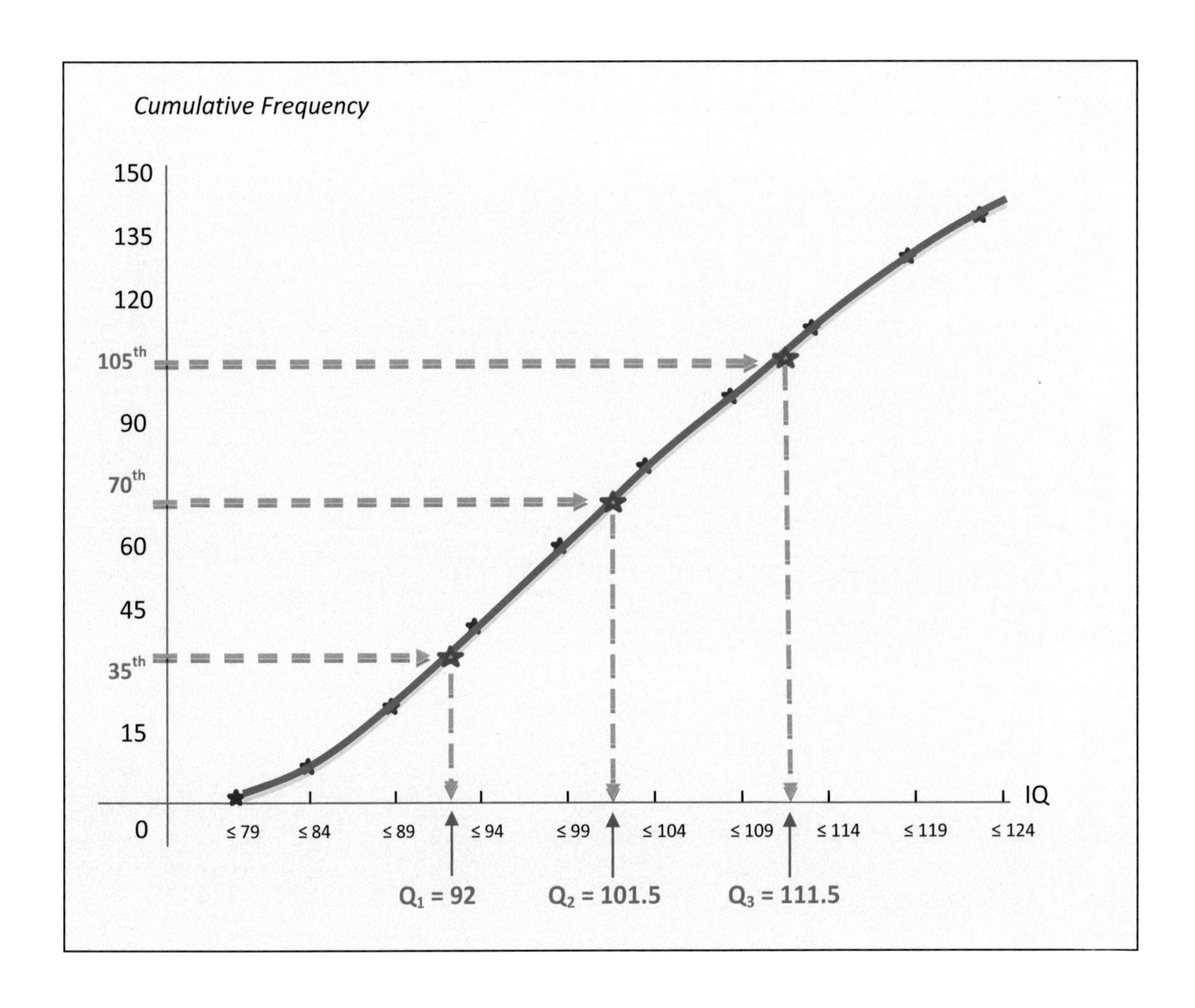

The quartiles are:

1. *Q_1 = ¼ (n) = ¼ (140) = 35th position i.e. Q_1 = 92 approx.*
2. *Q_2 = ½ (n) = ½ (140) = 70th position i.e. Q_2 = 101.5 approx.*
3. *Q_3 = ¾ (n) = ¾ (140) = 105th position i.e. Q_3 = 111.5 approx.*

2.7 MCQs and Solutions

1. Which of the following is not a measure of centrality?

(a) Mode
(b) Median
(c) Mean
(d) Range

2. Which of the following is not a measure of variation?

(a) Standard deviation
(b) Range
(c) Inter-Quartile range
(d) Median

3. The median of the following sample is...? *14 10 19 20 23 15*

(a) 19.5
(b) 17
(c) 16.83
(d) 13

4. The first quartile of the following sample is...? *2 9 7 15 14 10 5 3 8 12*

(a) 8.5
(b) 4.5
(c) 4
(d) 7

5. The second quartile of the following sample is...? *2 9 7 15 14 10 5 3 8 12*

(a) 8.5
(b) 4.5
(c) 4
(d) 7

6. The interquartile range is equal to:

(a) Maximum value minus the minimum value of a sample
(b) The square root of the variance
(c) The third quartile minus the first quartile
(d) The third quartile minus the first quartile and the result divided by 2

7. If I organise data into classes and assign a number of items to each class, then I have created a:

(a) Frequency distribution/Frequency table
(b) Histogram
(c) Box Plot
(d) Stem and leaf plot

8. Consider the following classes: 10 to 19, 20 to 29...which of the following is incorrect?

(a) The class width is 10
(b) The class boundaries for the first class are 9.5 to 19.5
(c) The class midpoint for the first class is 14.5
(d) The class width is chosen by dividing the total number of values by the selected number of classes.

9. If we are constructing a relative frequency distribution, then:

(a) Each class frequency is divided by 100
(b) Each class frequency is divided by the total frequency
(c) Each successive class frequency is added to the preceding class frequency
(d) Each class frequency is multiplied by the midpoint of each respective class

10. What is the least level of measurement *(Nominal/Ordinal/Interval/Ratio)* necessary to calculate the mode?

(a) At least a nominal level
(b) At least an ordinal level
(c) At least a ratio level
(d) At least an interval level

11. What is the least level of measurement *(Nominal/Ordinal/Interval/Ratio)* necessary to calculate the median?

(a) At least a nominal level
(b) At least an ordinal level
(c) At least a ratio level
(d) At least an interval level

12. The mean is computed by finding:

(a) The most frequently occurring score
(b) The score that is located exactly halfway *(of an arranged set of scores)*
(c) Summing the scores and dividing by 2
(d) Summing the values and dividing by the number of values

13. What is the least level of measurement *(Nominal/Ordinal/Interval/Ratio)* necessary to calculate the mean?

(a) At least a nominal level
(b) At least an ordinal level
(c) At least a ratio level
(d) At least an interval level

14. A Five number summary requires

(a) Q1, Q2 and Q3 along with the maximum and minimum values
(b) Q1, Q2 and Q3 along with Q1 – 1.5 (IQR) and Q3 + 1.5 (IQR) and lower and upper adjacent values
(c) The 3 measures of centrality along with 2 measures of variation
(d) Mean and the interquartile range

15. The box and whisker plot requires

(a) Q1, Q2 and Q3 along with the maximum and minimum values
(b) Q1, Q2 and Q3 along with Q1 – 1.5 (IQR) and Q3 + 1.5 (IQR) and lower and upper adjacent values
(c) The 3 measures of centrality along with 2 measures of variation
(d) Mean and the interquartile range

16. The standard deviation is equal to:

(a) The square root of the variance
(b) The variance squared
(c) Mean deviation
(d) Square root of the mean

17. The times (minutes) that it took a random sample of students to complete a class quiz were

23 35 14 37 28 37 20 29 49 40

Our calculations of the mean and median were _______ and _______ respectively. Therefore, the distribution can be described as ___________________________. The interquartile range and standard deviation are _______ and _______ respectively.

(a) 31.2 and 32, not symmetric (negatively skewed), 15.5, 10.43
(b) 31.2 and 37, not symmetric (negatively skewed), 17, 10.43
(c) 31.2 and 32, not symmetric (Positively skewed), 15.5, 10.43
(d) None of the above

18. The following frequency distribution summarises the time spent on Facebook of a sample of second level students. What is the approximate mean and standard deviation of this distribution?

Time - (minutes)	Frequency
20 – 40	2
40 – 60	4
60 – 80	6
80 – 100	4
100 - 120	2

(a) 3.6 and 564.70 respectively
(b) 6.0 and 312.72 respectively
(c) 100 and 70 respectively
(d) 70 and 23.09 respectively

19. Which of the following best explains how Jack performed?

(a) I got 80 out of 100 in Statistics
(b) 90% of the class got less than 80 in Statistics (80 is jacks score)
(c) I got 20 marks above the class average (class average = 60 and jack got 80)
(d) None of the above

20. Which of the following gives meaning to Jacks Statistics result?

(a) The percentile rank of his score
(b) The distance of his score from the class average
(c) The absolute value of his score
(d) The spread of scores around the class average

MCQ Solutions

1. (d)	6. (c)	11. (b)	16. (a)
2. (d)	7. (a)	12. (d)	17. (a)
3. (b)	8. (d)	13. (d)	18. (d)
4. (b)	9. (b)	14. (a)	19. (b)
5. (a)	10. (a)	15. (b)	20. (a)

2.8 Test Questions and Solutions

Q1. Summarising Data – Nominal variable

A sample of 200 teen deaths from a population of teen deaths of 2,000 in a large city in 2012 revealed the following information:

Cause of death	Frequency
Car / Bike Accident	62
Suicide	86
Medical Illness	8
Street Violence	44
	200

(a) Use Excel to chart:
- A bar chart *(using the frequency distribution)*
- A bar chart *(using a relative frequency distribution)*
- A pie chart

(b) What is the mode of this frequency distribution

Q2. Summarising Data – Ordinal variable

Consider the frequency distribution of grades for the 2011 graduates of a BBS degree programme.

Class (Grades)	Frequency
Fail	8
III	10
II.2	13
II.1	12
I	6

(a) Construct a relative frequency distribution
(b) Construct a cumulative frequency distribution
(c) Construct a cumulative relative frequency distribution
(d) Use Excel to chart
- A bar chart *(using a relative frequency distribution)*
- A bar chart *(using a cumulative frequency distribution)*
- A bar chart *(using a cumulative relative frequency distribution*

(e) What is the mode of the frequency distribution
(f) What is the median of the frequency distribution

Q3. Summarising Data – Quantitative variable

Consider the variable *Time taken on Make-up* which is a quantitative *continuous* variable. A sample of 65 female students revealed the following raw data which was subsequently converted into distribution tables.

22	***29***	*16*	*15*	*18*	*17*	*12*	*13*	*17*	*16*	*15*
19	*17*	***10***	*21*	*15*	*14*	*17*	*18*	*12*	*20*	*14*
16	*15*	*16*	*20*	*22*	*14*	*25*	*19*	*23*	*15*	*19*
18	*23*	*22*	*16*	*16*	*19*	*13*	*18*	*24*	*24*	*26*
13	*18*	*17*	*15*	*24*	*15*	*17*	*14*	*18*	*17*	*21*
16	*21*	*25*	*19*	*20*	*27*	*16*	*17*	*16*	*21*	

Distribution Tables

Class	Frequency	Relative frequency	Cumulative frequency		Cum Rel Freq	
10 – 12	3	3/65 = .05	≤ 12	3	≤ 12	.05
13 – 15	14	14/65 = .22	≤ 15	17 (3 + 14)	≤ 15	.27 (.05 + .22)
16 – 18	23	23/65 = .35	≤ 18	40 (17 + 23)	≤ 18	.62 (.27 +. 35)
19 – 21	12	12/65 = .18	≤ 21	52 (40 + 12)	≤ 21	.80 (.62 + .18)
22 – 24	8	8/65 = .12	≤ 24	60 (52 + 8)	≤ 24	.92 (.80 + .12)
25 – 27	4	4/65 = .06	≤ 27	64 (60 + 4)	≤ 27	.98 (.92 + .06)
28 – 30	1	1/65 = .02	≤ 30	65 (64 + 1)	≤ 30	1.00 (.98 + .02)
	65	1.0				

(a) Use excel to chart the following:
  I. Histogram *(Frequency Histogram)*
  II. Frequency Polygon
  III. Ogive

(b) Calculate appropriate measure of centrality
  I. Mean
  II. Mode
  III. Median

(c) Calculate appropriate measures of variation
  I. Standard Deviation
  II. Variance
  III. Interquartile range *(calculate this from the distribution tables)*
  IV. Semi – interquartile range

(d) Calculate the percentile rank for a score of 26

(e) Construct the Five number summary from the original data

(f) Construct a Box and Whisker plot from the original data

(g) Construct the Stem and Leaf diagram from the original data

Solutions

Q1. Summarising Data – Nominal variable

Cause of death	Frequency	Relative frequency
Car / Bike Accident	62	0.31
Suicide	86	0.43
Medical illness	8	0.04
Street Violence	44	0.22
	200	

Q1 (a)

Bar chart

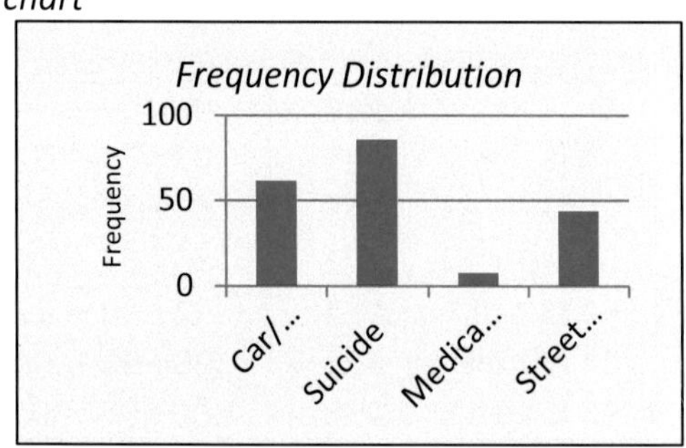

The horizontal axis is divided into 4 even distances. We then place a column of equal width in each of the 4 spaces. The column has a height equal to the frequency of each category.

Bar Chart

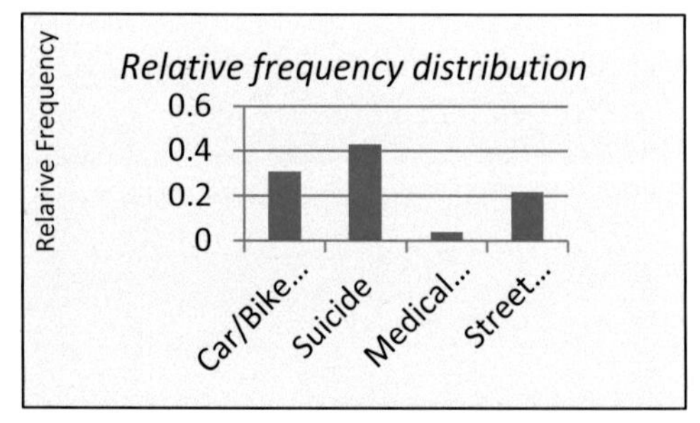

This is the same as the chart above but the columns have a height equal to the relative frequencies.

Pie chart

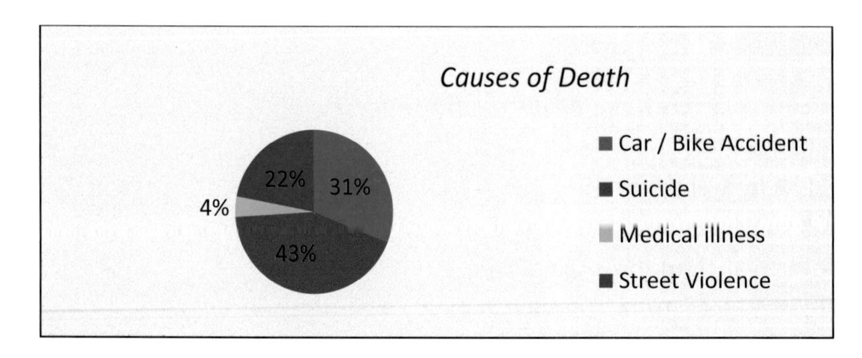

Appropriate measures of centrality

(b) The mode *(most frequently occurring observation)* is *Suicide (Suicide has the highest frequency).*

Q2. Summarising Data – Ordinal variable

Consider the frequency distribution of grades for final year of a degree in business

(a) (b) (c)

Distribution Tables

Class (Grades)	Frequency	Relative Frequency	Cumulative Frequency	Cumulative Relative frequency
Fail	8	0.163	8	0.163
III	10	0.204	18	0.369
II.2	13	0.265	31	0.634
II.1	12	0.244	43	0.878
I	6	0.122	49	1.000
	49			

(d) Bar Charts

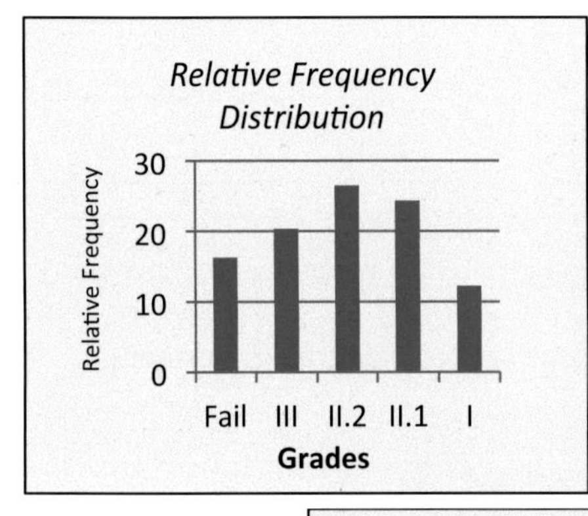

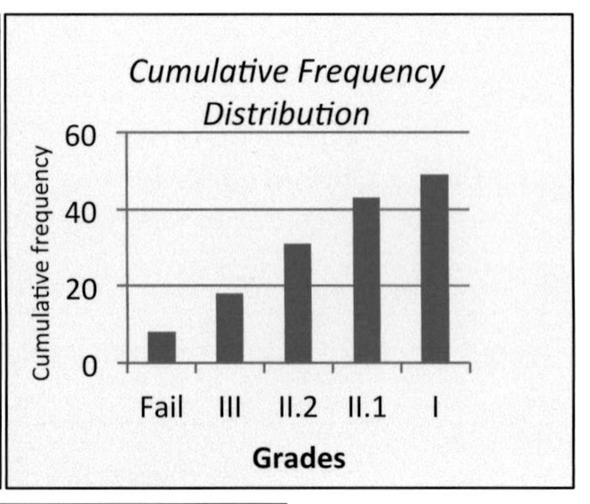

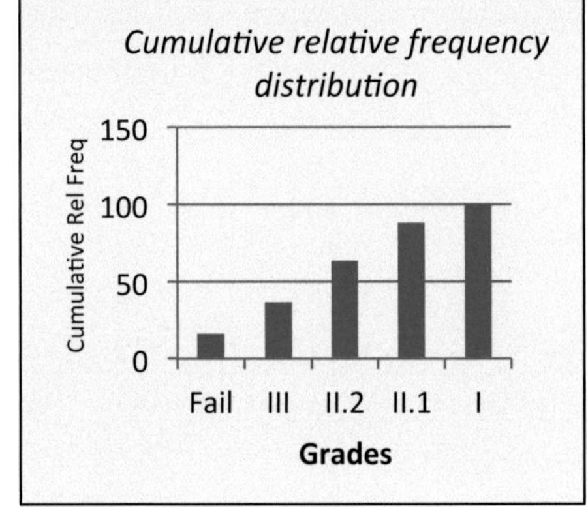

(e) *Appropriate measures of centrality*

The mode *(most frequently occurring observation)* is II.2 *(the Value 'II.2' has the highest frequency)*

(f) *Appropriate measures of centrality*

The median *(middlemost observation of the ordered data)* is 'II.2'

From the data set with size 49, the middlemost observation is the 25th $\left(\frac{49}{2}\right)$. According to the cumulative frequencies in the table, the first 18 observations were opposite the values Fail and III while the first 31 observations were opposite the values Fail and III and II.2. Consequently, the 25th observation is opposite II.2. Hence the median is 'II.2'

Q3. Summarising Data – Continuous variable

(a) Construct the following charts

i. Histogram *(Frequency Histogram)*
ii. Frequency Polygon

Distribution Tables

Class (Makeup speed)	Frequency	Relative frequency	Boundaries	Midpoint
10 – 12	3	3/65 = .05	9.5 – 12.5	11
13 – 15	14	14/65 = .22	12.5 – 15.5	14
16 – 18	23	23/65 = .35	15.5 – 18.5	17
19 – 21	12	12/65 = .18	18.5 – 21.5	20
22 – 24	8	8/65 = .12	21.5 – 24.5	23
25 – 27	4	4/65 = .06	24.5 – 27.5	26
28 – 30	1	1/65 = .02	27.5 – 30.5	29
	65	1.0		

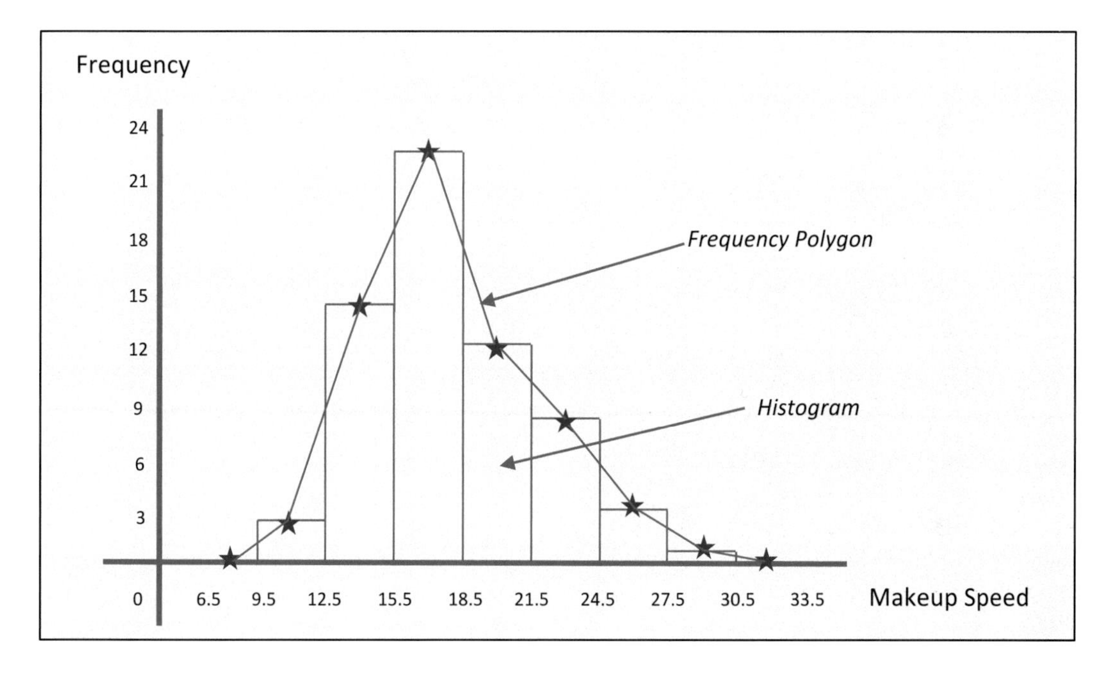

iii. Ogive

An extra class is added when constructing this chart since the Ogive must begin at 0.

Distribution Tables

Class	Frequency	Cumulative frequency	
7 – 9	0	≤ 9	0
10 – 12	3	≤ 12	3
13 – 15	14	≤ 15	17 (3 + 14)
16 – 18	23	≤ 18	40 (17 + 23)
19 – 21	12	≤ 21	52 (40 + 12)
22 – 24	8	≤ 24	60 (52 + 8)
25 – 27	4	≤ 27	64 (60 + 4)
28 – 30	1	≤ 30	65 (64 + 1)
	65		

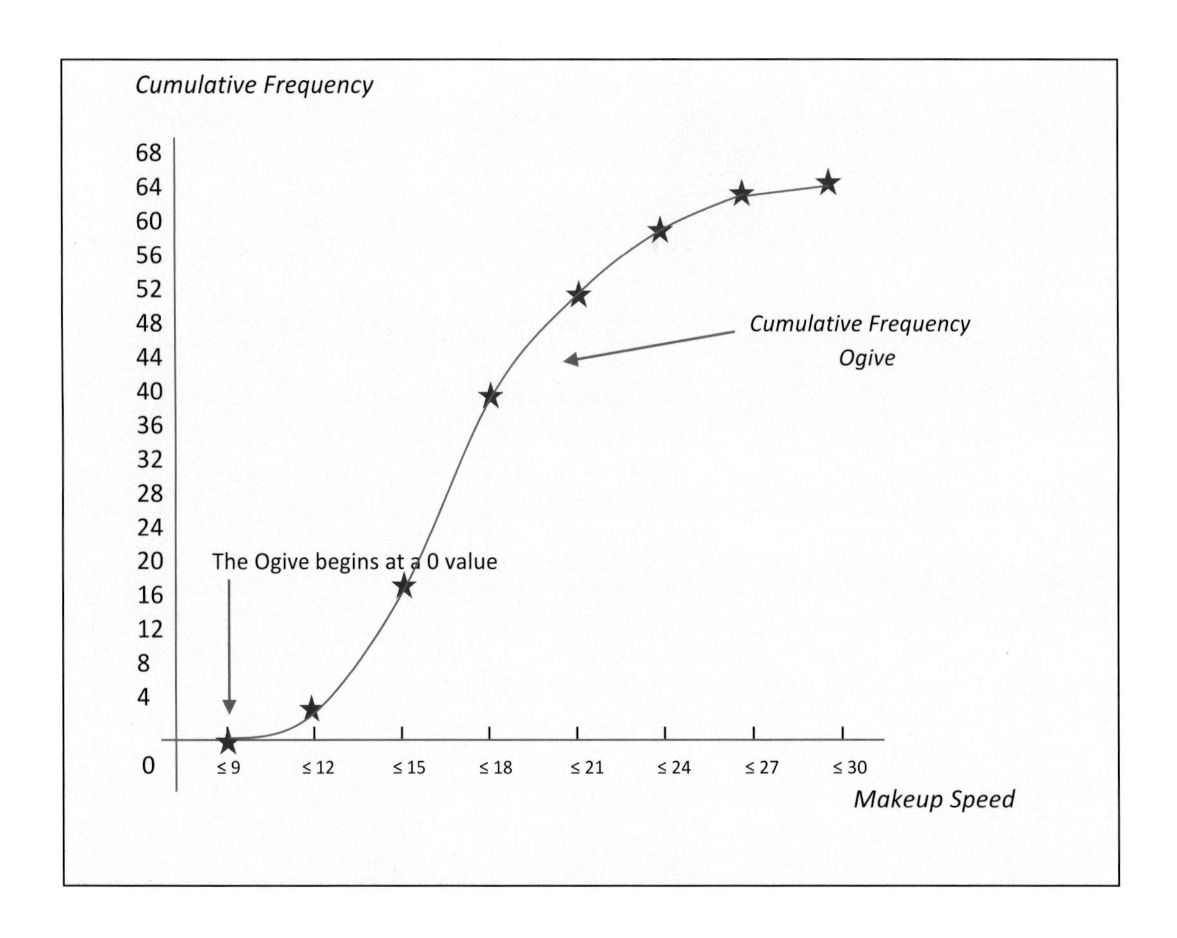

(b) Calculate appropriate measure of centrality

i. Mean

Distribution Table

Class	Frequency = f	Midpoint	fx
10 – 12	3	11	33
13 – 15	14	14	196
16 – 18	23	17	391
19 – 21	12	20	240
22 – 24	8	23	184
25 – 27	4	26	104
28 – 30	1	29	29
	∑f = 65		∑fx = 1177

$$\text{Mean} = \frac{\sum fx}{\sum f} = \frac{1177}{65} = 18.1$$

ii. Mode

Distribution Tables

Class	Frequency	Relative frequency
10 – 12	3	3/65 = .05
13 – 15	14	14/65 = .22
16 – 18	23	23/65 = .35
19 – 21	12	12/65 = .18
22 – 24	8	8/65 = .12
25 – 27	4	4/65 = .06
28 – 30	1	1/65 = .02
	65	1.0

$$\text{Mode} = L + \left[\frac{D1}{D1+D2}\right].C$$

$$\text{Mode} = 16 + \left[\frac{9}{9+11}\right].3 = 17.35$$

L = Lower limit (16) of modal class
C = Modal class Width (18.5 – 15.5 = 3)
D1 = Highest freq - freq immediately preceding it (23 – 14 = 9)
D2 = Highest freq - freq immediately following it (23 – 12 = 11)

iii. Median

Distribution Tables

Class	Freq.	F = Cum. freq.	
10 – 12	3	≤ 12	3
13 – 15	14	≤ 15	17 (3 + 14)
16 – 18	23	≤ 18	40 (17 + 23)
19 – 21	12	≤ 21	52 (40 + 12)
22 – 24	8	≤ 24	60 (52 + 8)
25 – 27	4	≤ 27	64 (60 + 4)
28 – 30	1	≤ 30	65 (64 + 1)
	65		

$$\text{Median} = L + \left[\frac{\frac{N}{2} - Fm-1}{\text{fm}}\right].cm$$

$$\text{Median} = 16 + \left[\frac{\frac{65}{2} - 17}{23}\right].3 = 18.02$$

n/2 = 65/2 = 32.5 hence the median is in the 33th position
The Median Class contains the 33rd position i.e. 16 - 18
L = Lower limit of the median class = 16
Fm-1 = Cum. freq of class just prior to the median class i.e.1
Cm = Median class width = 3
f_m = frequency of median class = 23

(c). Calculate appropriate measures of variation

Distribution Tables

Class	Frequency = *f*	Midpoint = x	fx	x^2	$f.x^2$
10 – 12	3	11	33	121	363
13 – 15	14	14	196	196	2744
16 – 18	23	17	391	289	6647
19 – 21	12	20	240	400	4800
22 – 24	8	23	184	529	4232
25 – 27	4	26	104	676	2704
28 – 30	1	29	29	841	841
	∑f = 65		∑fx = 1177		$\sum f.x^2$ = 22331

i. Standard Deviation

$$S = \sqrt{\frac{\sum fx^2}{\sum f} - \left(\frac{\sum fx}{\sum f}\right)^2} = \sqrt{\frac{22331}{65} - \left(\frac{1177}{65}\right)^2} = 3.96$$

ii. Variance

$$S^2 = (3.96)^2 = 15.68 = \text{Variance}$$

iii. Interquartile Range = IQR

Class	Frequency	F = Cumulative frequency	
10 – 12	3	≤ 12	3
13 – 15	14	≤ 15	17 (3 + 14)
16 – 18	23	≤ 18	40 (17 + 23)
19 – 21	12	≤ 21	52 (40 + 12)
22 – 24	8	≤ 24	60 (52 + 8)
25 – 27	4	≤ 27	64 (60 + 4)
28 – 30	1	≤ 30	65 (64 + 1)
	65		

IQR = $Q_3 - Q_1$ = 21.19 – 15.84 = 5.35 (*Q_3 and Q_1 are derived as follows):*

A quartile can be calculated using the following formula:

$$Q = L_Q + \left[\frac{P_Q - F_{Q-1}}{f_Q}\right] . c_Q$$

Q = Quartile formula for grouped data
L_Q = Lower limit of the quartile class
P_Q = Position of quartile in the distribution
F_{Q-1} = Cumulative frequency of class just prior to the quartile class
f_Q = frequency of quartile class
c_Q = quartile class width

Q_1 is that value below which 25% of the data lie

The first quartile is located at $\left(\frac{1}{4}\right)$. n = $\left(\frac{1}{4}\right)$. 65 = 16.25th position *(P_Q = 16.25)*. So Q_1 lies in the class 13 - 15 and L_Q = 13 F_{Q-1} = 3 f_Q = 14 c_Q = 3

$$Q_1 = L_Q + \left[\frac{P_Q - F_{Q-1}}{f_Q}\right] . c_Q = 13 + \left[\frac{16.25 - 3}{14}\right] . 3 = \mathbf{15.84}$$

Q_2 is that value below which 50% of the data lie

The second quartile is located at $\left(\frac{1}{2}\right)$. n = $\left(\frac{1}{2}\right)$. 65 = 32.5th position *(P_Q = 32.5)*. So Q_2 lies in the class 16 - 18 and L_Q = 16 F_{Q-1} = 17 f_Q = 23 c_Q = 3

$$Q_2 = L_Q + \left[\frac{P_Q - F_{Q-1}}{f_Q}\right] . c_Q = 16 + \left[\frac{32.5 - 17}{23}\right] . 3 = \mathbf{18.02}$$

Q_3 is that value below which 75% of the data lie

The third quartile is located at $\left(\frac{3}{4}\right)$. n = $\left(\frac{3}{4}\right)$. 65 = 48.75th position *(P_Q = 48.75)*. So Q_3 lies in the class 19 - 21 and L_Q = 19 F_{Q-1} = 40 f_Q = 12 c_Q = 3

$$Q_3 = L_Q + \left[\frac{P_Q - F_{Q-1}}{f_Q}\right] . c_Q = 19 + \left[\frac{48.75 - 40}{12}\right] . 3 = \mathbf{21.19}$$

iv. Semi - Interquartile Range *(SIQR)* or Quartile deviation

$$SIQR = \frac{Q3 - Q1}{2} = \frac{21.19 - 15.84}{2} = \frac{5.35}{2} = 2.6$$

(d). Calculate the percentile rank for a score of 26

If a student spends 26 minutes *(X = 26)* on her Makeup, what percentage of females were faster?

Class	Frequency	F = Cumulative frequency	
10 – 12	3	≤ 12	3
13 – 15	14	≤ 15	17 (3 + 14)
16 – 18	23	≤ 18	40 (17 + 23)
19 – 21	12	≤ 21	52 (40 + 12)
22 – 24	8	≤ 24	60 (52 + 8)
25 – 27	4	≤ 27	64 (60 + 4)
28 – 30	1	≤ 30	65 (64 + 1)
	65		

$$PR = \frac{Fx - 1 + \left[\frac{X - Xl}{Cx}\right] . fx}{n} \; x \; 100$$

$$PR = \frac{60 + \left[\frac{26-25}{3}\right] . 4}{65} \text{ x } 100 = 94.36$$

X = A given score in the question

F_{x-1} = Cum. Freq. of class just prior to the class containing X

Xl = Score at the lower limit of the class containing X

Cx = Width of class containing X

f_x = frequency of class containing X

(e) The raw data from the variable *time taken on make-up* has been ordered as follows

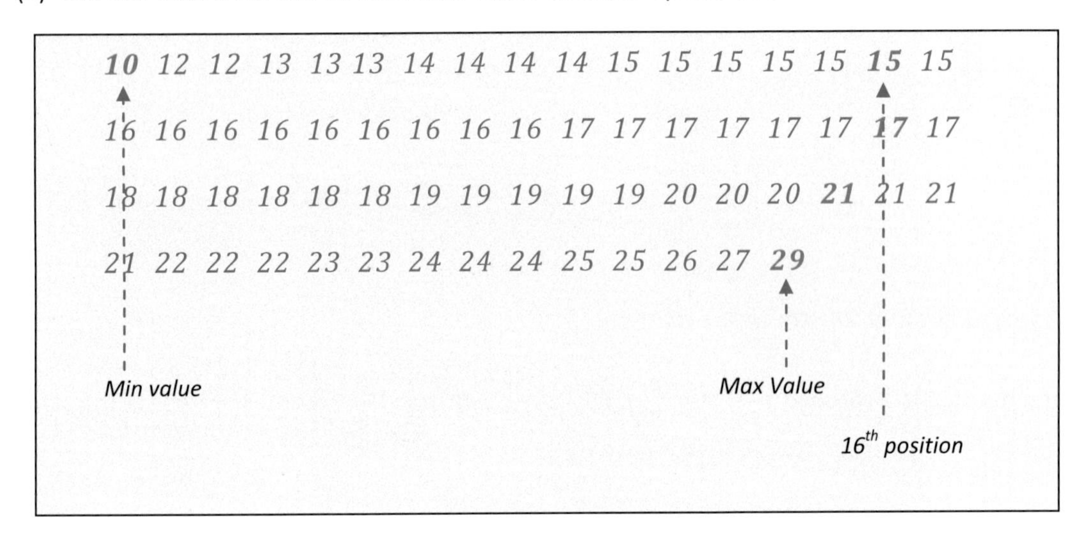

The Five – number summary requires the following 5 numbers:

1. Minimum number = 10
2. Maximum number = 29

16th position *.5 times the difference from next data point*

3. Q_1 = ¼ (n + 1) = ¼ (65 + 1) = 16.5th position i.e. Q_1 = 15 + .5 (15 - 15) = 15
4. Q_2 = ½ (n + 1) = ½ (65 + 1) = 33th position i.e. Q_2 = 17 = 17
5. Q_3 = ¾ (n + 1) = ¾ (65 + 1) = 49.5th position i.e. Q_3 = 21 + .5 (21 - 21) = 21

SPSS (Statistical Package for the Social Sciences) definitions for the calculation of the quartiles are adopted.

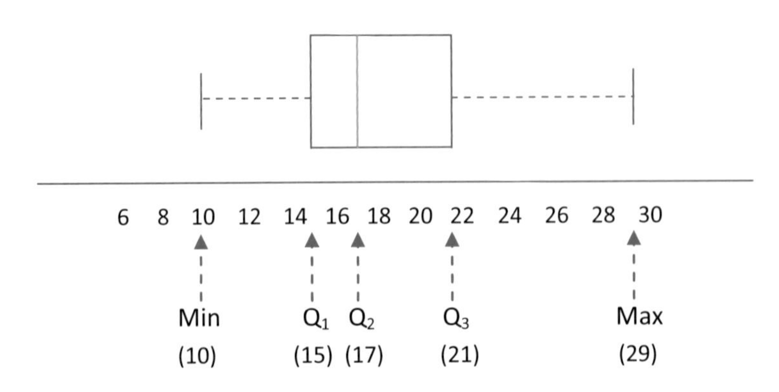

(f) The Box and whisker plot can be charted using the following numbers:

16th position .5 times the difference from next data point

1. $Q_1 = ¼ (n + 1) = ¼ (65 + 1) = 16.5^{th}$ position i.e. $Q_1 = 15 + .5 (15 - 15) = 15$
2. $Q_2 = ½ (n + 1) = ½ (65 + 1) = 33^{th}$ position i.e. $Q_2 = 17 = 17$
3. $Q_3 = ¾ (n + 1) = ¾ (65 + 1) = 49.5^{th}$ position i.e. $Q_3 = 21 + .5 (21 - 21) = 21$
4. IQR=Interquartile range = $Q_3 – Q_1 = 21 – 15 = 6$
5. Suspected Outliers are investigated if they are outside the lower and upper fences
   Lower fence = Q1 – 1.5 (IQR) = 15 – 1.5 (6) = 6
   Upper fence = Q3 + 1.5 (IQR) = 21 + 1.5 (6) = 30
6. Lower Adjacent Value LAV = Minimum Value = above the lower fence = 10 *(which is above 6)*
7. Upper Adjacent Value UAV = Maximum Value = below the upper fence = 29 *(which is below 30)*

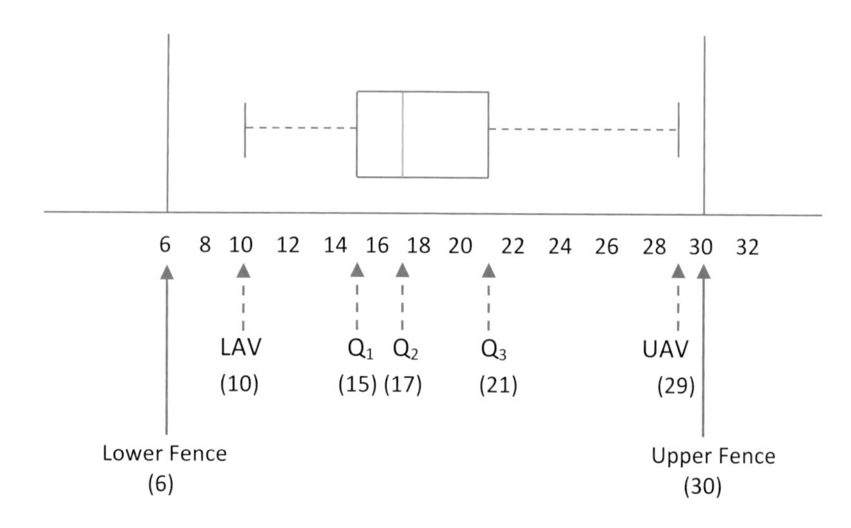

(g) The Stem and Leaf Display for the following ordered raw data set is presented below:

10 12 12 13 13 13 14 14 14 14 15 15 15 15 15 15 15

16 16 16 16 16 16 16 16 16 17 17 17 17 17 17 17 17

18 18 18 18 18 18 19 19 19 19 19 20 20 20 21 21 21

21 22 22 22 23 23 24 24 24 25 25 26 27 29

Option 1: Each line in the chart is a block of one *(e.g. Line 1 contains just 1 value i.e. 10)*

```
10 | 0
11 | 0 0
12 |
13 | 0 0 0
14 | 0 0 0 0
15 | 0 0 0 0 0 0 0
16 | 0 0 0 0 0 0 0 0 0
17 | 0 0 0 0 0 0 0 0
18 | 0 0 0 0 0 0
19 | 0 0 0 0 0
20 | 0 0 0
21 | 0 0 0 0
22 | 0 0 0
23 | 0 0
24 | 0 0 0
25 | 0 0
26 | 0
27 | 0
29 | 0
```

Option 2 - Each line in the chart is a block of two *(e.g. Line 1 is a block ranging from 10 to 11)*

```
1 | 0
1 | 2 2 3 3 3
1 | 4 4 4 4 5 5 5 5 5 5 5
1 | 6 6 6 6 6 6 6 6 6 7 7 7 7 7 7 7 7
1 | 8 8 8 8 8 8 9 9 9 9 9
2 | 0 0 0 1 1 1 1
2 | 2 2 2 3 3
2 | 4 4 4 5 5
2 | 6 7
2 | 9
```

2.10 IBM SPSS Statistics 20 – *Exploring your data*

Consider the raw data for the two quantitative *continuous* variables *(Make-up Times and Walking Times):* The tasks that the researcher must fulfil include:

1. Input each variable into IBM SPSS Statistics 20.
2. Derive a selection of descriptive statistics which are appropriate for each variable e.g. measures of centrality *(e.g. mean median)* and measures of variation *(variance, standard deviation, range, interquartile range)*.

   Derive a selection of charts which are appropriate for each variable *(e.g. Histogram, Box and Whisper Plot).*

Make-up times for 65 students

22 29 16 15 18 17 12 13 17 16 15
19 17 10 21 15 14 17 18 12 20 14
16 15 16 20 22 14 25 19 23 15 19
18 23 22 16 16 19 13 18 24 24 26
13 18 17 15 24 15 17 14 18 17 21
16 21 25 19 20 27 16 17 16 21

Walking Times for 100 students

40 40 40 40 40 40 41 41 41 41 41 42 42 42 42 42 42 42 42 43
43 43 43 43 44 44 44 44 44 44 44 44 44 45 45 45 45 46 46 47
47 47 47 47 47 47 48 48 48 48 50 50 50 50 50 50 51 51 51 51
51 52 52 52 53 53 53 53 54 55 55 57 57 57 60 60 61 62 63 64
65 65 66 68 70 70 70 71 71 72 74 76 76 77 77 83 87 88 95 96

IBM SPSS Statistics 20 Instructions

Step 1 – Open *IBM SPSS Statistics 20* select *Type in data* and click *OK*. Click *Variable View* at the bottom left corner and enter each variable. The column *Values* remains blank for *continuous* variables. Since each variable is *continuous*, *Scale* is selected under the column *Measure*.

Variable View Editor

	Name	Type	Width	Decimals	Label	Values	Missing	Columns	Align	Measure	Role
1	WalkTimes	Numeric	8	0	Walking Times	None	None	8	Right	Scale	Input
2	MakeUpTime	Numeric	8	0	Make-up times	None	None	8	Right	Scale	Input

Step 2 – Click *Data View* at the bottom left corner and enter the data for each variable.

Data View Editor

	WalkTimes	MakeUpTime
1	40	10
2	42	12
3	51	12
4	96	13
5	62	13
6	46	13
7	61	14
8	44	14
9	71	14
10	51	14
11	42	15
12	59	15
13	47	15
14	47	15
15	52	15

Step 3 – With *IBM SPSS Statistics 20* there are alternative approaches available to derive the same output.

Click *Analyse* and select *Descriptive Statistics* and select *Explore*.

(Alternative approach: Click *Analyse* and select *Descriptive Statistics* and select *Frequencies or Descriptives)*

Data View Editor

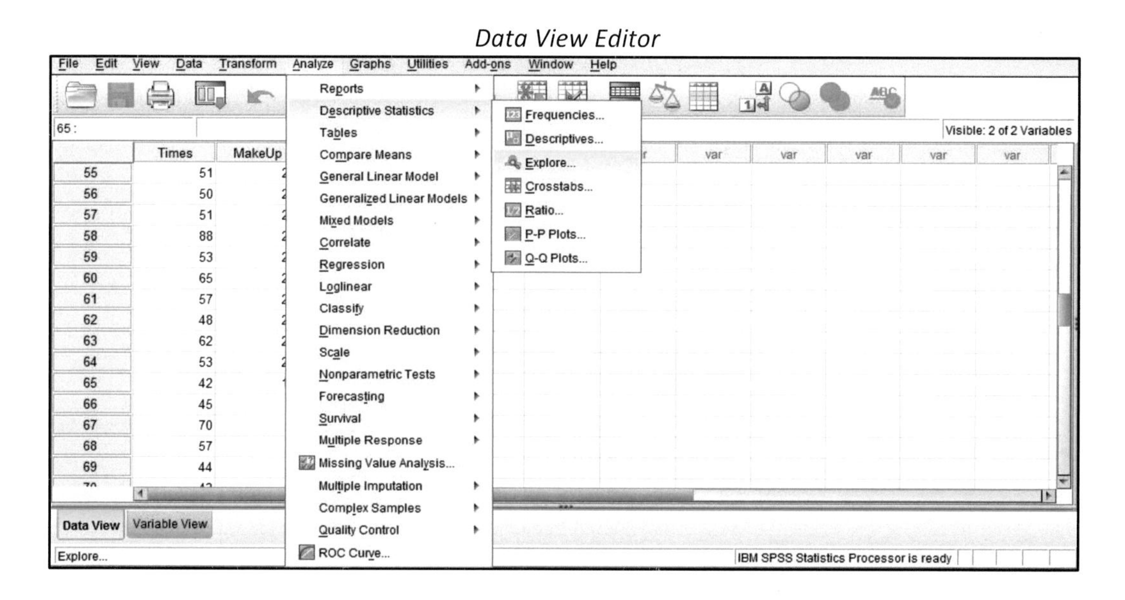

Step 4 – Place *only* one variable into the *Dependent List* in the *Explore* box. Place the variable *Walking Times* into the *Dependent List.*

Data View Editor

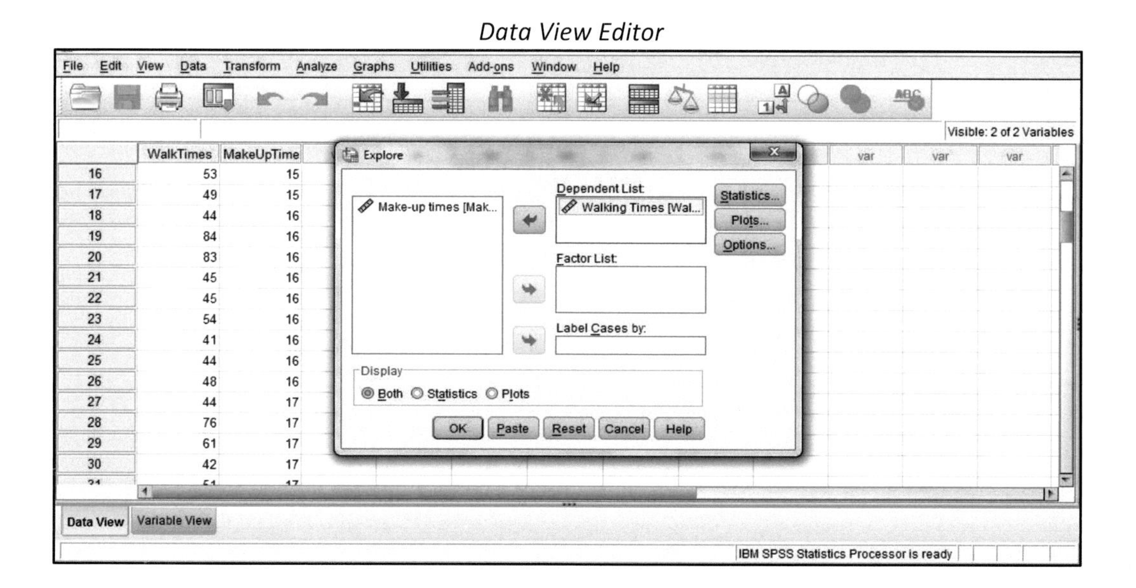

Step 5 – Click *Plots* and select *Histogram* and select *Normality plots with tests* and then click *Continue* and click *OK.*

Data View Editor

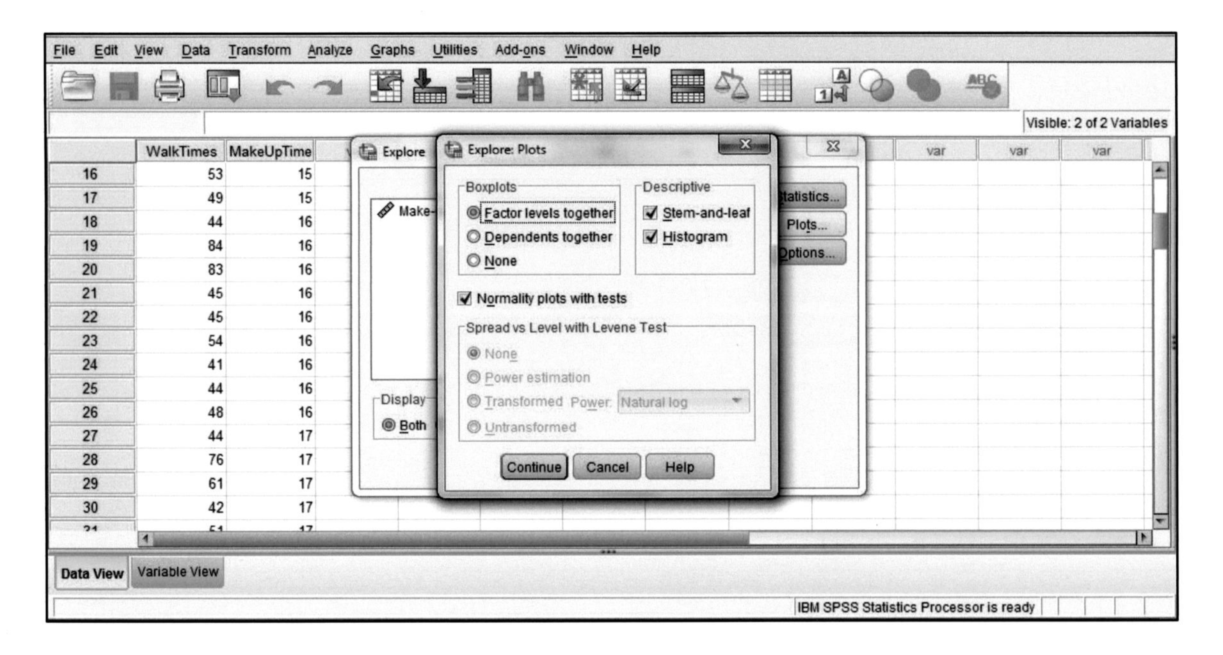

Step 6 – Repeat Step 3 through 5 for the variable *Make-up Times*. Remember to select *Reset* at Step 4

IBM SPSS Statistics 20 Output

Summary of SPSS output – Walking Times (n = 100)

Walking Times (n = 100)	*Statistic*	*Standard Error*
Mean	*53.57*	
Median	*49.50*	
Variance	*168.61*	
Standard Deviation	*12.985*	
Range	*56*	
Interquartile Range	*17*	
Minimum	*40*	
Maximum	*96*	
Skewness	*1.343*	*0.241*
Kurtosis	*1.324*	*0.478*

	Tests of Normality					
	Kolmogorov – Smirnov $n \geq 50$			*Shapiro – Wilk* $n < 50$		
	Statistic	*df*	*Sig.*	*Statistic*	*df*	*Sig.*
Walking Times	*0.178*	*100*	*0.000*	*0.854*	*100*	*0.000*

Histogram

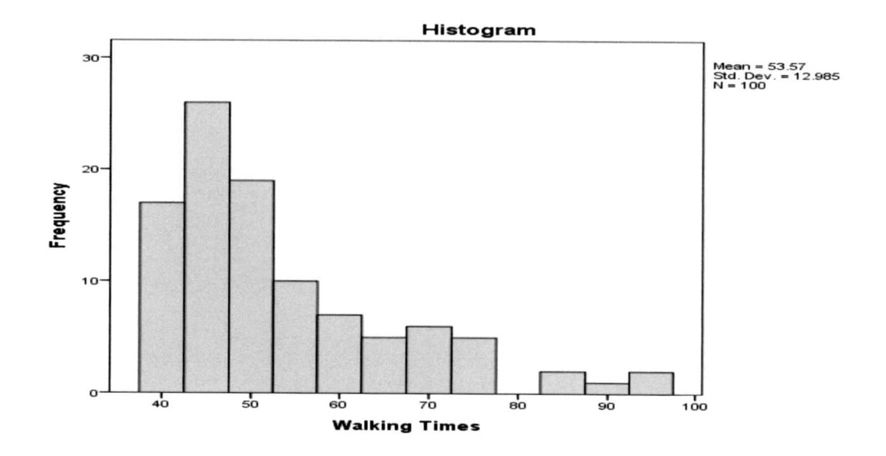

Box and Whisker Plot

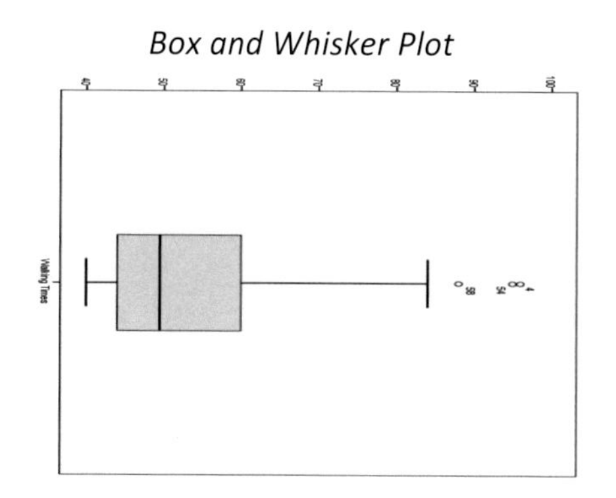

Normal Q-Q Plot

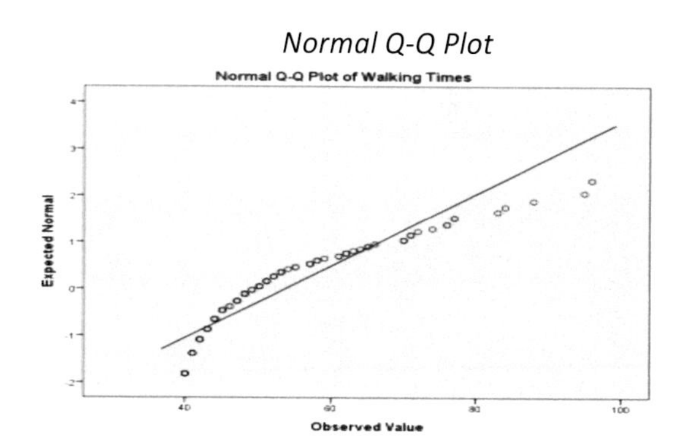

Summary of SPSS output – Make –up Times (n = 65)

Make-up Times (n = 65)	*Statistic*	*Standard Error*
Mean	*18.11*	
Median	*17.00*	
Variance	*15.69*	
Standard Deviation	*3.961*	
Range	*19*	
Interquartile Range	*6*	
Minimum	*10*	
Maximum	*29*	
Skewness	*0.601*	*0.297*
Kurtosis	*0.034*	*0.586*

	Tests of Normality					
	Kolmogorov – Smirnov n ≥ 50			*Shapiro – Wilk n < 50*		
	Statistic	*df*	*Sig.*	*Statistic*	*df*	*Sig.*
Make-up times	*0.133*	*65*	*0.006*	*0.965*	*65*	*0.062*

Histogram

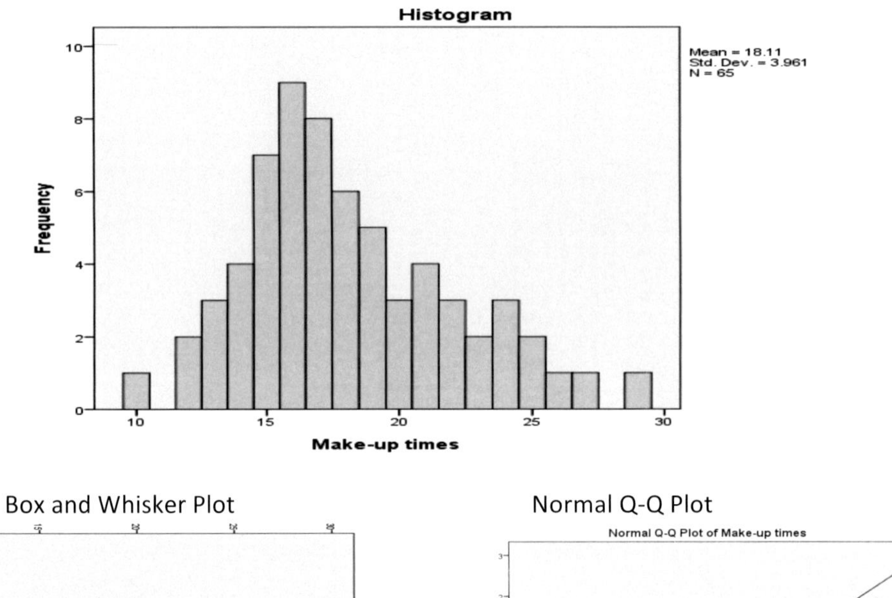

Box and Whisker Plot

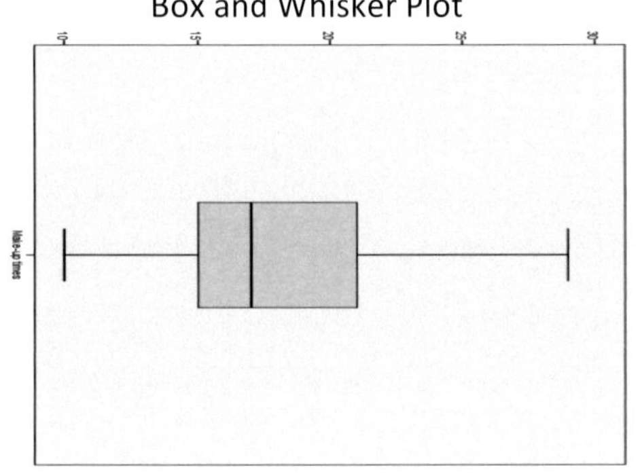

Normal Q-Q Plot

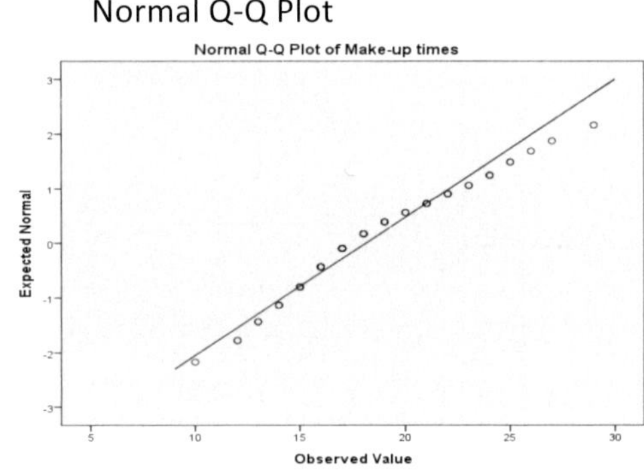

Excel 2010 – *Charts*

Exercise 1

Derive a histogram for the variable *Intelligence Quotient* from the following distribution table using *Microsoft Excel 2010*:

Distribution Table

IQ Score	Class Boundaries	Freq.
80 – 84	79.5 – 84.5	12
85 – 89	84.5 – 89.5	14
90 – 94	89.5 – 94.5	16
95 – 99	94.5 – 99.5	18
100 – 104	99.5 – 104.5	20
105 – 109	104.5 – 109.5	18
110 – 114	109.5 – 114.5	16
115 – 119	114.5 – 119.5	14
120 – 124	119.5 – 124.5	12

2.10 Excel 2010: Charts

Step 1 – Place the highlighted data in the distribution table into *Excel 2010*.

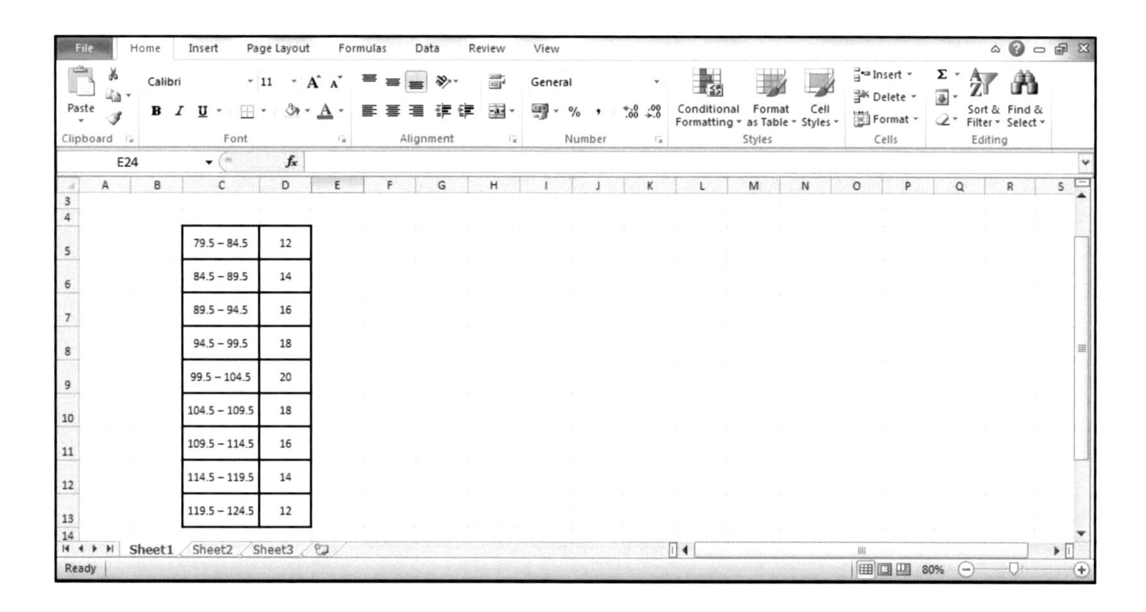

Step 2 – Highlight the imported cells as shown. Click *Insert* and then *Column* and select the first chart listed under *2 – D Column*.

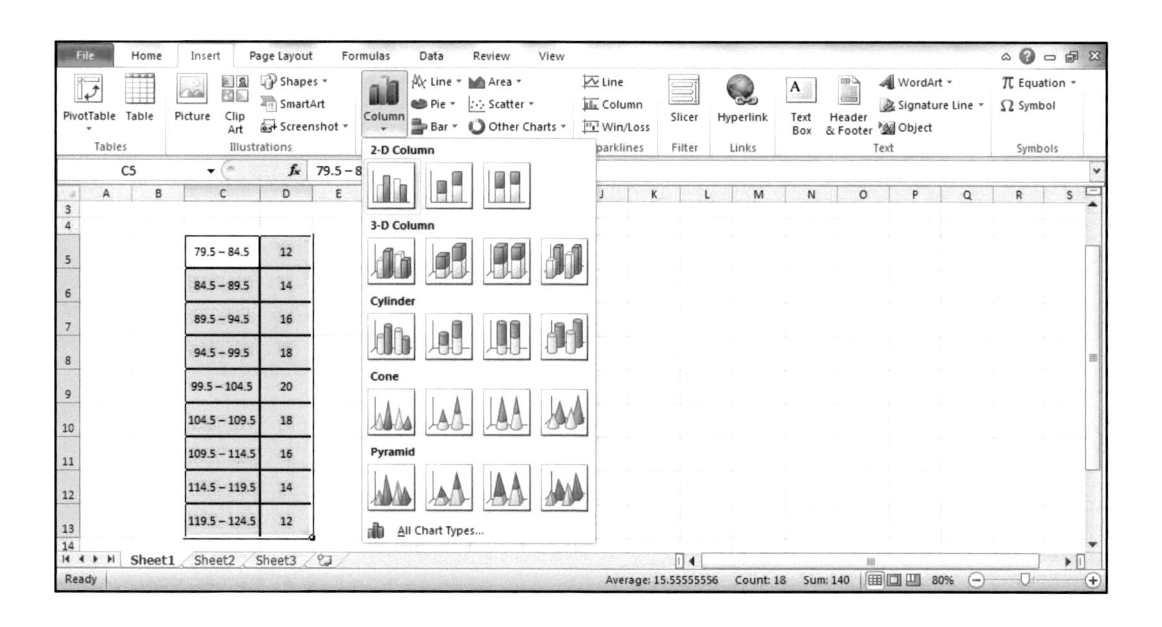

Step 3 – Double click on one of the bars in the chart and adjust the *Gap Width* to *No Gap* and click *Close*.

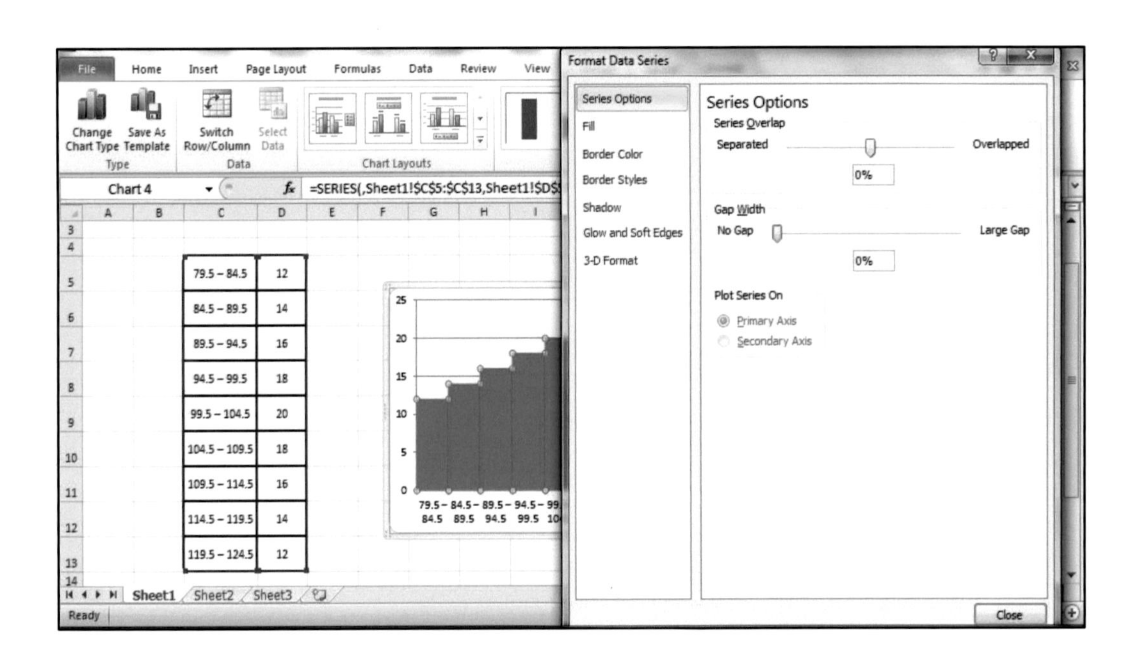

Step 4 – Double click the horizontal axis displaying the class boundaries and click *Alignment*. Click *Text direction* and select *ABA – Rotate all text 270°*. Then click *Close*.

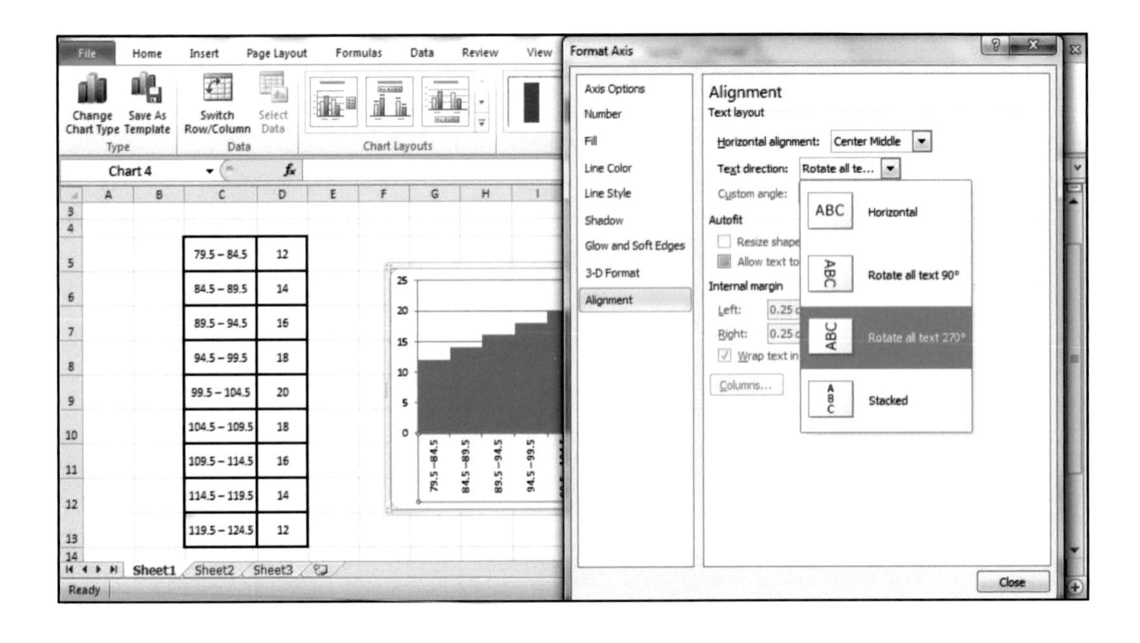

Step 5 – The histogram can be enhanced by manipulating *Chart Tools*. For example, by selecting a particular *Chart Style* the histogram can be enhanced for presentation purposes.

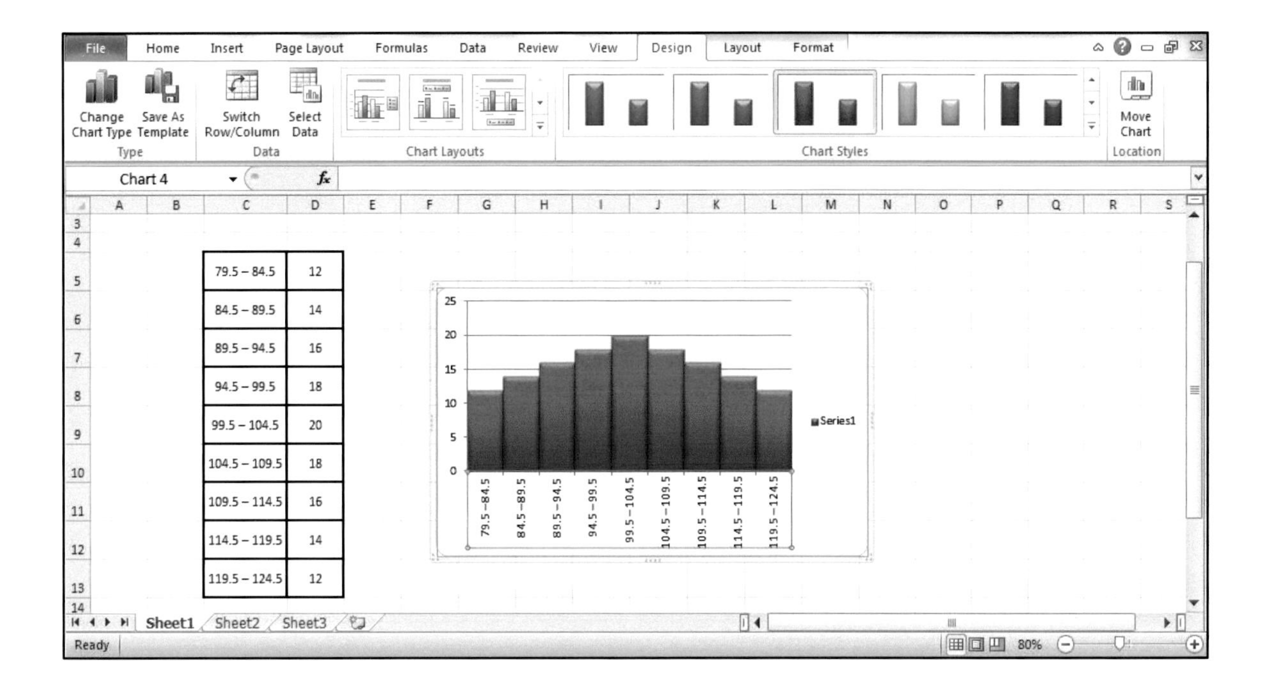

Exercise 2

Derive the following charts for the single variable *Blood Group* using *Microsoft Excel 2010*:

1. Bar Chart
2. Pie Chart

Distribution table

Blood Group 1	Frequency 2
Group O	880
Group A	840
Group B	200
Group AB	80
	2000

Excel 2010 Instructions

Step 1 – Place the highlighted data in the distribution table into *Excel 2010*.

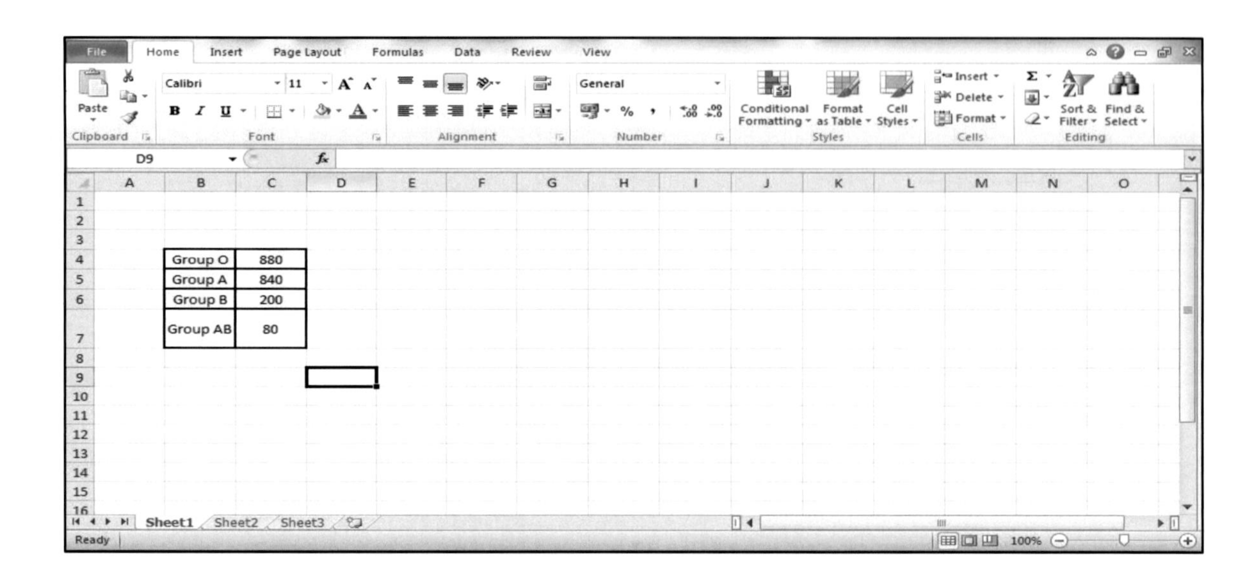

Step 2 – Highlight the imported cells as shown. Click *Insert* and then *Column* and select the first chart listed under *2 – D Column*.

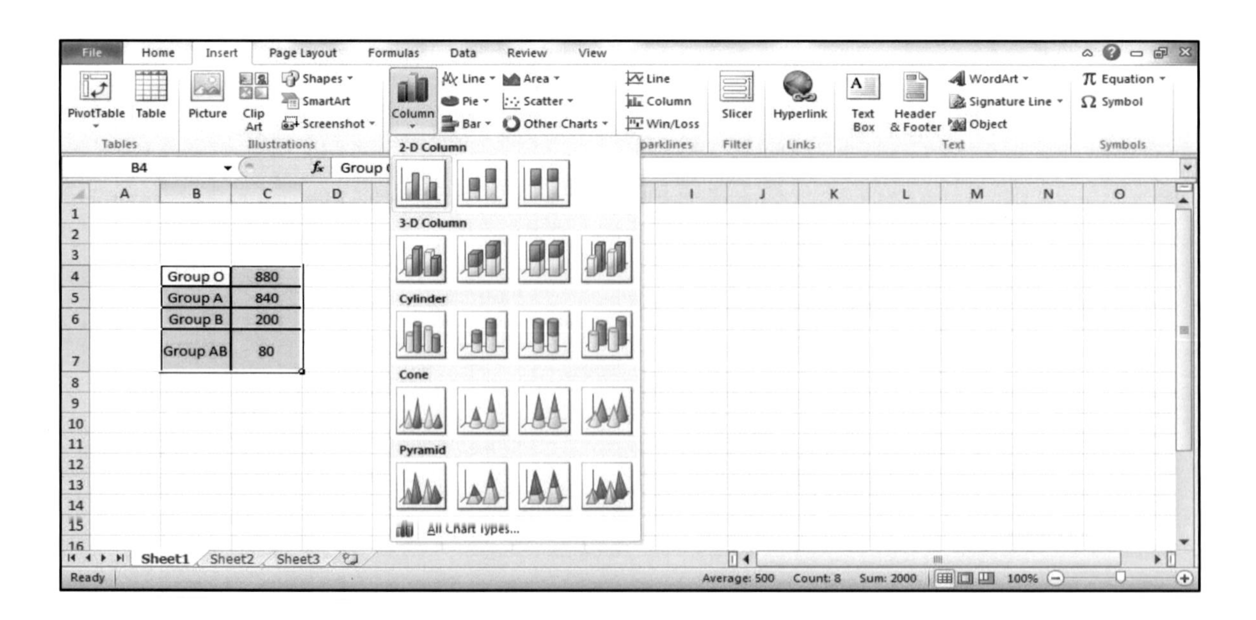

Step 3 – The bar chart can be enhanced by clicking the chart which makes the *Chart Tools* facility available.

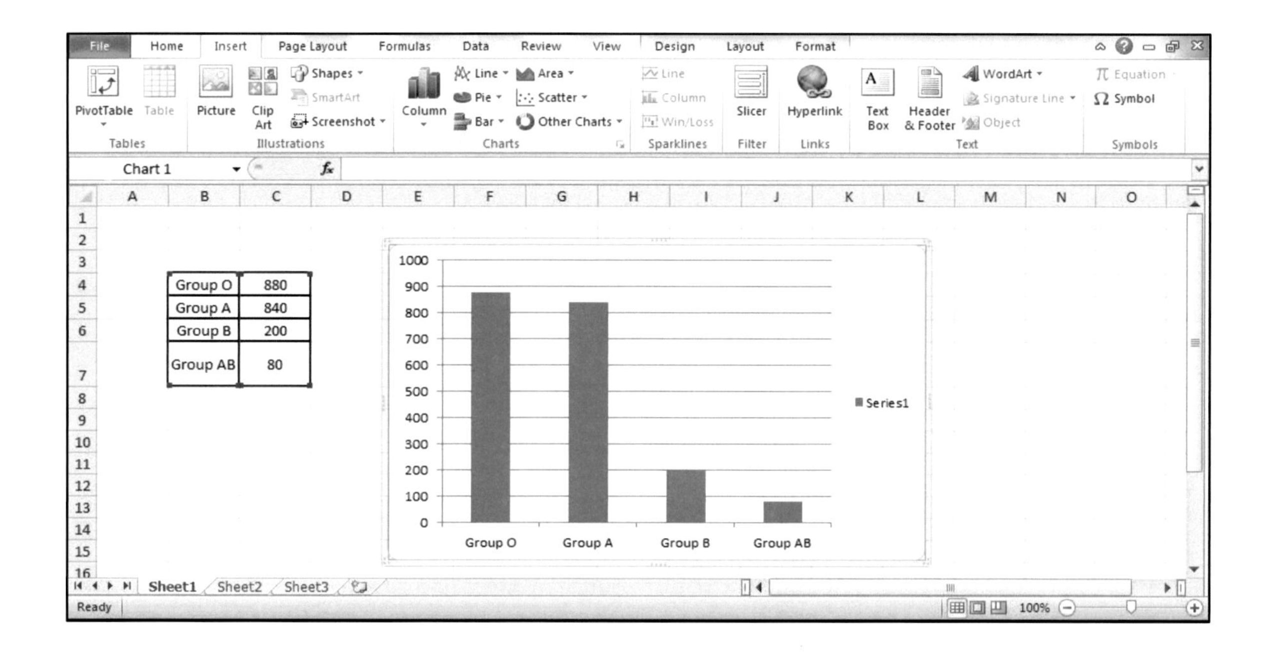

Step 4 – Repeat Steps 1 through Step 3 to derive the pie chart.

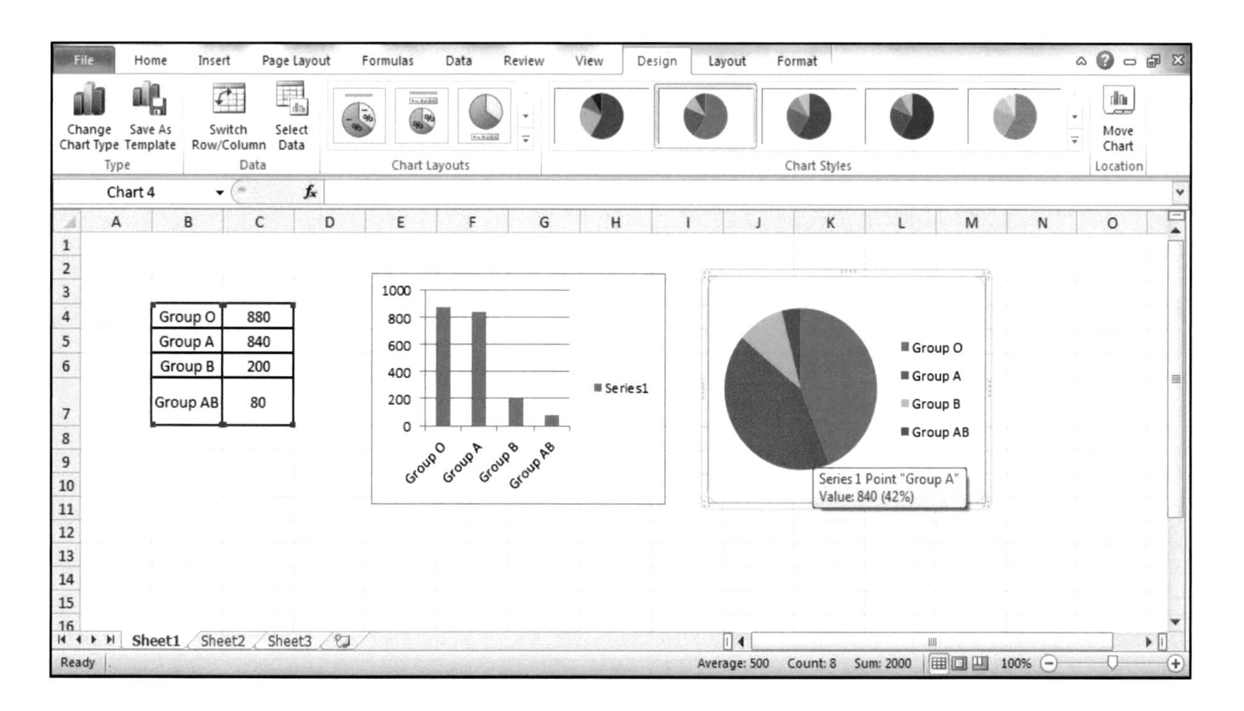

Exercise 3

Derive the following charts for two qualitative nominal variables *(Survival and Gender)* using *Microsoft Excel 2010*:

1. Bar Chart
2. Stacked Bar Chart

Contingency Table - Survival by Gender

	Lost	*Survived*	Total
Men	659	146	805
Women	106	296	402
Total	765	442	1207

Excel 2010 Instructions

Step 1 – Copy the highlighted columns in the distribution table and paste into *Excel 2010*.

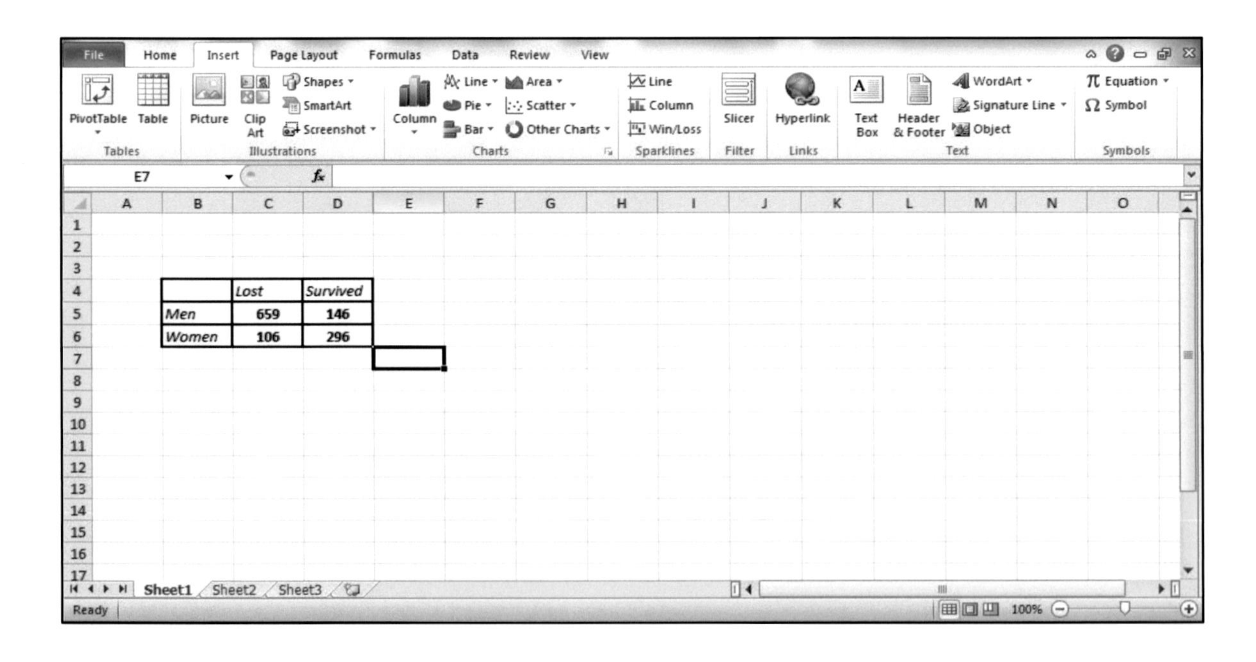

Step 2 – Highlight the imported cells as shown. Click *Insert* and then *Column* and select the first chart listed under *2 – D Column*.

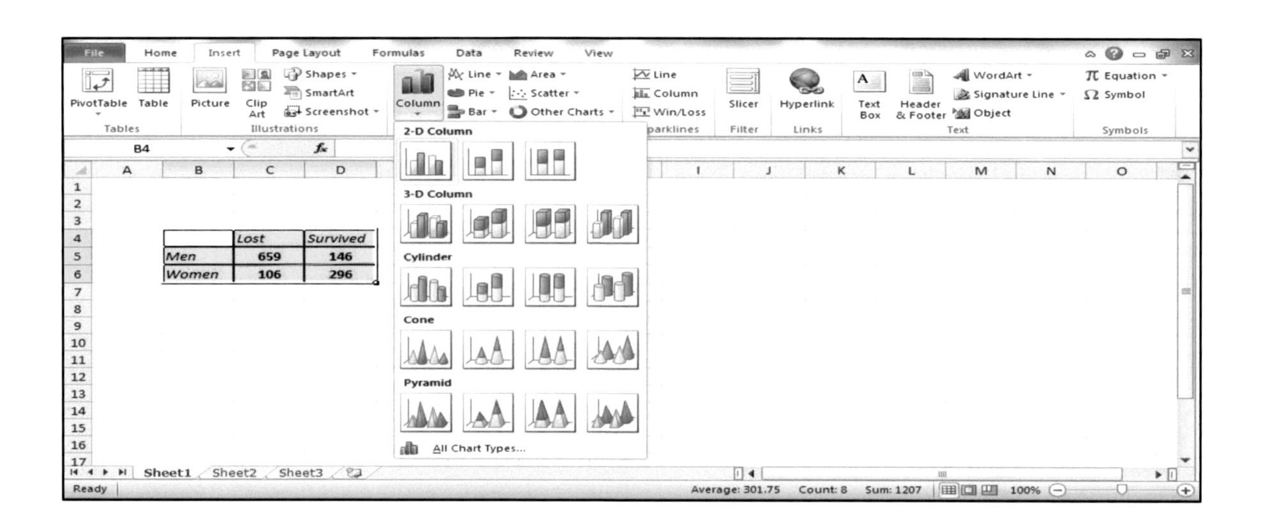

Step 3 – The bar chart can be enhanced by clicking the chart which makes the *Chart Tools* facility available.

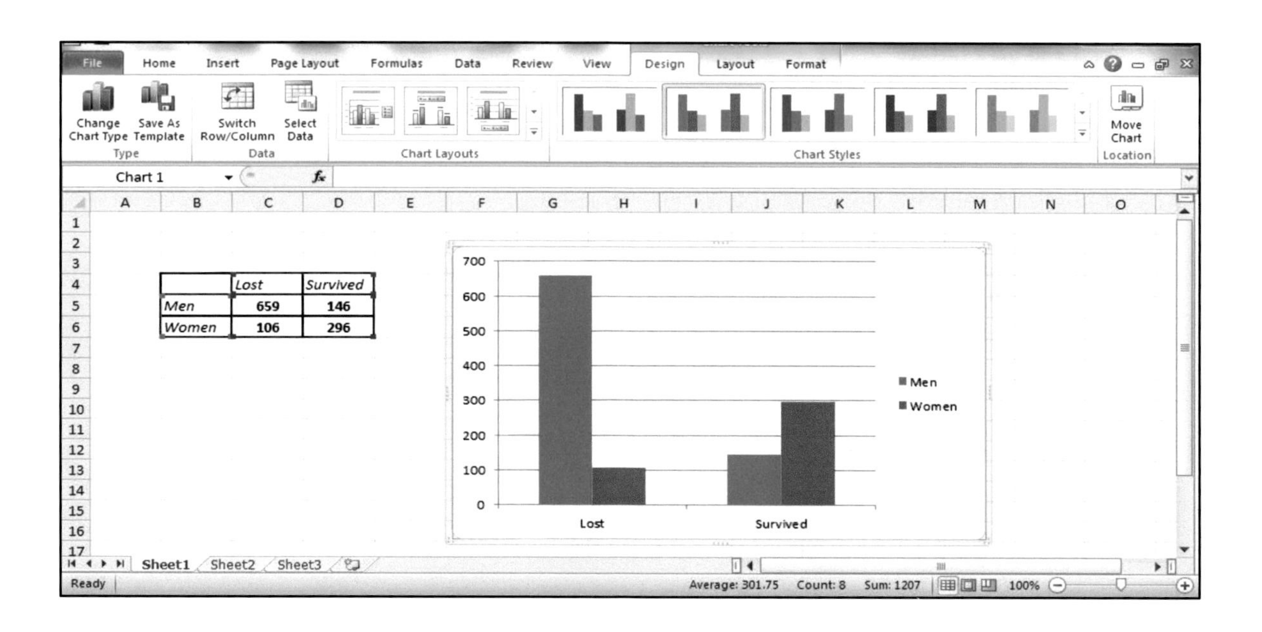

Step 4 – Repeat Steps 1 through Step 3 to derive the stacked bar chart.

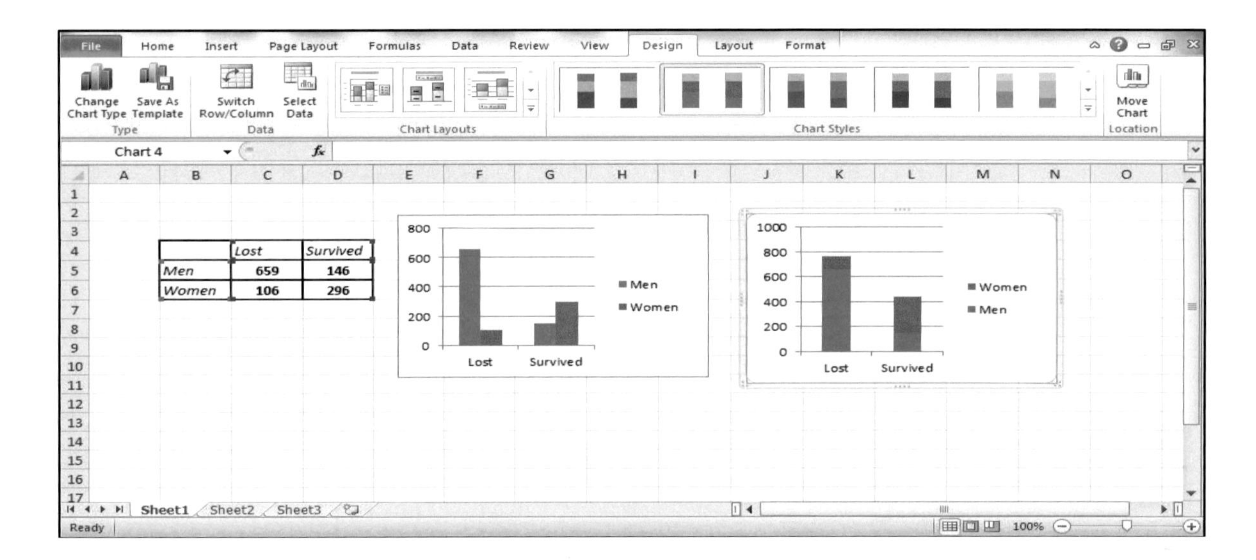

Exercise 4

Derive summary statistics for the following quantitative variable *Time Taken* using *Microsoft Excel 2010*. A random sample of 23 students sitting a *MCQ test in Statistics* was selected. Their time to complete the test was recorded and is presented as follows:

Time Taken to complete an MCQ Test for n = 23
15 16 17 19 20 21 22 22 23 23 23 24 24 25 25 26 28 29 30 32 34 38 39

Excel 2010 Instructions

Step 1 – Enter the 23 observations into *Excel 2010.*

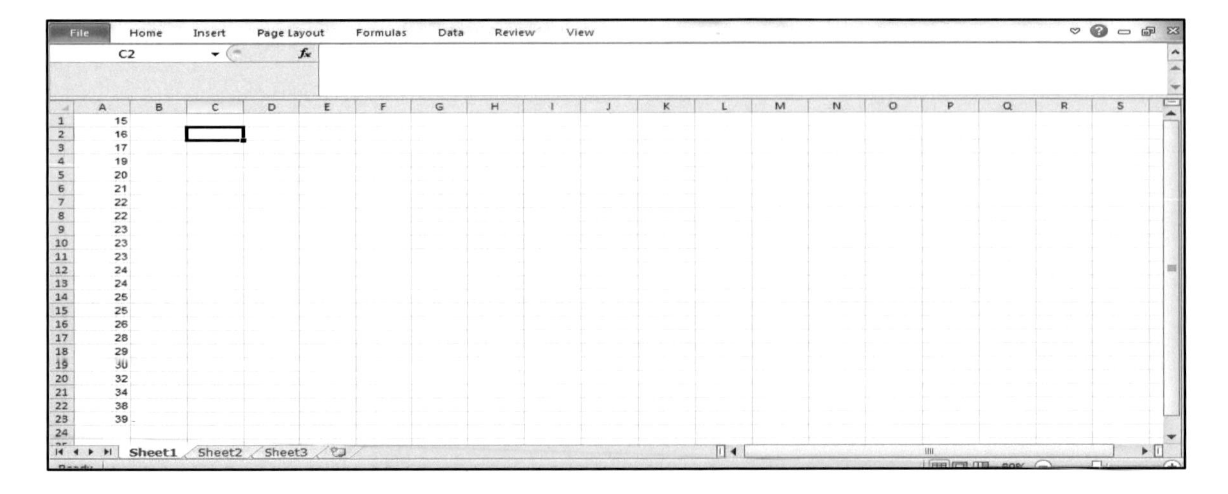

Step 2 – To ensure that *Excel 2010* is properly set up to supply you with summary statistics, carry out the following instructions in the Excel worksheet:

1. Click *File* and select *Options* then select *Add-Inns* and then select *Analysis ToolPaK* and click *Go*
2. Under *Add-ins available* select both *Analysis ToolPak* and *Analysis ToolPak – VBA* and click *OK*
3. Click *Data* and select *Data Analysis* then select Descriptive *Statistics* and then click *OK*
4. Into the *Input range* identify the cell range of the observations – in this instance I identify the cell range *A1:A23*
5. Under the Output option select *Output Range* and identify any cell *(other than the cells containing the observations)*, in this instance I identify cell *C3 (or any cell of your choice other than A1 to A23.*
6. Select *Summary statistics* and click *OK* and the following should appear.

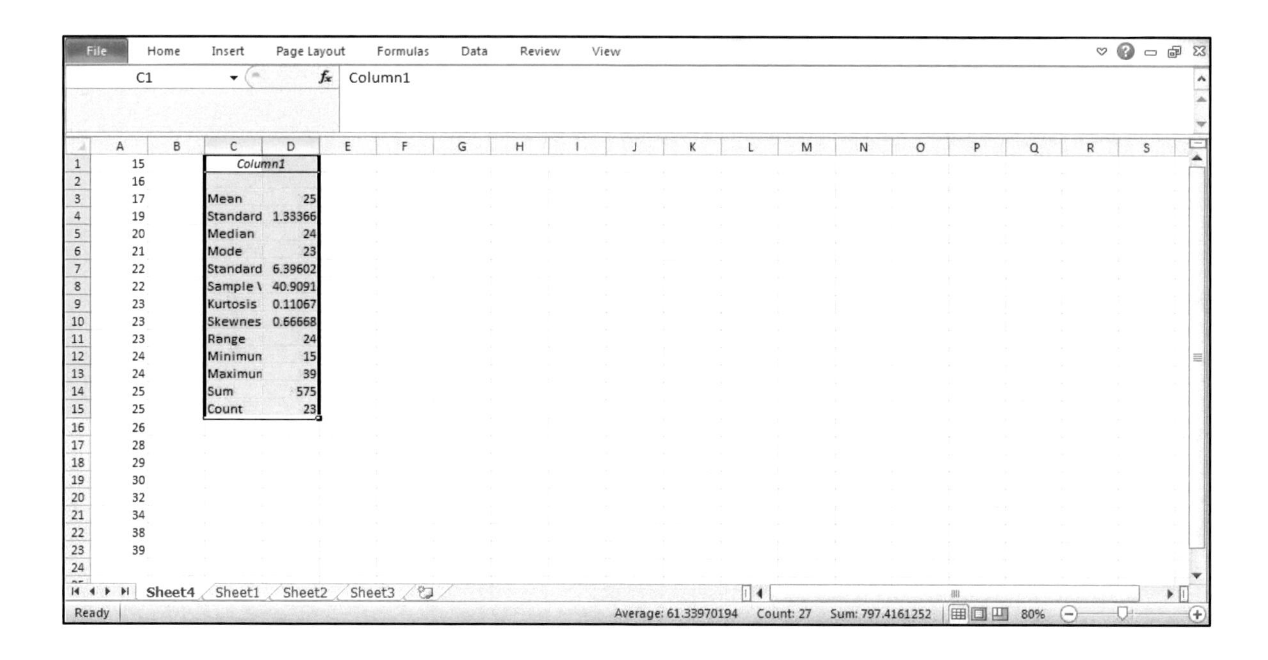

Chapter 3 – Descriptive Statistical Techniques 2

'Then there is the man who drowned crossing a stream with an average depth of six inches.'

W.I.E. Gates (1955 -)

Interpreting the output from descriptive statistical techniques only relates to the sample data that has been collected.

3.1 Interpreting Tables: *Qualitative/Quantitative Variable(s)*

In this section we will interpret the tables that we derived in Chapter 2. We will begin with the tables derived for both one and two qualitative nominal scaled variable(s). The data values or observations we derive from a nominal variable are merely coded values. There is no natural underlying order to these categories/coded values and subtraction between these coded values is meaningless. The variable Blood Group has 4 categories which we assume has no underlying order.

Nominal Variable

Tables for one nominal variable (Blood Group)

A researcher selected a random sample of 2,000 students from the population of 20,000 third level students. He converted the raw data into the following distribution tables.

Distribution tables

Blood Group 1	Frequency 2	Relative Frequency 3	Percentage 4
Group O = 1	880	0.44	44%
Group A = 2	840	0.42	42%
Group B = 3	200	0.10	10%
Group AB = 4	80	0.04	4%
	2000		

(Adapted from Kinnear and Gray, 2011)

Interpretation

We can make the following statements about this table:

1. *44% of the sample will fall into blood Group O.*
2. *If I select a student from a lottery drum, the probability that that student would fall into blood group B is 10%.*
3. *The mode (most frequently occurring score) is Group O.*

The mode is one of 3 measures of average or central tendency. A measure of average gives us a sense of the 'typical' value in the dataset. No calculation or ordering of the data is required to get the mode. A dataset has with just one mode is unimodal, two modal values is bimodal, and more than two modal values multimodal.

Table for two qualitative nominal scaled variables (Gender and Survival)

An appropriate table for two qualitative nominal scaled variables is the contingency table. A contingency table allows us to combine two qualitative nominal scaled variables. Consider the following contingency table:

Contingency Table - Survival by Gender

		Lost	*Survived*	Total
Men	Count	**659**	**146**	805
	% within gender	81.9%	18.1%	
Women	Count	**106**	**296**	402
	% within gender	26.4%	73.6%	
Total	Count	765	442	1207

(Compiled from British Board of Trade Report, 1912)

Interpretation of % within gender

This contingency table enables us to explore the presence or absence of association *(or dependence)* between two qualitative nominal scaled variables. In other words, is survival more associated with one gender over another or is survival dependent or influenced by the gender of a person.

It is clear from the above table that the percentage of females that survived *(73.6% =* $\frac{296}{402}$ *x 100)* far exceeds the percentage of males that survived *(18.1% =* $\frac{146}{805}$ *x 100)*. Therefore, it appears that survival *(dependent or explained nominal variable)* is influenced by gender *(independent or explanatory nominal variable)*. The contingency table can be extended in the following manner:

Contingency Table - Survival by Gender

		Lost	*Survived*	Total
Men	Count	**659**	**146**	805
	% within gender	81.9%	18.1%	
	% within survival	86.1%	33.03%	
Women	Count	**106**	**296**	402
	% within gender	26.4%	73.6%	
	% within survival	13.9%	66.97%	
Total	Count	765	442	1207

(Compiled from British Board of Trade Report, 1912)

Interpretation of % within survival

Of those that survived *(442)* the percentage that were male *(33.03% =* $\frac{146}{442}$ *x 100)* compared to the percentage that were female *(66.97% =* $\frac{296}{442}$ *x 100)*. There is a difference between the percentage of male survivors *(18.1%)* and the percentage of survivors that were male (33.03%). The contingency table can be further extended as follows:

Contingency Table - Survival by Gender

		Lost	*Survived*	Total
Men	Count	**659**	**146**	805
	% within gender	81.9%	18.1%	
	% within survival	86.1%	33.03%	
	% of total	54.6%	12.1%	
Women	Count	**106**	**296**	402
	% within gender	26.4%	73.6%	
	% within survival	13.9%	66.97%	
	% of total	8.78%	24.5%	
Total	Count	765	442	1207

Compiled from British Board of Trade Report (1912)

Interpretation of % of total

Of the total *(1207)*, male survivors accounted for *(12.1% =* $\frac{146}{1207}$ *x 100)* compared to female survivors who accounted for *(24.5% =* $\frac{296}{1207}$ *x 100).*

Ordinal Variable

Here we interpret the tables derived for both one and two qualitative *(one nominal and one ordinal)* variable*(s)*. The data values or observations we derive from an ordinal variable are merely coded values. There is a natural underlying order to these categories/coded values but subtraction between these coded values is meaningless. The variable *Lecturer explains things clearly* has 5 categories which we assume does have an underlying order.

Tables for one ordinal scaled variable (Lecturer explains things clearly)

A sample of 131 students was selected from a population of 13,100 students. The students were asked to indicate their views about the communication skills of their lecturer. The raw data was converted into the following distribution tables.

Distribution Tables

'Lecturer explains things clearly'	Freq.	Rel. Freq.	Percent	Cum. Freq.	Cum. Rel. Freq.	Cum. Percent
Strongly Disagree = 1	8	0.06	6%	8	0.06	6%
Disagree = 2	13	0.10	10%	21	0.16	16%
Neutral = 3	21	0.16	16%	42	0.32	32%
Agree = 4	52	0.40	40%	94	0.72	72%
Strongly Agree = 5	37	0.28	28%	131	1.00	100%
	131	1.00				

Interpretation

We can make the following statements about this table:

1. *6% of students strongly disagree with the statement that 'Lecturer explains things clearly'*
2. *If I select a student at random from a lottery drum, the probability that that student will express a favourable view of the lecturer (i.e. give a rating of 4 or 5 to the statement) if 68%.*
3. *21 students rated the statement 'Lecturer explains things clearly' with a 1 or 2.*
4. *16% of students rated the statement 'Lecturer explains things clearly' with a 1 or 2.*
5. *68% of students rated the statement 'Lecturer explains things clearly' with a 4 or 5. This percentage I can infer from simply adding 40% + 28% in the percentage column.*
6. *The mode* (most frequently occurring score) *is Agree*
7. *The median (middlemost observation of the ordered data) is 'Neutral' (as per calculations in Chapter 2)*

The median is one of 3 measures of average or central tendency. The data must be arranged in a 'natural' order *(ascending or descending).* The median splits the ordered dataset into two equal-sized groups.

Table for two qualitative variables (one nominal and one ordinal)

The appropriate table for two qualitative variables is the contingency table. A contingency table allows us to combine two qualitative variables *(one nominal and one ordinal).*

Contingency Table - Opinion by Gender

	Lecturer explains things clearly					
	Strongly disagree	Disagree	Neutral	Agree	Strongly agree	Total
Male students	8	12	8	30	17	75
Female students	6	8	8	40	18	80
Total	14	20	16	70	35	155

Interpretation

This contingency table enables us to explore the presence or absence of association *(or dependence)* between two qualitative variables *(one nominal and one ordinal).* In other words, is a favourable opinion more associated with one gender over another, or is opinion dependent or influenced by the gender of a person?

Quantitative Variable

Here we interpret the tables derived for a quantitative variable. The data values or observations we derive from a quantitative variable are ordinary 'real' numbers *(uncoded values).* The data values or observations derived from a quantitative variable may be discrete or continuous. The variable IQ of first year college students can be assumed to be a quantitative continuous variable. A sample of 140 students was selected from a population of 1,400 students. The data was converted into the following distribution tables.

Distribution Tables

IQ Score	*Freq.*	*Rel. Freq.*	*Cum. Freq.*		*Cum. Rel. Freq.*		*Cum. Percent*	
			*UCL**	*Cum. F*	*UCL**	*Cum. RF*	*UCL**	*Cum. %*
80 – 84	*12*	*0.09*	*≤ 84*	*12*	*≤ 84*	*0.09*	*≤ 84*	*9%*
85 – 89	*14*	*0.10*	*≤ 89*	*26*	*≤ 89*	*0.19*	*≤ 89*	*19%*
90 – 94	*16*	*0.11*	*≤ 94*	*42*	*≤ 94*	*0.30*	*≤ 94*	*30%*
95 – 99	*18*	*0.13*	*≤ 99*	*60*	*≤ 99*	*0.43*	*≤ 99*	*43%*
100 – 104	*20*	*0.14*	*≤ 104*	*80*	*≤ 104*	*0.57*	*≤ 104*	*57%*
105 – 109	*18*	*0.13*	*≤ 109*	*98*	*≤ 109*	*0.70*	*≤ 109*	*70%*
110 – 114	*16*	*0.11*	*≤ 114*	*114*	*≤ 114*	*0.81*	*≤ 114*	*81%*
115 – 119	*14*	*0.10*	*≤ 119*	*128*	*≤ 119*	*0.91*	*≤ 119*	*91%*
120 – 124	*12*	*0.09*	*≤ 124*	*140*	*≤ 124*	*1.00*	*≤ 124*	*100%*
	140	*1.00*						

**UCL = Upper class limit*

Interpretation

We can make the following statements about this table:

1. *9% of students scored between 80 and 84 on the IQ test*
2. *If I select a student at random from a lottery drum, the probability that that student will score ≤ 104 is 57%*
3. *42 students scored ≤ 94*
4. *30% of students scored between 80 and 94. 30% of students scored ≤ 94*

3.2 Interpreting graphs: *Constructed from grouped data*

Quantitative Variable

A sample of 140 students was selected from a population of 1,400 students. The data was converted into the distribution table below. On this occasion the researcher opted to choose 9 classes or class intervals based on his own judgement rather than apply the scientific approach to selecting the number of classes. The scientific approach would have recommended 8 classes.

80 80 81 81 81 82 82 82 82 83 83 83 84 85 85 86 86 86 87 87 87 88
88 89 89 89 89 90 90 90 91 91 92 92 92 93 93 93 93 94 94 94 94 95
95 96 96 96 97 97 97 97 98 98 98 98 98 99 99 99 99
100 100 100 100 101 101 101 101 102 102 102 103 103 103 103 104
104 104 104 104 105 105 105 105 106 106 106 107 107 108 108 108
109 109 109 109 109 110 110 111 111 111 111 111 112 112 112 113
113 114 114 114 114 114 115 115 115 115 116 116 117 117 118 118
119 119 119 119 120 120 120 120 121 121 121 122 122 123 123 124

Distribution Table

IQ Score	Class Boundaries	Freq.
80 – 84	79.5 – 84.5	12
85 – 89	84.5 – 89.5	14
90 – 94	89.5 – 94.5	16
95 – 99	94.5 – 99.5	18
100 – 104	99.5 – 104.5	20
105 – 109	104.5 – 109.5	18
110 – 114	109.5 – 114.5	16
115 – 119	114.5 – 119.5	14
120 – 124	119.5 – 124.5	12

The Histogram

The histogram is a graph which resembles adjoining tower blocks in a major city. Each tower block or skyscraper represents a count of the data points *(represented by the height of the skyscraper)* falling within a range or class *(represented by the base of the skyscraper)*. Each range or class is known as a *bin.* The shape of the histogram is influenced by the number of bins or classes selected and the sample size. If the bins or classes *(base)* are too wide, important information may become camouflaged or concealed. If the bins are too narrow, seemingly important information might be assigned inflated relevance and given undeserved attention. Ideally, the researcher should experiment with a variety of bin widths to understand and determine how the shape of the histogram is sensitive to bin/class width.

Why inspect the histogram?

1. A step in the process of assessing the *normality* of the data/variable. The data/variable can be suspected to achieve *normality* if the superimposed *bell shaped* curve approximately matches the histogram. Many powerful statistical tests *(the subject matter of later chapters)* require the assumption that the population*(s)* from which our sample*(s)* are drawn achieve *normality* or are *normally distributed.*

2. To determine if any values/scores appear to be out of place *(i.e. an outlier)*. Extreme values or *outliers* may prevent us from declaring that our data achieves *normality*, thus limiting us to using less powerful statistical techniques. It is vital that extreme values or *outliers* are investigated and dealt with appropriately *(Tabachnick and Fidell, 2005).* Statistical tests that involve calculating a mean*(s)* are of particular concern. The mean may be highly influenced by extreme values. The researcher must decide in advance whether the mean is the appropriate measure to represent the *typical* person in a particular research situation.

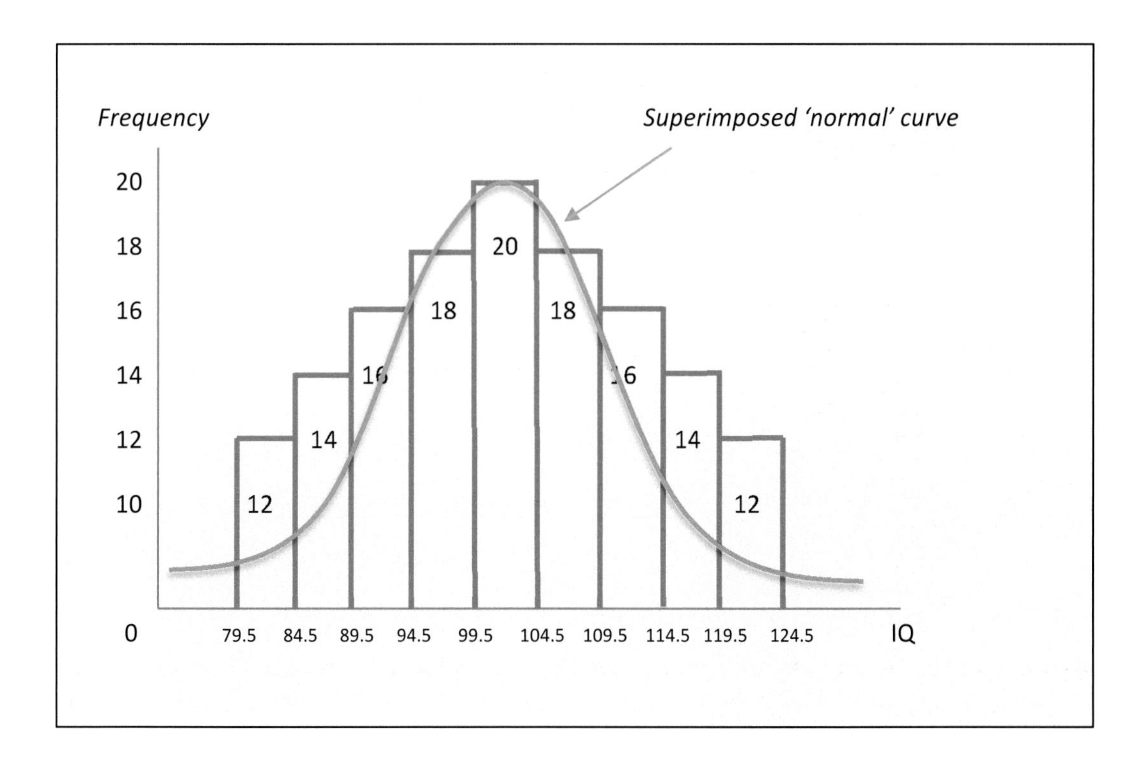

The shape of the histogram reflects how the sample data is distributed *('distributed' refers to the shape of the histogram).*

The following possible shapes can arise:

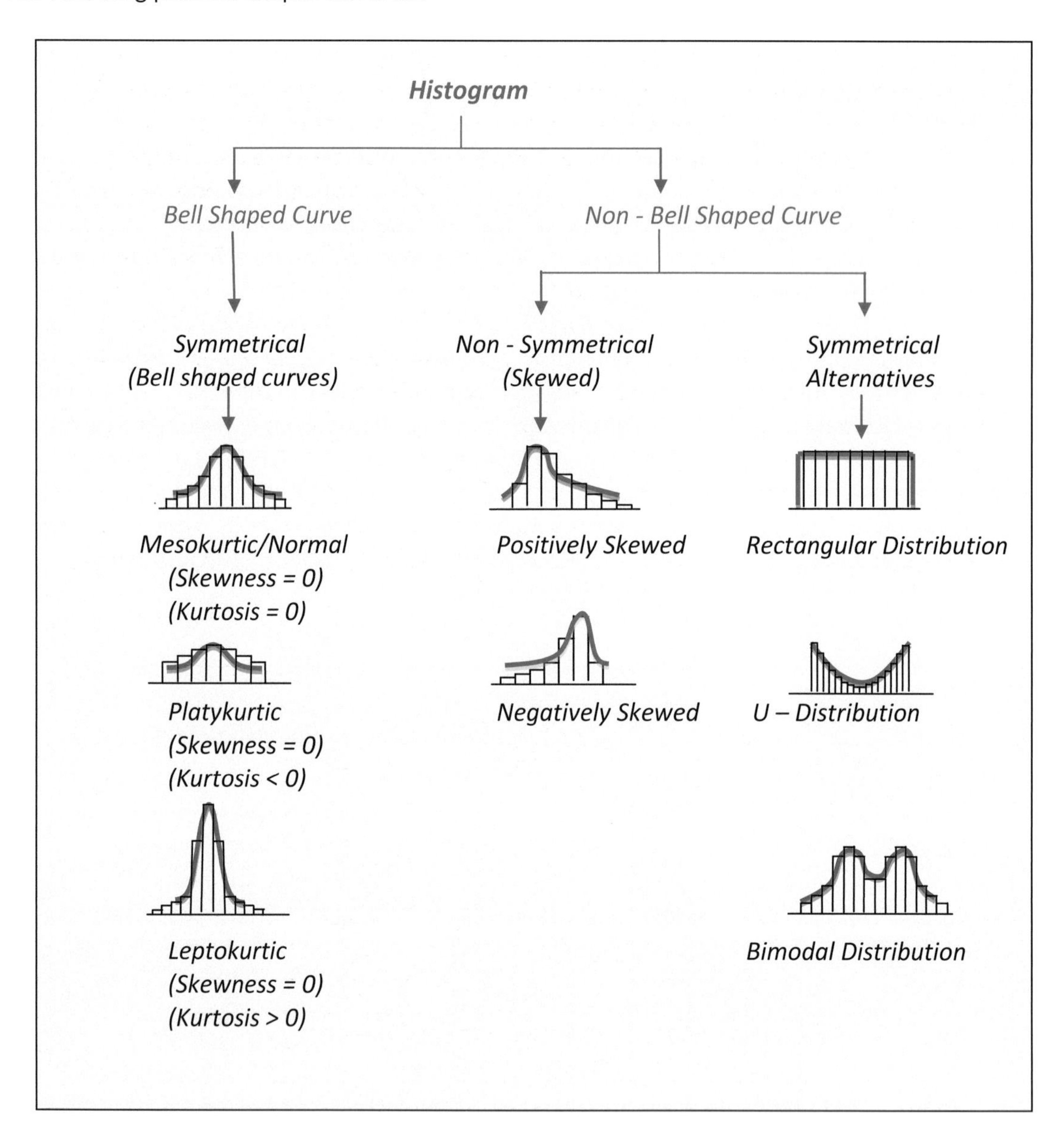

Let's put the histogram of IQs to the test:

Based on a visual inspection we can conclude that the histogram of IQs is best matched with a bell shaped curve. An initial inspection suggests that the distribution of the sample IQ scores *appears* to achieve *normality*. Whilst one must undertake further inspections, an initial impression suggests that the sample data *may* have come from a population which is *normally distributed*. There is a family of powerful statistical tests *(parametric tests)* that require assumptions about the population*(s)* from which we select a sample to be achieved. Therefore, one must always check how the sample data is distributed as these *parametric tests* require the sample data achieves *normality*. If it is declared that the sample data does not achieve *normality*, alternative courses of action must be taken including:

1. Use *distribution-free* statistical tests. These alternative tests are sometimes referred to as *non-parametric tests*. They are less powerful in the sense that they may fail to detect differences or associations between variables when such differences or associations are present.
2. Transform the original data such that the transformed data achieves or resembles *normality*. A popular option is to mathematically transform the measurement to a different scale using, for example, a logarithmic transformation so that the assumption of *normality* is achieved. The type of transformation used depends on the shape of your distribution *(Pallant, 2005)*. There is considerable debate relating to this alternative course of action *(Tabachnick and Fidell, 2005)*.
3. Ignore the failure to achieve *normality* and use the powerful parametric tests by invoking the *Central Limit Theorem* which presents theoretical justification to the application of these tests by virtue of sufficient sample size *(≥ 30)*.

We must, however, carry out further inspections before we can conclude that the population*(s)* from which our sample is drawn achieves normality or can be declared to be *normally distributed* or is *approximately normally distributed*.

Interpreting the Ogive

The ogive is derived from the following distribution table:

I Q	Frequency	Cumulative Frequency	
		UCL*	Cum. F
75 - 79	0	≤ 79	0
80 - 84	12	≤ 84	12
85 - 89	14	≤ 89	26
90 - 94	16	≤ 94	42
95 - 99	18	≤ 99	60
100 - 104	20	≤ 104	80
105 - 109	18	≤ 109	98
110 - 114	16	≤ 114	114
115 - 119	14	≤ 119	128
120 - 124	12	≤ 124	140
	140		

**UCL = Upper Class Limit*

Interpretation

The following can be derived from the graph below *(derived estimates are approximations):*

1. To find out the number of students that scored less than or equal an IQ of 119, I locate 119 on the horizontal axis and draw a line upwards to the ogive and then go horizontally across. Therefore, I estimate that approximately 130 students scored less than or equal to 119.
2. If I scored 117 in this IQ test, what percentage of students scored lower? I locate 117 on the horizontal axis and draw a line upwards to the ogive and then go horizontally across. Therefore, I estimate that 84% ($\frac{126}{150}$ x 100) students scored lower than me.
3. To find the IQ below which 60 of the students scored, I locate 60 on the vertical axis and draw a horizontal line across to the Ogive and then drop down vertically. Therefore, I estimate that 60 students scored less than or equal to 98.

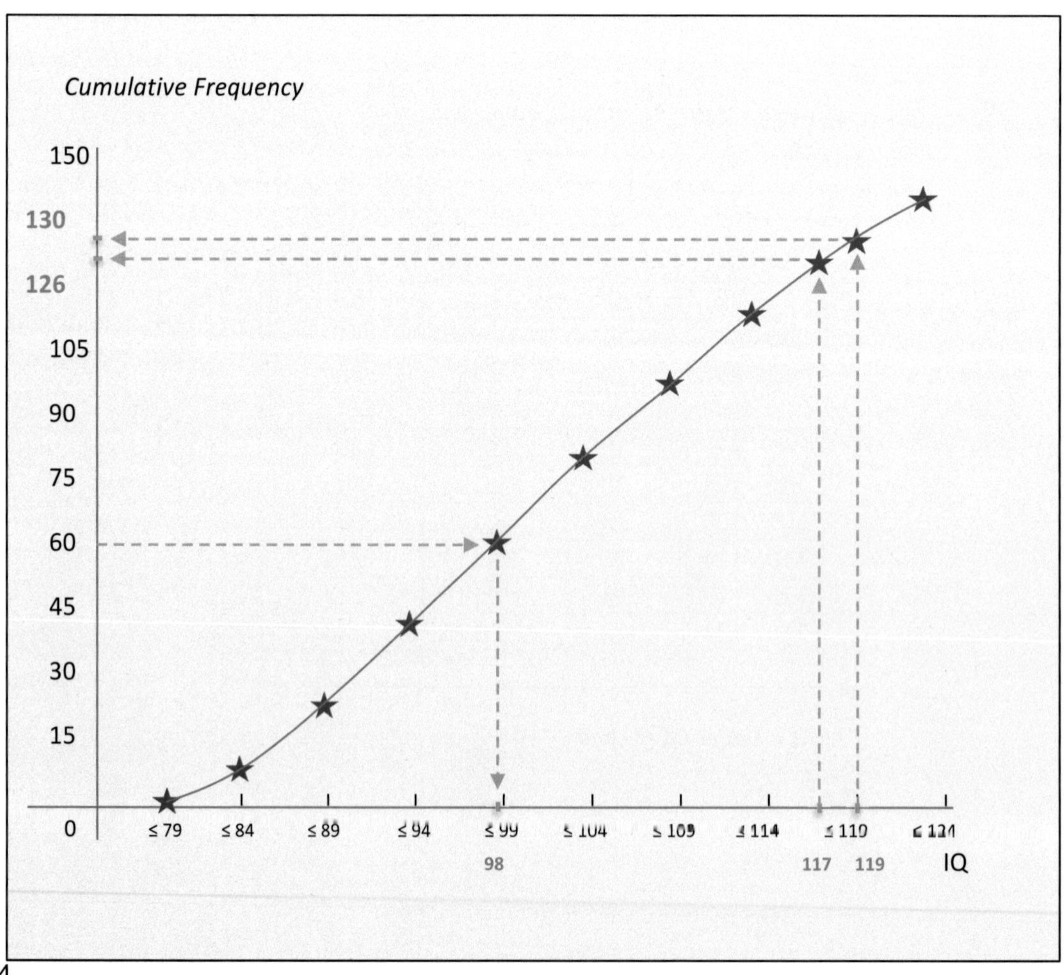

3.3 **Interpreting graphs:** *Constructed from ungrouped data*

Interpreting the Five-Number Summary

The five-number summary chart was constructed using the following raw data on *Walking Times*.

Walking Times for 100 students

40	40	40	40	40	40	41	41	41	41	41	42	42	42	42	42	42	42	42	43
43	43	43	43	44	44	44	44	44	44	44	44	44	45	45	45	45	46	46	47
47	47	47	47	47	47	48	48	48	48	50	50	50	50	50	50	51	51	51	51
51	52	52	52	53	53	53	53	54	55	55	57	57	57	60	60	61	62	63	64
65	65	66	68	70	70	70	71	71	72	74	76	76	77	77	83	87	88	95	96

The five-number summary chart divides the *Walking Times* into four quarters.

1. *25% of the walking times are between 40 and 44*
2. *25% of the walking times are between 44 and 49*
3. *25% of the walking times are between 49 and 60*
4. *25% of the walking times are between 60 and 96*

The middle 50% of values of the variable *Walking Times (44 to 60)* is represented by a rectangle *(the vertical green line indicates the location of the median = Q_2 = 49)*. This summary reveals that the top 25% of *Walking Times (60 to 96)* is more spread out compared to the bottom 25% of *Walking Times (40 to 44)* which is the least spread out of the four quarters *(i.e. more closely clustered)*.

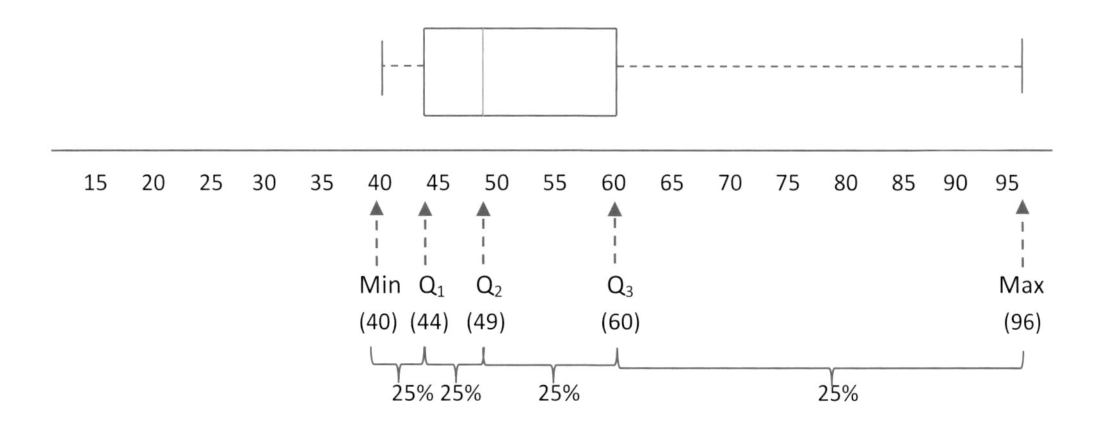

Interpreting the Box and Whisker Plot

The box and whisker plot was constructed using the raw data on *Walking Times*.

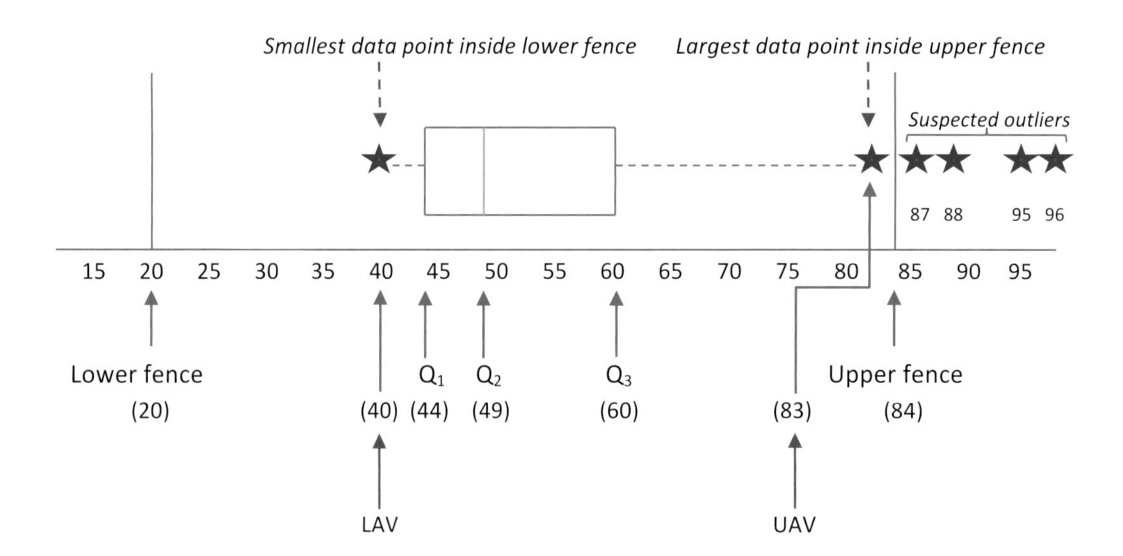

This chart reveals more than the five-number summary. *Outliers* can be identified. In addition, this chart gives us an indication of the symmetry of the sample dataset. The following can be derived from the box and whisker chart:

1. An *outlier* is any value that falls below the lower and above the upper fences.

   $Q_1 - 1.5$ (IQR) = Lower fence ➡ No *outliers*
   $Q_2 + 1.5$ (IQR) = Upper fence ➡ Four *outliers (87 88 95 and 96)*

   Once identified, an outlier needs to be omitted if it is an error or otherwise if a justifiable reason for its exclusion can be reasonably made. If you judge an outlier to be *valid*, you must consider all the implications of excluding it or including it. An *outlier* that is valid can be adjusted upwards or downwards towards its nearest *non-outlier* if the researcher wishes to preserve the person as part of the group under study.

2. The whiskers *(the dashed horizontal lines which extend outwards from the rectangle)* extend from the rectangle to the minimum and maximum values *(towards the lower and upper adjacent values which are not outliers)*.

   LAV = Lower Adjacent Value = the lowest value which is not an outlier
   UAV = Upper Adjacent Value= the highest value which is not an outlier

3. The rectangle *(defined in length by Q_3 minus Q_1 is also known as the Interquartile range)* contains the middle 50% of the scores. The median *(the vertical green line inside the rectangle)* divides the total number of scores into two equal parts.

4. For the variable *Walking Times,* the right side whisker is much longer than the left side whisker which reveals that the data is skewed to the right *(positively skewed or right tail of the polygon is extended)* and / or if the portion of the rectangle to the right of the median is longer than the portion of the rectangle to the left of the median, then sample dataset can be judged to be skewed to the right *(positively skewed).*

What possible shapes can a Box and Whisker Plot take on?

The box and whisker plot reveals whether the scores in the sample dataset are symmetrically distributed, however, the precise shape of the distribution of the data/variable is best revealed by an inspection of the histogram and / or the stem and leaf display.

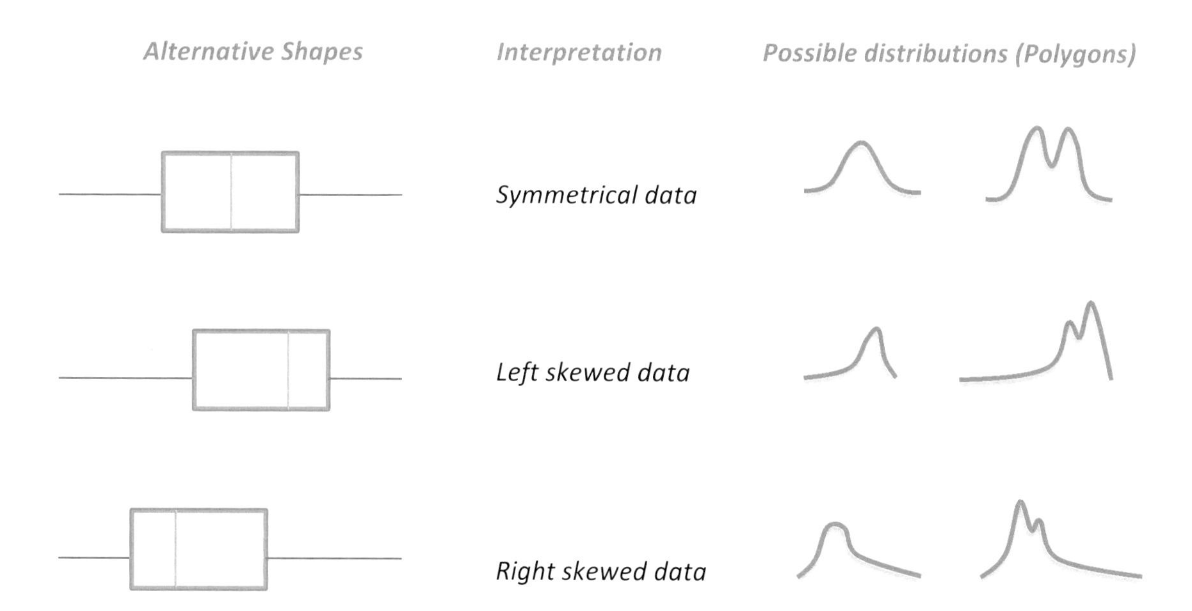

Interpreting the Stem and Leaf Display

The stem and leaf display was constructed from the data gathered for the variable *Walking Times.* Each line in the chart is a block of ten *(e.g. Line 1 is a block ranging from 40 to 49).*

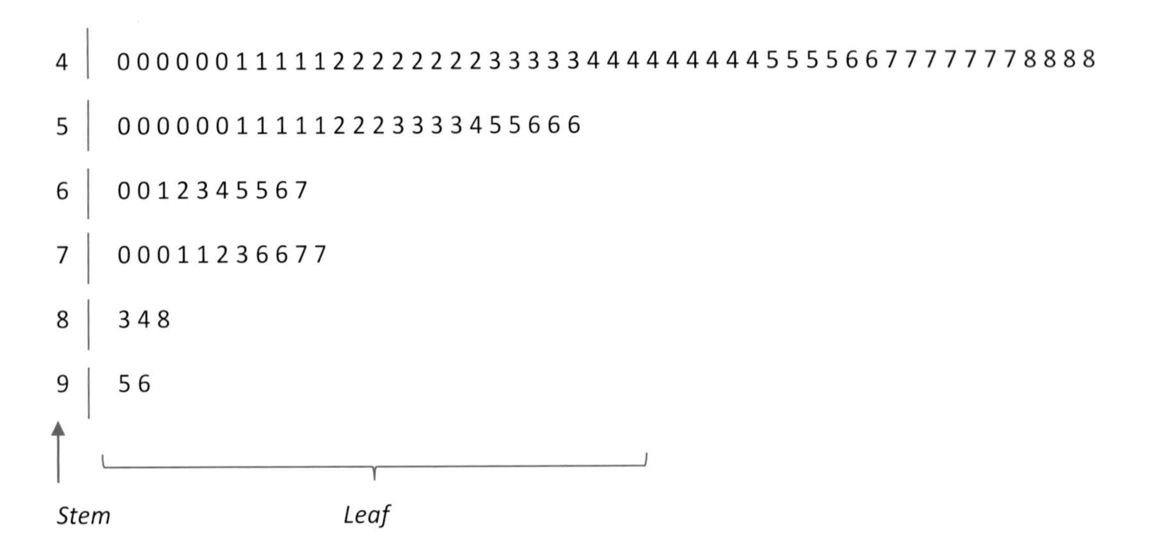

If this chart was rotated 90° counter clockwise, it would resemble the histogram. The stem and leaf display, however, retains all the original values of the variable *Walking Times*. The distribution of *Walking Times* can be judged to be positively skewed *(skewed to the right).*

3.4 Interpreting measures: *Centrality and variation from grouped data*

Centrality

The following three measures of central tendency were calculated in Chapter 2. The calculations were made from the following distribution tables. These calculations are just estimates of the three measures of central tendency. If the calculations were made directly from the raw data then the three measures of central tendency would be precise.

Distribution Tables

IQ	Freq = f	F = Cum. Freq.	Midpoint = x	fx
80 - 84	12	12	82	984
85 - 89	14	26	87	1218
90 - 94	16	42	92	1472
95 - 99	18	60	97	1746
100 - 104	20	80	102	2040
105 - 109	18	98	107	1926
110 - 114	16	114	112	1792
115 - 119	14	128	117	1638
120 - 124	12	140	122	1464
	$\sum f = 140$			$\sum fx = 14280$

Measures of Centrality

Mean = 102
Mode = 102.5
Median = 102.5

Interpretation

These three estimated measures of central tendency are approximately equal. These three measures provide a very useful indicator of the symmetry of the distribution of data. Consider the following three polygons/frequency curves which can represent possible shapes of histograms. A perfectly symmetric curve will have all three measures of central tendency located at one point. A skewed curve will be caused by the mean pulling one tail of the curve either to the right *(positively skewed)* or to the left *(negatively skewed)*.

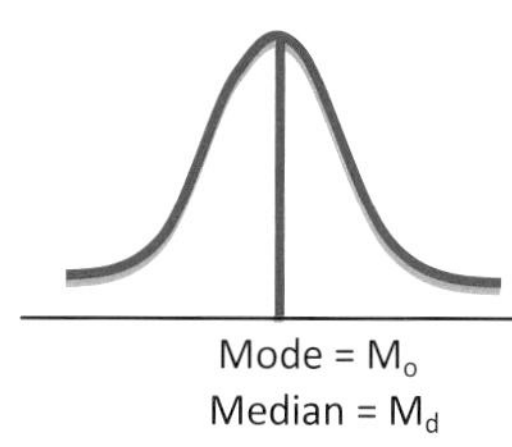

Symmetric

M_n M_d M_o

Negatively skewed

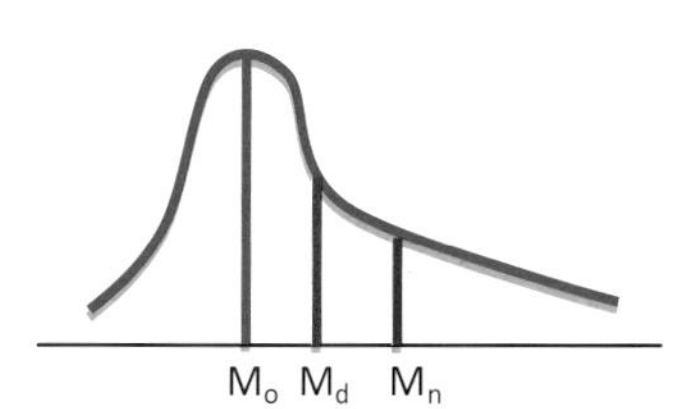

Positively skewed

The *mean* is the most appropriate measure of central tendency when the distribution is symmetric or approximately symmetric. The *median* is the most appropriate measure of central tendency when the distribution is skewed.

Interpretation

These measures of variation were derived from the distribution tables and not from the original raw data scores. Therefore, these calculations are just estimates and if the calculations were made directly from the raw data the calculated measures of variation would be precise. To fully describe our distribution of IQ scores, we must go beyond the measures of central tendency and observe how the IQ scores are dispersed or spread about the chosen measure of central tendency.

Accepted principle for quantitative 'continuous' variables

1. *If we judge a quantitative 'continuous' variable to be 'normally distributed', then the most appropriate measure of central tendency and variation are the mean and standard deviation respectively. Such a judgement enables us to go directly to the most powerful statistical tests (parametric tests).*

2. *If we judge a quantitative 'continuous' variable to be 'skewed', then the most appropriate measure of central tendency and variation are the median and interquartile range respectively. Such a judgement will direct us to use distribution free tests (non-parametric tests).*

Assessing the normality of collected data determines the route one takes in selecting inferential statistical techniques later on, i.e. whether they are parametric or non-parametric.

3.5 Interpreting measures: *Centrality and variation from ungrouped data*

Measures of central tendency *(sample sizes are kept small strictly for demonstration purposes)*

The following measures of central tendency were calculated in Chapter 2. Consider the following set of scores recorded for nine students who attempt the 1st hole at a local 'Crazy Golf' course:

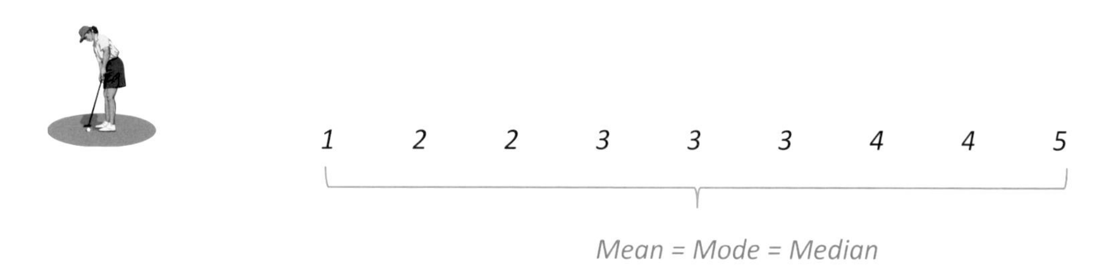

General notes on measures of centrality

1. In the example above, the 3 measures of central tendency are equal. This is one indicator of the symmetry of a distribution. These scores display a *symmetric* pattern or distribution.

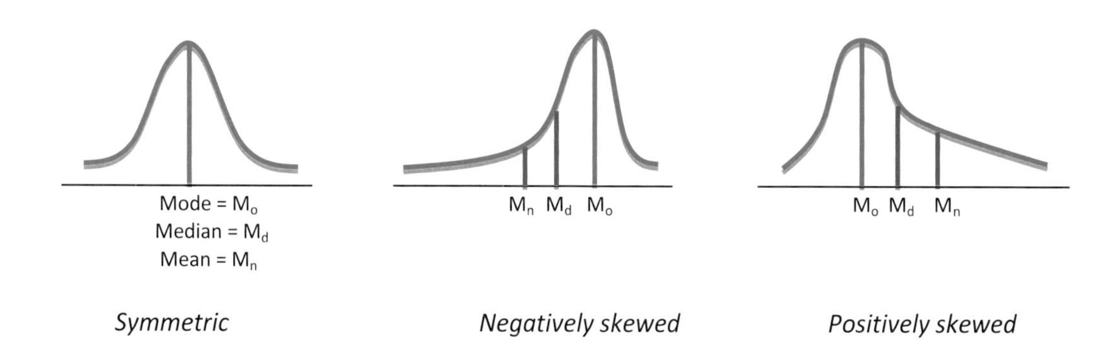

2. The mean is the most appropriate measure of central tendency in the absence of mild or extreme values *(outliers)*. All the values or scores are included in the calculation of the mean. The mean becomes less useful *(less representative)* when mild to extreme values *(outliers)* are present. Mild to extreme values *(outliers)* drag the distribution leftwards *(negatively skew or skewed to the left)* or rightwards *(positively skewed or skewed to the right)*. In the absence of *outliers*, the mean is the most appropriate measure of centrality when the distribution is symmetric or approximately symmetric.

The effects of an extreme score – consider the following alternative scores at the 1st hole at a local 'Crazy Golf' course

.

	$\{1, 2, 2, 3, 3, 3, 4, 4, 5\}$	$\{1, 2, 2, 3, 3, 3, 4, 4, 50\}$
Mean = $\bar{x}$	3	27.55

The mean is no longer capable of representing the typical or average score since an extreme score is included in its calculation.

3. The median does not involve a mathematical calculation. It is most appropriate when mild or extreme values are present. The median splits a dataset into two equal halves. The median is most appropriate when the distribution is skewed *(the presence of mild or extreme values drag the distribution leftwards or rightwards.* The median is not influenced by extreme scores *(outliers)*. The median is that score which is positioned or located exactly half way *(for arranged data)*. The median of an odd *ordered* set of scores is the middle score.

	$\{1, 2, 2, 3, 3, 3, 4, 4, 5\}$	$\{1, 2, 2, 3, 3, 3, 4, 4, 50\}$
Median	3	3

The median is very capable of representing the typical score when extreme values are present.

4. The mode, like the median, is not a *mathematical average* and is most appropriate for highlighting the most popular value. The mode in the following example is not influence by extreme values *(outliers)*.

	$\{1, 2, 2, 3, 3, 3, 4, 4, 5\}$	$\{1, 2, 2, 3, 3, 3, 4, 4, 50\}$
Mode	3	3

5. The mean has a special partnership with the standard deviation, the median with the interquartile range, but the mode has no special link with a particular measure of variation.

In general, the mean is a preferred measure of central tendency since it enables the researcher to consider more powerful statistical test procedures. In circumstances where the distribution is symmetrical, the three measures will be identical. Under these circumstances the mean should be employed. The mode is appropriate whenever an immediate or approximate estimate of central tendency is required.

Measures of Variation

The following measures of variation were calculated in Chapter 2. Consider the following set of scores recorded for nine students who attempt the 1st hole at a local 'Crazy Golf' course:

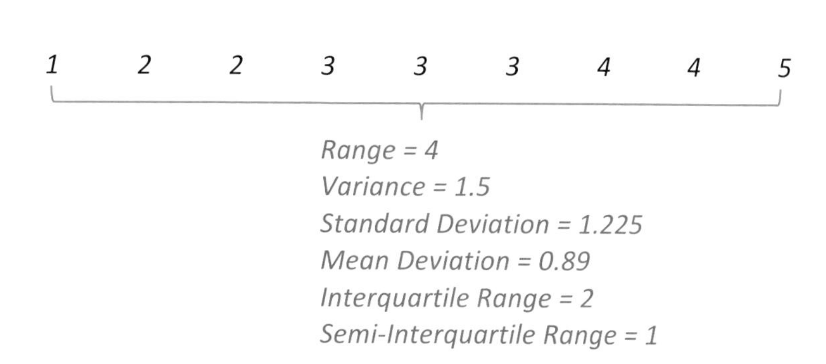

General notes on measures of variation

1. To fully describe any pattern or distribution of scores, we must go beyond the measures of central tendency. We must observe how a set of scores are dispersed or spread about a particular measure of central tendency.

2. The standard deviation is preferred over the variance *(which is the square of the standard deviation)*. The variance is not expressed in the same units as original raw scores but is expressed in the square of the original raw scores.

3. As with the mean, all the values or scores are included in the calculation of the standard deviation. The standard deviation becomes less useful (less representative) when mild to extreme values are present. These extreme values will generate a larger value for the standard deviation as seen in the example above.

Accepted principle for quantitative 'continuous' variables

1. *If we judge a quantitative 'continuous' variable to be 'normally distributed', then the most appropriate measure of central tendency and variation are the mean and standard deviation respectively. Such a judgement enables us to go directly to the most powerful statistical tests (parametric tests).*

2. *If we judge a quantitative 'continuous' variable to be 'skewed', then the most appropriate measure of central tendency and variation are the median and interquartile range respectively. Such a judgement will direct us to use distribution free tests (non-parametric tests).*

Empirical rule for a normally distributed population

If we declare, from a thorough examination of our sample data set, that that the population from which the sample was drawn can be described by a mean μ and a standard deviation σ and is 'normally distributed', then we can infer that:
a. *68.26% of the population of scores will fall within the interval* $[\mu \pm 1\sigma]$ b. *95.44% of the population of scores will fall within the interval* $[\mu \pm 2\sigma]$ c. *99.73% of the population of scores will fall within the interval* $[\mu \pm 3\sigma]$ *Since the population mean μ and a standard deviation σ are rarely known, we can use estimates of these parameters instead (i.e. we can use the* $\overline{X}$ *and s of the random sample)*

Application of the Empirical rule

Consider a random sample of 40 electric mileages *(mpg)* that have been achieved by a new small fuel efficient model.

48.5	52.3	53.5	50.5	50.5	49.6	51.0	48.3	50.6	50.2
52.5	47.5	50.9	49.8	50.0	50.8	53.0	50.9	49.9	50.1
50.7	48.2	51.5	49.0	51.7	53.2	51.1	52.6	51.2	49.5
49.4	51.9	52.0	48.8	46.8	51.3	49.3	54.0	49.2	51.4

Mean = $\overline{X} = \frac{\sum x}{n} = \frac{48.5+52.3+53.5+\cdots+51.4}{40} = 50.575$

Standard deviation = s = $\sqrt{\frac{\sum(x-\bar{x})^2}{n-1}} = \sqrt{\frac{(48.5-50.6)^2+(52.3-50.6)^2+\cdots+(51.4-50.6)^2}{40-1}} = 1.644$

Empirical Rule

68.26% of all mileages will fall within the interval $[\overline{X} \pm 1s]$ = $[50.575 \pm 1(1.644)]$ =$[48.931\ to\ 52.219]$

95.44% of all mileages will fall within the interval $[\overline{X} \pm 2s]$ = $[50.575 \pm 2(1.644))]$ =$[47.287\ to\ 53.863]$

99.73% of all mileages will fall within the interval $[\overline{X} \pm 3s]$ = $[50.575 \pm 3(1.644))]$ =$[45.644\ to\ 55.506]$

3.6 Assessing Normality

The approaches outlined in this section should be simultaneously considered when assessing the normality of data derived for a quantitative continuous variable. The most powerful statistical techniques assume that the pattern or distribution of population values match a normal 'bell shaped' pattern. A breach of the normality assumption may deem any attempts at interpretation or deriving inferences from parametric statistical tests unreliable or invalid.

Normality or a normal 'bell shaped' pattern implies that the collected data *(which represents and reflects the population of values, assuming a proper random sample has been conducted)* assumes a symmetrical, bell shaped mesokurtic pattern. This curve is symmetrical *(provides a perfect match when folded about its mean)* and its tails extend to infinity *(tails will appear to never touch the horizontal axis).* Since the researcher may never have access to the actual shape of the population of values, he must attempt to detect whether a variable of interest possesses the pattern of normality.

Many variables measuring natural qualities or characteristics will tend to possess the pattern of normality including: intelligence, height, weight, pulse rates, etc. A variety of approaches are available to the researcher in his quest to declare normality for a particular variable and hence provide the justification for applying the more powerful statistical techniques *(parametric tests).* On occasion, these approaches to assessing normality may present conflicting results. However, a combination of these approaches along with the accumulated experience of the researcher should assist the task of assessing normality.

Approach 1 – Visual inspection

An inspection of a variety of charts is a useful starting point. Once the histogram appears reasonably bell shaped *(remember that with larger samples, the histogram is more likely to reflect the true population shape)*, then you can move on to visually inspecting other charts to seek support for this suspected 'bell-shaped' pattern. The box and whisker plot may lend support to your investigation since it provides an indication of symmetry *(remember that a symmetrical distribution can be either bell shaped or non-bell shaped).* The normal Quantile-Quantile plot *(Q-Q plot)* provides a diagonal line along which the sample values should fall and should not reveal a tendency or pattern to deviate in an obvious non-linear pattern. The detrended Q-Q plot indicates how each sample value deviates from normality *(normal being zero in the diagram).* Most values should hover around the line in this chart and the values should be evenly spread out along the range of the line. Remember that this visual approach is not conclusive and must be complemented with other approaches.

Assessing	Visual inspection of the	Typical notes made from the visual inspection
1. Symmetry	*Box and Whisker plot*	*1. Symmetry may not imply normality.* *2. This plot may reveal outliers that ought to be investigates and perhaps justifiably omitted.*
2. Bell Curve	*Histogram*	*1. A histogram with too many bars may disguise normality.* *2. A truly normal variable will be best reflected in histograms which are constructed from increased sample sizes.*
	Stem & Leaf plot	
	Normal Q-Q plot	*This plot may reveal outliers that ought to be investigates and perhaps justifiably omitted.*
	Detrended Normal Q-Q plots	*This plot may reveal outliers that ought to be investigates and perhaps justifiably omitted.*

The experienced researcher should avoid the temptation to automatically declare that the 'data are skewed' when the histogram appears slightly asymmetric *(not having the perfect symmetry of a perfect bell shaped curve)*. An experienced researcher will understand that even in samples drawn from a symmetric population, the histogram may not be an exact mirror image of the population. The shape of the histogram is influenced by the number of bins/classes selected and the sample size.

Approach 2 – Descriptive Measures

A review of a variety of descriptive measures can reveal a pattern for the distribution of values for the variable under investigation. It is worth comparing the mean with the 5% trimmed mean *(Calculated by SPSS: 5% of values are removed from each end of the sample of values and the mean is recalculated)*. This will immediately present an alert to the presence of potential outliers *(particularly if the mean is very different to the 5% trimmed mean)*. If the mean and median are identical then the distribution of values is symmetric. Remember that a symmetrical distribution can be unimodal, bimodal, or can assume a variety of other shapes *(rectangular, u-shaped, etc.)*. Once again, the experienced researcher will avoid declaring that the data are skewed when the sample mean is slightly different to the sample median.

Statistical packages provide values for skewness and kurtosis. A perfectly normal distribution will achieve a value of zero for each of these measures *(skewness and kurtosis)*. A positive value for skewness implies that the distribution of sample values is positively skewed *(tail is extended to the right – values tending to be gathered or clustered towards the lower values of the variable range)*. A positive value for kurtosis implies that the distribution of sample values are inclined towards peakedness *(values of the variable are gathered or clustered at the centre)*. A negative value for skewness implies that the distribution of sample values is negatively skewed *(tail is extended to the left – values tending to be gathered or clustered towards the upper values of the variable range)*. A negative value for kurtosis implies that the distribution of sample values is inclined towards flatness *(values of the variable are not gathered or clustered at the centre).*

Assessing	*Visual inspection of the*	*Typical notes made from the visual inspection*
1. Symmetry	*Mean* *Median*	*If the mean = median then the distribution is symmetric, but this does not imply normality.*
2. Normality	*Mean* *Median* *Mode* *Skewness*: measures symmetry* *Kurtosis: measures peakedness*	*1. If the mean = median = mode then the distribution is symmetric and unimodal. The mode, as a measure of centrality for a continuous variable, should be set aside.* *2. A perfectly normal distribution will achieve a value of zero for both skewness and kurtosis (rarely observed occurrence)* *3. The value for skewness (G_1)* provided by Excel and SPSS, when used in conjunction with a certain table (see below), can be used as a test of departure from normality.*

* G_1 = *Adjusted Fisher-Pearson standardized moment coefficient* = $\frac{n}{(n-1)(n-2)}\left[\sum\left(\frac{x-\bar{x}}{s}\right)^3\right]$

Both Excel and SPSS provide a value for sample skewness *(i.e. G_1 = Adjusted Fisher-Pearson standardized moment coefficient).* G_1 will enable the researcher to infer that:

1. *Its sign reflects the direction of skewness.*
2. *It compares the sample with a normal (symmetric) distribution.*
3. *Values far from zero suggest a non-normal (skewed) population.*
4. *The statistic has an adjustment for sample size (this adjustment is of little consequence in large samples).*

Interpretation of G_1 - Useful when the researcher has access to the original raw data

The statistic G_1 when used in conjunction with the following table *(90% Range for Sample Skewness Coefficient G_1)* can be used as a test of departure from normality, *(Doane and Seward, 2011).* According to Doane and Seward (2011, p. 8) the researcher can use this table to decide whether or not G_1 *(skewness value)* 'is far enough from zero to conclude that the sample probably did not come from a normal population'. The table *(90% Range for Sample Skewness Coefficient G_1)* begins at a sample size of 20 since 'skewness is hard to judge in smaller samples'. 'In samples drawn from a normal population, the expected range of G_1 decreases as sample size increases and vice versa'. The statistic G_1 in conjunction with this table 'is not a general test of symmetry, because the table refers only to a normal population'.

Suggested interpretation of G_1 in conjunction with the '90% range' table – if your sample is from a normal population, the skewness coefficient G_1 would fall within the stated range 90% of the time. Values of G_1 outside this range suggest non-normal skewness.

90% Range (highlighted) for Sample Skewness

Sample Size	*Lower Tail*			*Upper Tail*		
n	*0.01*	*0.05*	*0.10*	*0.90*	*0.95*	*0.99*
20	*-1.23*	*-0.83*	*-0.63*	*0.63*	*0.83*	*1.23*
30	*-1.03*	*-0.70*	*-0.53*	*0.53*	*0.70*	*1.03*
40	*-0.90*	*-0.61*	*-0.47*	*0.47*	*0.61*	*0.90*
50	*-0.81*	*-0.55*	*-0.42*	*0.42*	*0.55*	*0.81*
60	*-0.74*	*-0.50*	*-0.39*	*0.39*	*0.50*	*0.74*
70	*-0.69*	*-0.47*	*-0.36*	*0.36*	*0.47*	*0.69*
80	*-0.65*	*-0.44*	*-0.34*	*0.34*	*0.44*	*0.65*
90	*-0.60*	*-0.42*	*-0.32*	*0.32*	*0.42*	*0.60*
100	*-0.57*	*-0.39*	*-0.30*	*0.30*	*0.39*	*0.57*
150	*-0.47*	*-0.33*	*-0.25*	*0.25*	*0.33*	*0.47*
200	*-0.40*	*-0.28*	*-0.22*	*0.22*	*0.28*	*0.40*
300	*-0.33*	*-0.23*	*-0.18*	*0.18*	*0.23*	*0.33*
400	*-0.28*	*-0.20*	*-0.16*	*0.16*	*0.20*	*0.28*
500	*-0.26*	*-0.18*	*-0.14*	*0.14*	*0.18*	*0.26*

90% Range (highlighted) for Sample Kurtosis

Sample Size	*Lower Tail*			*Upper Tail*		
n	*0.01*	*0.05*	*0.10*	*0.90*	*0.95*	*0.99*
40	*-1.09*	*-0.89*	*-0.76*	*0.91*	*1.36*	*2.46*
50	*-1.01*	*-0.82*	*-0.70*	*0.82*	*1.21*	*2.17*
60	*-0.95*	*-0.76*	*-0.64*	*0.77*	*1.14*	*2.04*
70	*-0.90*	*-0.72*	*-0.61*	*0.72*	*1.05*	*1.89*
80	*-0.86*	*-0.68*	*-0.58*	*0.66*	*0.98*	*1.69*
90	*-0.82*	*-0.65*	*-0.55*	*0.64*	*0.93*	*1.63*
100	*-0.79*	*-0.63*	*-0.52*	*0.61*	*0.87*	*1.51*
150	*-0.68*	*-0.53*	*-0.44*	*0.51*	*0.71*	*1.22*
200	*-0.61*	*-0.47*	*-0.39*	*0.45*	*0.63*	*1.04*
300	*-0.52*	*-0.40*	*-0.33*	*0.37*	*0.51*	*0.82*
400	*-0.46*	*-0.35*	*-0.29*	*0.31*	*0.43*	*0.67*
500	*-0.42*	*-0.32*	*-0.26*	*0.28*	*0.38*	*0.61*

Note: Percentiles are based on author's simulation using 50,000 samples of each sample size using R version 2.13.0 with Fisher-Pearson skewness and kurtosis routines from CRAN library 1071 (same formulas as Excel). The simulation is based on the methodology described in David P. Doane and Lori E. Seward (2011), "Measuring Skewness: A Forgotten Statistic?" Journal of Statistics Education, Vol 19, No. 2.

- A skewness value *(G_1)* of 1.343 is provided by SPSS for the variable Walking Times *(n = 100)* and this skewness value is well outside the range required for normality *(i.e. -0.39 to 0.39)*.

Summary of SPSS output – Walking Times (n = 100)

Walking Times (n = 100)	*Statistic*	*Standard Error*
Mean	*53.57*	
Median	*49.50*	
Variance	*168.61*	
Standard Deviation	*12.985*	
Range	*56*	
Interquartile Range	*17*	
Minimum	*40*	
Maximum	*96*	
Skewness	*1.343*	*0.241*
Kurtosis	*1.324*	*0.478*

When visual displays appear ambiguous *(i.e. neither highly skewed nor definitely symmetric)* and when the sample mean is seemingly close to the sample median, the skewness measure G_1, used in conjunction with the '90% range table', is very useful to the task of detecting skewness. A discussion on kurtosis will be suspended in this text. In any case, *Horswell and Looney (1993, p. 437)* note that 'The performance of skewness tests is shown to be very sensitive to the kurtosis of the underlying distribution' and *Balanda and MacGillivray (1988)* suggest that kurtosis is essentially 'a property of symmetric distributions'.

Interpretation of Sk_2 - Useful when the researcher does not have access to the original raw data

The sample statistics G_1 when used in conjunction with the *90% range* table allows the researcher to infer whether or not the sample came from a normal population. However, G_1 is only useful when the researcher is working from the original raw data. In the event that the researcher is confronted with summarised data *(sample mean = $\bar{x}$, sample median = m and sample standard deviation = s)*, and that access to the original raw data is not possible, then *Pearson 2 skewness coefficient (Sk_2)*, used in conjunction with an appropriate *90% range* table, allows the researcher to infer whether or not the sample comes from a normal population. However, as Doane and Seward said, in 2011, *"the critical values of Sk_2 and G_1 lead to the same conclusion on average...the weakness of Sk_2 is that it lacks power"*. Despite this weakness, they suggest that *"a large skewness statistic casts doubt on the normality of the population"*. The sample statistic is $Sk_2 = 3\frac{(\bar{x}-m)}{s}$. Doane and Seward *(2011)* include a footnote in their *90% range* table, *"to make sure that it is interpreted correctly"*

90% expected range for Sk_2

n	*Lower Limit*	*Upper Limit*	*n*	*Lower Limit*	*Upper Limit*
10	-0.963	0.963	60	-0.463	0.463
20	-0.762	0.762	70	-0.437	0.437
30	-0.643	0.643	80	-0.407	0.407
40	-0.554	0.554	90	-0.385	0.385
50	-0.506	0.506	100	-0.367	0.367

Note: If your sample is from a normal population, the skewness coefficient Sk_2 would fall within the stated range 90% of the time. Values of Sk_2 outside this range suggest non-normal skewness.

Approach 3 – Tests of Normality

This approach to assessing normality should not be used in isolation. There are a variety of tests of normality available *(almost 40 tests can be sourced in statistical literature Dufour et al, 1998)* and each one has value under certain situations but not in others. Indeed different tests can provide different contradictory conclusions. Some writers have attempted to create a league table *(league table below derived from findings by Razali and Wah, 2011)* for these tests based on usefulness criteria. The most common tests of normality are listed in the following table.

A study by *Razali and Wah (2011)* concluded that amongst these four tests, Shapiro-Wilk test is the most powerful test for all types of distributions *(symmetric and asymmetric)* and sample sizes whereas the Kolmogorov – Smirnov test is the least powerful. In spite of the accolades for the Shapiro Wilk test, when it comes to small sample sizes *($n \leq 30$)*, the Shapiro – Wilk has low power *(power being the capacity to detect deviations from normality when they exist).*

Other studies including *Mendes and Pala (2003)* and *Keskin (2006)* had also elevated the Shapiro – Wilk to the top of the league table *(a table listing the most powerful tests of normality).* Razali and Wah *(2011)* also remind researchers that the four normality tests do not perform well for small sample sizes *($n \leq 30$).*

Tests – League Table (based on most powerful @ 5% & 10% level of significance)	*Notes*
Shapiro – Wilk test	*1. This test is the most powerful for all sample sizes* *2. Originally restricted for sample sizes of < 50* *3. Lower power for sample sizes < 30* *4. Demonstrated to be very powerful for large sample sizes*
Anderson-Darling test	*This test matches the power of the Shapiro – Wilk test*
Lilliefors test	*This test is outperforms the Kolmogorov – Smirnov test*
Kolmogorov – Smirnov test	*1. This test is the least powerful for all sample sizes* *2. Generally considered for sample sizes ≥ 50* *3. May detect minor departures from normality (providing a Sig. < 0.05) in very large samples.*

SPSS presents the following tests of normality: Kolmogorov – Smirnov and Shapiro – Wilk tests

	Tests of Normality					
	Kolmogorov – Smirnov $n \geq 50$			*Shapiro – Wilk $n < 50$*		
	Statistic	*df*	*Sig.*	*Statistic*	*df*	*Sig.*
Walking Times	*0.178*	*100*	*0.000*	*0.854*	*100*	*0.000*

The interpretation of both tests: If Sig. > 0.05 then one can assume normality.

The Chi-square test *(goodness of fit test)* can also be used to discover, for example, if a pattern of observed frequencies 'fits' a pattern of expected frequencies that conforms to a normal distribution. This chi-square test *(goodness of fit test)* may be undertaken under the following two scenarios:

1. *When one is investigating whether the observed distribution (i.e. the sample data) comes from a normal population where the mean and standard deviation is known (specified).*
2. *When one is investigating whether the observed distribution (i.e. the sample data) is normal. In this test type, the mean and standard deviation is unknown (unspecified) and must be estimated.*

This approach is not treated in this book.

Approach 4 – Central Limit Theorem

Many researchers invoke the CLT in instances where they are working with sample sizes ≥ 30 to justify their application of powerful parametric test procedures (notably in situations involving tests about population mean(s)). Some parametric statistical tests *(one-sample and two-sample t-test)* are known to be robust against the assumption of normality especially if sample sizes are reasonably large. However just because a method is robust is no assurance that the method is still powerful when the population is non-normal *(Conover, 1999)*. A statistical test procedure should not be preferred over another simply on the basis of robustness. Larger samples confers more power and insistence on justifying a parametric test procedure may be unnecessary when less powerful tests *(non-parametric)* can match the outcome of more powerful tests when sample sizes become increasingly larger.

3.7 MCQs and Solutions

1. Consider the following tests of normality for the variable *Make-up Times* ($n = 65$). What would be your conclusion about the distribution of the data?

	Tests of Normality					
	Kolmogorov – Smirnov $n \geq 50$			*Shapiro – Wilk* $n < 50$		
	Statistic	*df*	*Sig.*	*Statistic*	*df*	*Sig.*
Make-up times	*0.133*	*65*	*0.006*	*0.965*	*65*	*0.062*

(a) This sample is normally distributed
(b) This sample is not normally distributed
(c) This sample is negatively skewed
(d) None of the above

2. If a bell shaped distribution is very peaked, then we can describe it as:

(a) Leptokurtic
(b) Platykurtic
(c) Mesokurtic
(d) None of the above

3. If the distribution is symmetric and unimodal, then ...?

(a) Mean = Median = Mode
(b) Mean < Median < Mode
(c) Mean > Median > Mode
(d) None of the above

4. If your sample is normally distributed and has no extreme scores, then the most appropriate measure of centrality is...?

(a) Mean
(b) Mode
(c) Median
(d) None of the above

5. Which of the following measures of centrality is sensitive to extreme scores?

(a) Mean
(b) Mode
(c) Median
(d) None of the above

6. A normal distribution should have which of the following properties?

(a) Bell shaped
(b) Symmetrical
(c) Have a skewness and kurtosis value of zero
(d) All of the above

7. If your distribution of scores appears to be positively skewed then:

(a) The right tail is extended
(b) Mean > Median > Mode
(c) The left tail is extended
(d) (a) and (b) are correct

8. The skewness value is a measure of:

(a) The symmetry of a distribution
(b) The peakedness of a distribution
(c) Average distance between the 3 measures of centrality in a non-normal distribution
(d) None of the above

9. The kurtosis value is a measure of:

(a) The symmetry of a distribution
(b) The peakedness of a distribution
(c) Average distance between the 3 measures of centrality in a non-normal distribution
(d) None of the above

10. What is the most likely shape of a distribution which has a mean IQ = 100, median IQ = 95 and a mode IQ = 90?

(a) Skewed to the right
(b) Skewed to the left
(c) Symmetric
(d) Bimodal

11. Consider the box and whisker plot

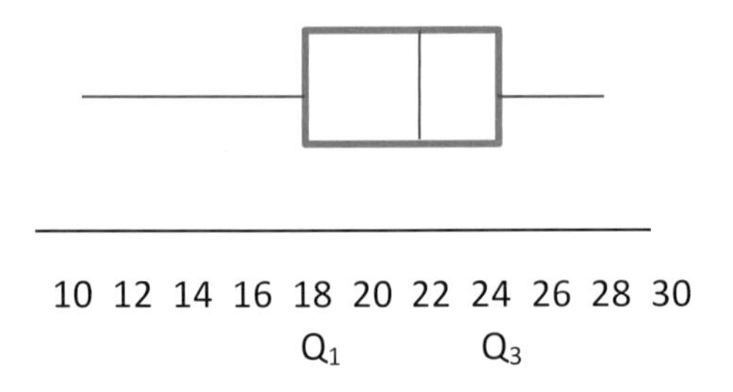

Which of the following statements are true?

(a) The distributing is skewed to the right *(positively skewed)*
(b) The distributing is skewed to the left *(negatively skewed)*
(c) The Interquartile range is about 24
(d) The median is about 8

12. Parametric statistical tests assume that the populations from which samples are drawn are:

(a) Symmetrical
(b) Positively skewed
(c) Negatively skewed
(d) Normally distributed

13. Distribution free tests are employed when we are dealing with a dataset which is:

(a) Symmetrical
(b) A skewed distribution
(c) Normally distributed
(d) None of the above

14. Which of the following is untrue?

(a) The dataset $\{2, 3, 5, 7, 9\}$ has a Quartile 1 = 2.5 and Quartile 3 = 8 using the SPSS formula
(b) The dataset $\{3, 5, 7, 9\}$ has a Quartile 1 = 3.5 and Quartile 3 = 8.5 using the SPSS formula
(c) If the variance is 81 then the standard deviation is 9
(d) If the semi-interquartile range is 2 then the interquartile range is 1

15. Which of the following is untrue?

(a) My percentile rank of 85 in statistics tells me that 85% of students scored lower than me
(b) An outlier is identified if it falls outside $Q_1 - 1.5$ (IQR) and $Q_3 + 1.5$ (IQR)
(c) The interquartile range = $Q_3 - Q_1$
(d) The shape of the distribution of a dataset can be seen more clearly from a box and whisker plot than a stem and leaf display

16. Consider the following curve *(frequency polygon)*

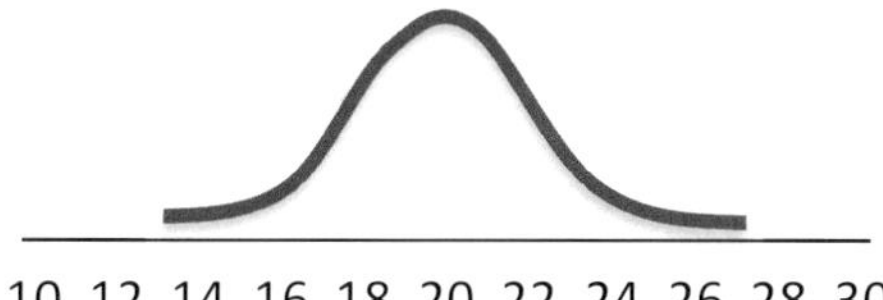

Which of the following is untrue?
(a) Mean (20) = Median (20) = Mode (20)
(b) This distribution is symmetric about the value 20
(c) This distribution has a skewness value of approximately zero
(d) Non parametric tests would most likely be appropriate with this dataset

17. Consider the following curve *(frequency polygon)*

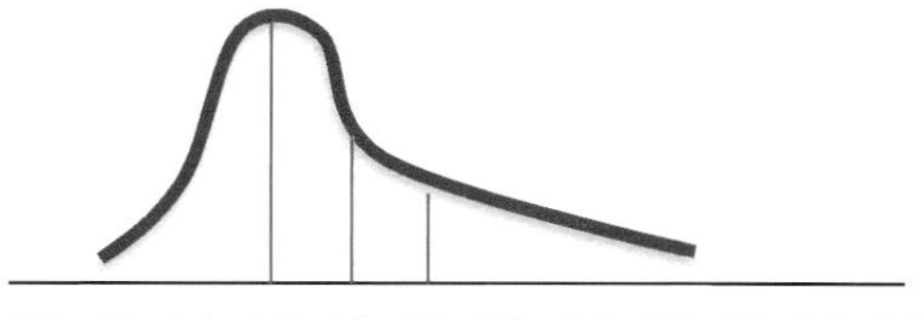

Which of the following is untrue?
(a) Mean (20) = Median (18) = Mode (16)
(b) This distribution is positively skewed *(skewed to the right)*
(c) This distribution has a negative skewness value
(d) Non parametric tests would most likely be appropriate with this dataset.

18. Consider the following curve *(frequency polygon)*

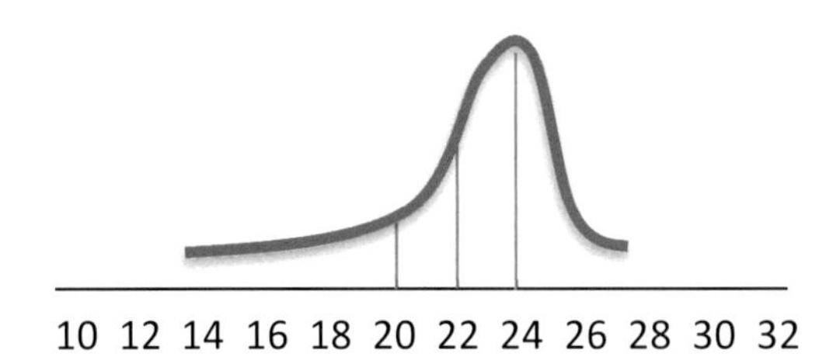

Which of the following is untrue?

(a) Mean (20) = Median (22) = Mode (24)
(b) This distribution is negatively skewed *(skewed to the left)*
(c) This distribution has a negative skewness value
(d) Parametric tests would most likely be appropriate with this dataset

19. Consider the following curve (frequency polygon)

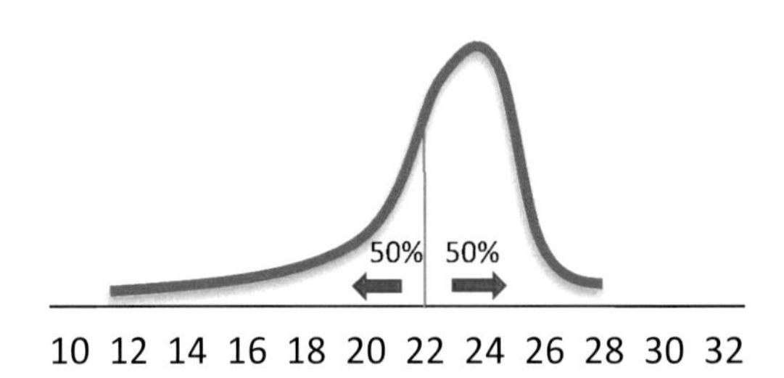

Which of the following is untrue?

(a) The mode is the highest point in the distribution
(b) The median divides the distribution of scores into two equal halves
(c) The interquartile range is an appropriate measure of variation for skewed data
(d) The mean is an appropriate measure of centrality for skewed data

20. Consider the following raw data alternatives:

Descriptives	$\{1, 2, 2, 3, 3, 3, 4, 4, 5\}$	$\{1, 2, 3, 3, 3, 4, 4, 4, 4, 5\}$	$\{2, 3, 3, 3, 4, 4, 5, 6\}$
n = sample size	9	10	8
Mean	3	3.3	3.75
Median	3	3.5	3.5
Mode	3	4	3
Range	4	4	4
Variance	1.5	1.35	1.64
St. Dev	1.22	1.16	1.28
IQR	2	1.25	1.75
Q1	2	2.75	3
Q2	3	3.5	3.5
Q3	4	3	4.75
Frequency Polygon			

Sample sizes are kept small strictly for demonstration purposes.

Which of the following analysis is incorrect?

(a) Raw data 1 displays a symmetrical pattern (mean = median = mode). The appropriate measure of centrality and variance will be the mean and standard deviation respectively. The histogram reveals a frequency polygon which suggests that the sample appears to have come from a population which is normally distributed.

(b) Raw data 2 displays a negative skew (mean < median < mode). The appropriate measure of centrality and variance will be the median and interquartile range respectively. The histogram reveals a frequency polygon which suggests that the sample appears to have come from a population which is not normally distributed.

(c) Raw data 3 displays a positive skew (mean > median > mode). The appropriate measure of centrality and variance will be the median and interquartile range respectively. The histogram reveals a frequency polygon which suggests that the sample appears to have come from a population which is not normally distributed.

(d) Raw data alternatives 2 and 3 display skewed distributions (mean ≠ median ≠ mode). The appropriate measure of centrality and variance will be the mode and variance respectively. The histograms reveal frequency polygons which suggest that the samples appear to have come from populations which are not normally distributed.

MCQ Solutions

1. (b)	6. (d)	11. (b)	16. (d)
2. (a)	7. (d)	12. (d)	17. (c)
3. (a)	8. (a)	13. (b)	18. (d)
4. (a)	9. (b)	14. (d)	19. (d)
5. (a)	10. (a)	15. (d)	20. (d)

Chapter 4 – Probability Distributions

'Doubt is not a pleasant condition, but certainty is absurd.'

Voltaire (1694 – 1778)

Inferential statistics is that part of the statistical method which equips us with the techniques that allow us to generalise from the sample to the wider population

4.1 Schematic Chart: *Overview of probability and Alternative Distributions*

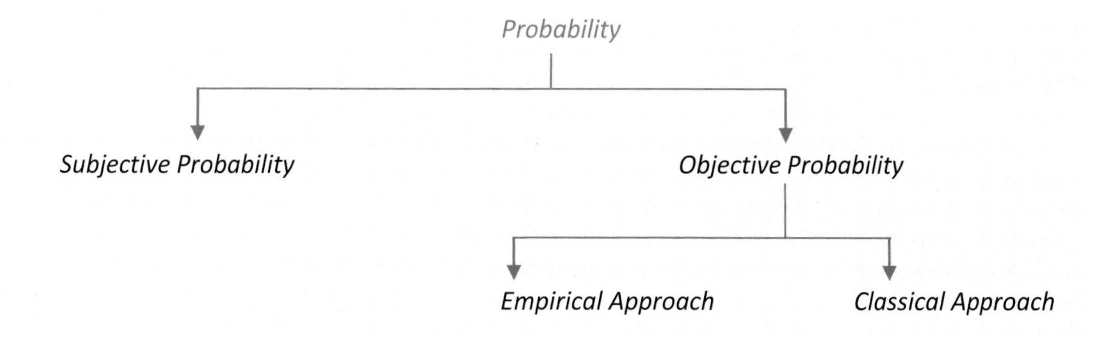

Alternative Distributions

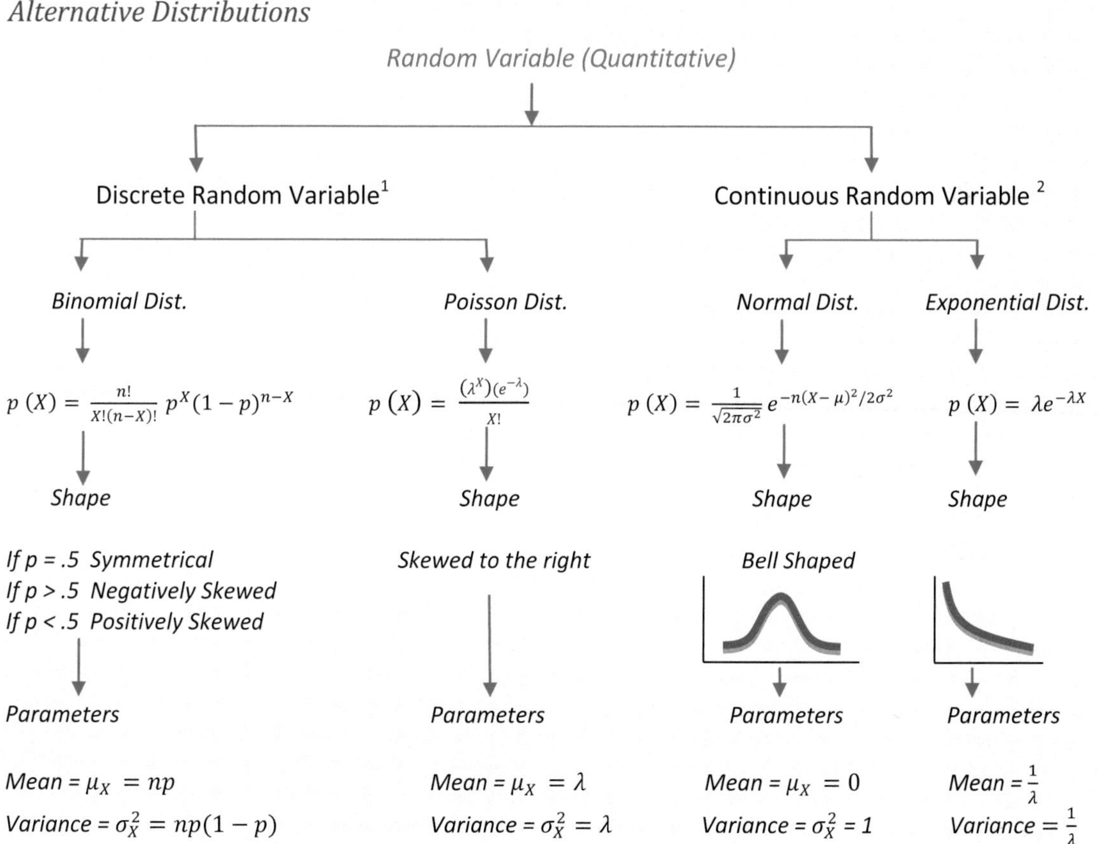

Figure 4.1 - Random Variables

1. *With discrete random variables, we can calculate the probability of occurrence of a single outcome from the sample space (Random experiment = Rolling a die, Sample space = 1, 2, 3, 4, 5, 6, variable type = discrete random variable.)*
2. *With continuous random variables, we can only calculate the probability of occurrence of a single outcome from within a specified range or above or below a specified value.*

4.2 Overview

Introduction

The probability or chance *(p)* of an *event* occurring will fall somewhere along the following spectrum:

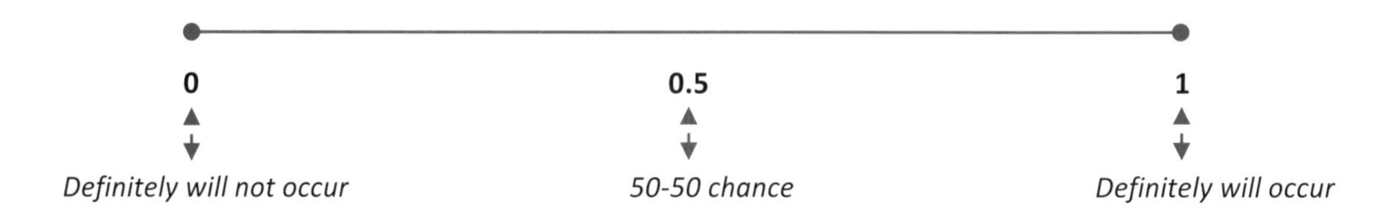

The probability is always expressed as a value which lies somewhere between $0 \leq p \leq 1$ *(between 0 and 1 inclusive)*. Consider the probability of the following *events* occurring:

a. *p(night follows day) = 1*
b. *p(death follows life) = 1*
c. *p(night does not follows day) = 0*
d. *p(death does not follows life) = 0*

If p is the probability that an event will occur, then q will represent the probability that the event will not occur *($q = 1 - p$)*. Remember that $p + q$ must always equal 1.

Probability Theory

Probability Theory is concerned with the possible outcomes of experiments. Two types of experiment can be considered.

1. Known population experiment (all possible outcomes are known)

The probability or likely occurrence of an event in this type of experiment is estimated using the formula:

$$p(event) = \frac{number\ of\ outcomes\ favouring\ the\ chosen\ event}{total\ number\ of\ possible\ outcomes} = \frac{e}{N}$$

This type of experiment involves a single trial *(i.e. the outcome from just one toss of a coin is observed, the outcome from just one throw of a die is observed, the outcome from just one selection from a pack of cards is observed).*

Known population experiment

Experiment	*p(event)*	**Sample Space Known(N)*	*Favouring the Event (e)*	*p(event)* = $\frac{e}{N}$
Toss a coin	*p(tail)*	*2 possible outcomes*	*One possible tail*	*p(tail)* = $\frac{1}{2}$ = *0.5*
Throw a die	*p(three)*	*6 possible outcomes*	*One possible three*	*p(three)* = $\frac{1}{6}$ = *0.166*
Throw a die	*p(odd)*	*6 possible outcomes*	*Three possible odds*	*p(odd)* = $\frac{3}{6} = \frac{1}{3}$ = *0.333*
Select a card	*p(jack)*	*52 possible outcomes*	*Four possible Jacks*	*p(jack)* = $\frac{4}{52}$ = *0.076*
Select a letter	*p(t)*	*26 possible outcomes*	*One possible t*	*p(t)* = $\frac{1}{26}$ = *0.038*
Select a letter	*p(vowel)*	*26 possible outcomes*	*Five possible vowels*	*p(vowel)* = $\frac{5}{26}$ = *0.192*
Select a vowel	*p(u)*	*5 Possible outcomes*	*One possible u*	*p(u)* = $\frac{1}{5}$ = *0.2*

**Sample Space = Population of possible outcomes*

2. Unknown population experiment (all possible outcomes are not known)

The probability or frequency of occurrence of an event in this type of experiment is estimated using the formula:

$$p(event) = \frac{number\ of\ outcomes\ favouring\ the\ chosen\ event}{total\ number\ of\ sample\ outcomes} = \frac{e}{n}$$

The type of experiment involves many trials *(the outcomes from observing 100 sampled students)*

Unknown population experiment

Experiment (n = 100)	*p(event)*	*Sample Space (N)*	*Favouring the Event (e)*	*p(event)* = $\frac{e}{n}$
**Observing a Sample*	*p(blue-eyed student)*	*Unknown*	*30 are blue-eyed*	*p (BE)* = $\frac{30}{100}$ = *0.30*

** (A random sample of 100 students is selected from a population of 3000 students)*

Approaches to probability

(a) *Theoretical or Classical Approach – Known population experiment*

With the *Known population experiments* the probability is estimated based on intuitive reasoning. If we were to conduct the same experiment *(i.e. toss a coin)* an infinite number of times, then the likely theoretical relative frequency $\left[\frac{frequency}{total\ frequency}\right]$ of a head would approach ½ or 0.5.

This assignment is based on an intuitive reasoning which suggests that if we repeat the experiment towards infinity and if each outcome can be assured an equal likelihood of occurrence, then the relative frequency of a head would approach 0.5.

(b) Empirical Approach – Unknown population experiment

With the *Unknown population experiments* the probability is estimated based on empirical findings. If we simply count the number of blue-eyed students from the 100 selected students, then the proportion of occurrences i.e. the relative frequency $\left[\frac{frequency}{total\ frequency}\right]$ can be estimated i.e. $\frac{30}{100}$ = 0.30

These two approaches to probability are considered *objective approaches* since a probability is assigned to an event based on either historical or theoretical relative frequency. These approaches are in contrast to the *subjective approach*, which assigns a probability to an event based on opinions or beliefs held or other information considered pertinent.

Reporting probability

Probability can be reported or expressed in variety of ways. The probability of selecting a *blue-eyed* student can therefore be written in any one of the following formats:

	p(blue-eyed student)	
Expressed a proportion	*0.30*	
Expressed a percentage	*30%*	
Per 100	*30 times per 100*	
Odds for	*30 to 70 or 0.43 to 1*	*Odds* = $\frac{p}{1-p}$
Odds against	*70 to 30 or 2.33 to 1*	*Odds Against* = $\frac{1-p}{p}$

4.3 Rules of probability

In section 4.1, we looked at the probability of a single event from one experiment. Now we examine the probability of combination of events from either one experiment or two experiments.

Multiplication Rule (Independent Events)

Known population experiments

Two experiments are undertaken and the outcomes are observed. The experiments are conducted such that the two events will be independent of each other *(the occurrence of an event from one experiment does not impact on the occurrence of an event from another experiment).*

Example 1 - One toss of a coin and one throw of a die (two experiments)

Independent events 1st Event = Toss a coin
2nd Event = Throw a die

Consider the experiments 'tossing a coin' and 'throwing a die'

What is the probability of getting a three *(A)* **and** a tail *(B)*?

*Multiplication Rule $_{Independent\ Events}$ = P (A **and** B) = P (A) x P (B) also written P (A ∩ B) = P (A) x P (B)*

P (Three **and** Tail) = *P* (Three) x *P* (Tail) = $\frac{1}{2} x \frac{1}{6} = \frac{1}{12}$ = 0.5 x 0.166 = 0.083 or 8.3%

Example 2 – Select a ball and select a ball (two experiments)

Independent events 1st Event = Select a ball/record/replace the ball
2nd Event = Select a ball/record/replace the ball

Consider the experiments 'select a ball from a lottery drum' and 'select another ball from a lottery drum'

A lottery drum contains 7 balls *(numbered 0 to 6)*. Select a ball and record the number then return the ball. Select a second ball and record the number.

What is the probability of getting a three *(A)* **and** a three *(B)*?

*Multiplication Rule $_{Independent\ Events}$ = P (A **and** B) = P (A) x P (B) also written P (A ∩ B) = P (A) x P (B)*

P (Three **and** Three) = *P* (Three) x *P* (Three) = $\frac{1}{7} x \frac{1}{7} = \frac{1}{49}$ = 0.0204 or 2.04%

General Multiplication Rule (Non-independent Events)

Known population experiments

Two experiments are undertaken and the outcomes are observed. The experiments are conducted such that the events are not independent of each other *(the occurrence of an event from one experiment does impact on the occurrence of an event from another experiment).*

Example 3 – Select a ball and select a ball (two experiments)

Not Independent Events   1st Event = Select a ball/record/do not replace
2nd Event = Select a ball/record

Consider the experiments 'select a ball from a lottery drum and do not replace it' and 'select another ball from a lottery drum'

A lottery drum contains a population of 7 balls *(numbered 0 to 6)*. Select one ball and record the number, but do not return the ball. Select a second ball and record the number.

What is the probability of getting a three *(A)* and then a two *(B)*?

General Multiplication Rule $_{\textit{Not Independent Events}}$ = *P (A* **and** *B) = P (A) x P (B|A)*   *where P (B|A) is the probability of B given that A has occurred*   *(P (B|A) is also referred to as conditional probability)*

P (Three **and** Two) = *P* (Three) x *P* (Two|Three) = $\frac{1}{7}\ x\ \frac{1}{6} = \frac{1}{42}$ = 0.0238 or 2.38%

Addition Rule (Mutually Exclusive Events – events that cannot occur at the same time)

Known population experiments

Example 4 – 'tossing a coin' (one experiment)

Consider the experiment 'tossing a coin'

What is the probability getting a head *(A)* **or** a tail *(B)*?

Addition Rule $_{\textit{Mutually Exclusive Events}}$ = *P (A* **or** *B) = P (A) + P (B) also written P (A U B) = P (A) + P (B)*

P (Head or Tail) = *P* (H) + *P* (T) = $\frac{1}{2} + \frac{1}{2}$ = 0.5 + 0.5 = 1

Example 5 – 'tossing a coin' (one experiment)

Consider the experiment 'throwing a die'

What is the probability of getting a 4 *(A)* **or** 5 *(B)*?

Addition Rule $_{Mutually\ Exclusive\ Events}$ *= P (A **or** B) = P (A) + P (B) also written P (A U B) = P (A) + P (B)*

P (4 or 5) = P (4) + P (5) = $\frac{1}{6} + \frac{1}{6} = \frac{2}{6}$ or 0.166 + 0.166 = 0.33 or 33%

Extended Addition Rule $_{Mutually\ Exclusive\ Events}$ *= P (A **or** B **or** C ...**or** Z) = P (A) + P (B) + P (C) + ... + P (Z)*

General Addition Rule (Non-Mutually Exclusive Events – events that can occur at the same time)

Known population experiments

Example 6 – 'Select a card from a shuffled pack' (one experiment)

Consider the experiment 'Select a card from a shuffled pack'

What is the probability of getting a King *(A)* **or** a Club *(B) (i.e. to select one or the other)*?

Since it is possible to select a king of clubs, then the probability of selecting this card must be subtracted.

Addition Rule $_{Mutually\ Exclusive\ Events}$ *= P (A **or** B) = P (A) + P (B) – P (A and B)* *Also written* *P (A U B) = P (A) + P (B) – P (A ∩ B)*

P (A or B) = P (A) + P (B) – P (A and B) = $\frac{4}{52} + \frac{13}{52} - \frac{1}{52} = \frac{16}{52}$

Addition Rule (Mutually Exclusive Events)

Unknown population experiments

Example 8 – 'Select a sample of 140 students' (one experiment)

A sample of 140 students was selected at random. The students undertook an IQ test and the following distribution table constructed.

I Q	Frequency *(e)*	Relative frequency = $\frac{e}{n}$
80 - 84	12	0.09
85 - 89	14	0.10
90 - 94	16	0.11
95 - 99	18	0.13
100 - 104	20	0.14
105 - 109	18	0.13
110 - 114	16	0.11
115 - 119	14	0.10
120 - 124	12	0.09
	(n) =140	1.00

Using the distribution table

What is the probability of selecting a student that will have an IQ which belongs to the intervals 95 – 99 *(A)* or 105 – 109 *(B)*?

Addition Rule $_{\textit{Mutually Exclusive Events}}$ *= P (A **or** B) = P (A) + P (B) also written P (A U B) = P (A) + P (B)*

P (95 - 99 or 105 - 109) = *P* (95 - 99) + *P* (105 - 109) = 0.13 + 0.13 = 0.26 or 26%

Complement Rule

Example 9 – 'tossing a coin' (one experiment)

This rule requires:

(a) Two events are mutually exclusive *(the two events cannot occur together)*
(b) Two events are collectively exhaustive *(there can only be two outcomes)*

Consider the experiment 'tossing a coin'

What is the probability of not getting a tail?

p*(tail)* = p*(A)* = probability of getting a tail
p*(not a tail)* = p$(\bar{A})$ = probability of not getting a tail

Complement Rule = $P(\bar{A}) = 1 - P(A)$ *where* $\bar{A} = not\ an\ A$

P (not a Tail) $= 1 - P$ (Tail) $= 1 - \frac{1}{2} = \frac{1}{2}$

Consider the experiment 'throwing a die'

What is the probability of not getting a two?

p*(two)* = p*(A)* = probability of getting a two
p*(not a two)* = p$(\bar{A})$ = probability of not getting a two

Complement Rule = $P(\bar{A}) = 1 - P(A)$ *where* $\bar{A} = not\ an\ A$

P (not a Two) $= 1 - P$ (Two) $= 1 - \frac{1}{6} = \frac{5}{6}$

4.4 Continuous Distributions – *Normal Distribution*

The concept of normally distributed data was introduced in Chapter 3. One of the most important assumptions that must be met for most parametric tests is that the distribution of values for the *continuous* variable under investigation matches the pattern of a normal distribution. The normal distribution is defined by the parameters μ *(mean)* and σ *(standard deviation)*. The normal distribution *(Gaussian)* is a continuous probability distribution and not a discrete probability distribution. The properties of the normal distribution include:

a. The total area under the curve is 1
b. The highest point of the curve coincides with the location of the mean, median, and mode
c. The width of the curve is determined by the standard deviation
d. The distribution is symmetric and perfectly bell shaped
e. The empirical rule (see Chapter 3) applies to the normal curve

In the following questions we assume that the assumption of normality holds true i.e. that the distribution of values for each *continuous* variable under investigation is normally distributed or takes the shape of the normal curve. The probability of occurrence of a value *(in a specified range or above or below a specified value)* is the corresponding area under the curve.

Questions

1. In which state exam did the student perform best in?

	*Mathematics *(HL)*	*Geography (HL)*	*Chemistry (HL)*
Students Score	80	65	75
Average = μ	85	55	60
Standard Deviation = σ	10	5	15

**HL = Higher level (assume the exam is available at higher and lower level)*
The average and standard deviation for the population of all students is calculated at a central office

2. What percentage of the population scored less than student in each subject?

3. What percentage of the population scored?

   a. Between 80 and 90 in Mathematics
   b. Below 45 in Geography
   c. Above 80 in Chemistry

4. Between what two scores do the middle 60% of the scores lie in Mathematics?

5. The top 15% of students in Mathematics get additional bonus points in their application to the engineering faculty of a prestigious university. What minimum mark must be reached to achieve these bonus points?

Answers

1. In which state exam did the student perform best in?

   Whilst it may be tempting to say *Mathematics* it would be wise to look again. At first glance, one does get a sense of how well the student has performed in each subject by simply relating the students score to the population average and standard deviation. To address the question *in which state exam did the student perform best in*, we must have a benchmark or standardised reference point. Therefore, the first step is to convert the subject scores that the student achieved into *standard scores* or *z scores*. This *z-score* is like a new unit of measurement derived using the formula [$z = \frac{X-\mu}{\sigma} = \frac{score-average}{standard\ veviation}$]. The following table reveals that the student performed best in Geography *(in relative terms)*.

	Mathematics (HL)	*Geography (HL)*	*Chemistry (HL)*
Score	80	65	75
Average	85	55	60
Standard Deviation	10	5	15
z score = $\frac{score-average}{standard\ veviation}$	-0.5	**+2.0**	+1.0

Interpretation of z-score

a. *A negative z-score indicates that the students score is below the mean.*
b. *A positive z-score indicates that the students score is above the mean.*
c. *A higher positive (negative) score indicates the students score is further above (below) the mean.*

The following bell shaped curve represents the *standard normal distribution* and the *standard score* or *z score* for each subject is compared to the standardised population average.

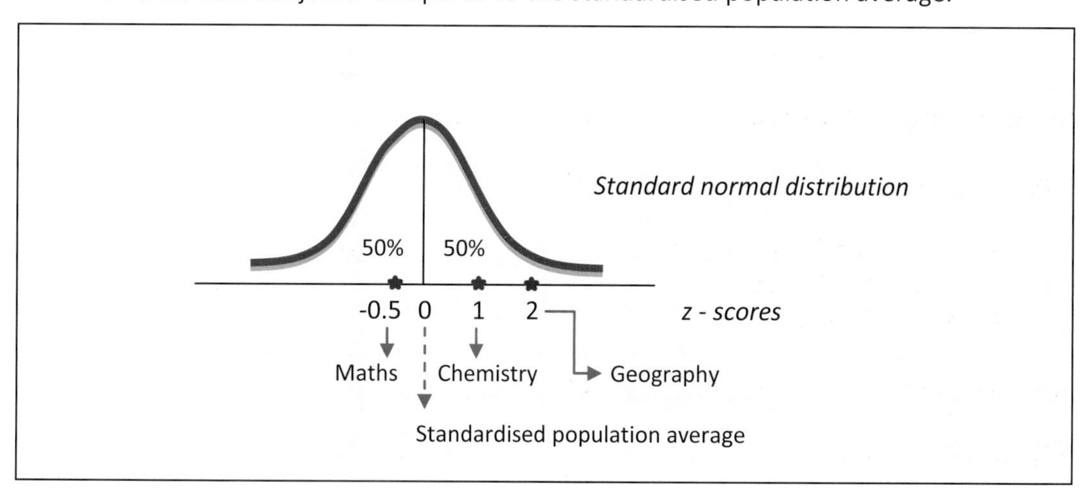

In relative terms, the student performed best in Geography.

2. What percentage of the population scored less than student in each subject?

The *z table* will be used to address this question. To use the *z table* each subject score must be converted into its standard score or *z score* as per question 1 above. The *z table* can now be used to derive the answers. Each subject will be examined separately.

	Mathematics (HL)	*Geography (HL)*	*Chemistry (HL)*
Score	80	65	75
z score	-0.5	+2.0	+1.0

a. Mathematics

It is useful to draw two identical bell curves and place all the relevant information pertaining to this question into the top diagram *(Mathematics score = 80 and the average score = 85)*, and place their equivalent *z scores* into the bottom diagram *(Standardised Mathematics score z =* $\frac{80-85}{10}$ *= -0.5 and the standardised average z =* $\frac{85-85}{10}$ *= 0)*.

The average score and its equivalent *z score* can be included or excluded from these diagrams *(it merely provides a reference point which can be useful)*. The question posed will help us to decide which portion or area under the curve is of interest. The question *what percentage of the population scored less in Mathematics* indicates that the area below the student's score of 80 *(equivalent z score = -0.5)* is of interest and this area can be shaded in both diagrams. Using the *z table,* the area under the curve that corresponds to a *z score* of -0.5 is 0.3085 which tells us that 30.85% of the population scored less in Mathematics.

When you look up a z score in the z table the proportion only refers to a tail area in 50% of the diagram

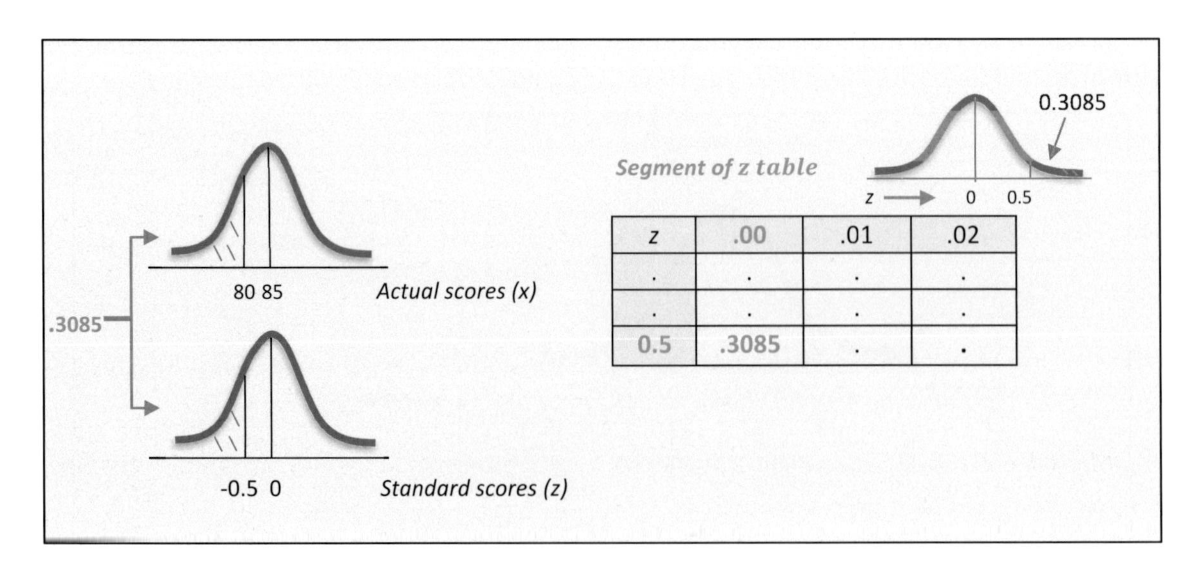

b. Chemistry

Once again it is useful to draw two identical bell curves and place all the relevant information pertaining to this question into the top diagram *(Chemistry score = 75 and the average score = 60)*, and place their equivalent *z scores* into the bottom diagram *(Standardised Chemistry score* $z = \frac{75-60}{15}$ *= 1 and the standardised average* $z = \frac{60-60}{15}$ *= 0).*

The question posed will help us to decide which portion or area under the curve is of interest. The question *what percentage of the population scored less in Chemistry* indicates that the area below 75 *(equivalent z score = 1)* is of interest and this area can be shaded in both diagrams. Using *the z table,* the area under the curve which corresponds to a *z score* of 1 is 0.1587. This proportion only refers to a tail area in 50% of the diagram. Therefore to derive the proportion of interest, we subtract 0.1587 from 1 *(total area under the curve)* to get 0.8413. Therefore, 84.13% of the population scored less than the student in Chemistry.

When you look up a z score in the z table the proportion only refers to a tail area in 50% of the diagram

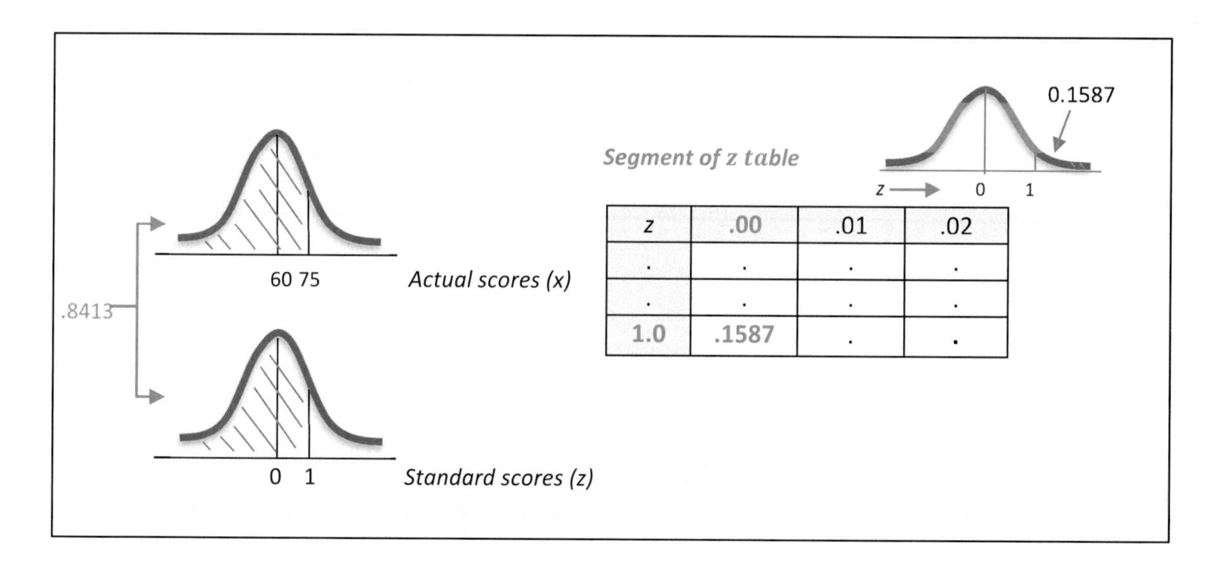

c. Geography

Once again it is useful to draw two identical bell curves and place all the relevant information pertaining to this question into the top diagram *(Geography score = 65 and the average score = 55)*, and place their equivalent *z scores* into the bottom diagram *(Standardised Geography score* $z = \frac{65-55}{5}$ *= 2 and the standardised average* $z = \frac{55-55}{5}$ *= 0).*

The question posed will help us to decide which portion or area under the curve is of interest. The question *what percentage of the population scored less in Geography* indicates that the area below 65 *(equivalent z score = 2)* is of interest and this area can be shaded in both diagrams. Using *the z table,* the area under the curve which corresponds to a *z score* of 2 is 0.0227. This proportion only refers to a tail area in 50% of the diagram. Therefore to derive the proportion of interest, we subtract 0.0227 from 1 *(total area under the curve)* to get 0.9773. Therefore, 97.73% of the population scored less than the student in Geography.

When you look up a z score in the z table the proportion only refers to a tail area in 50% of the diagram

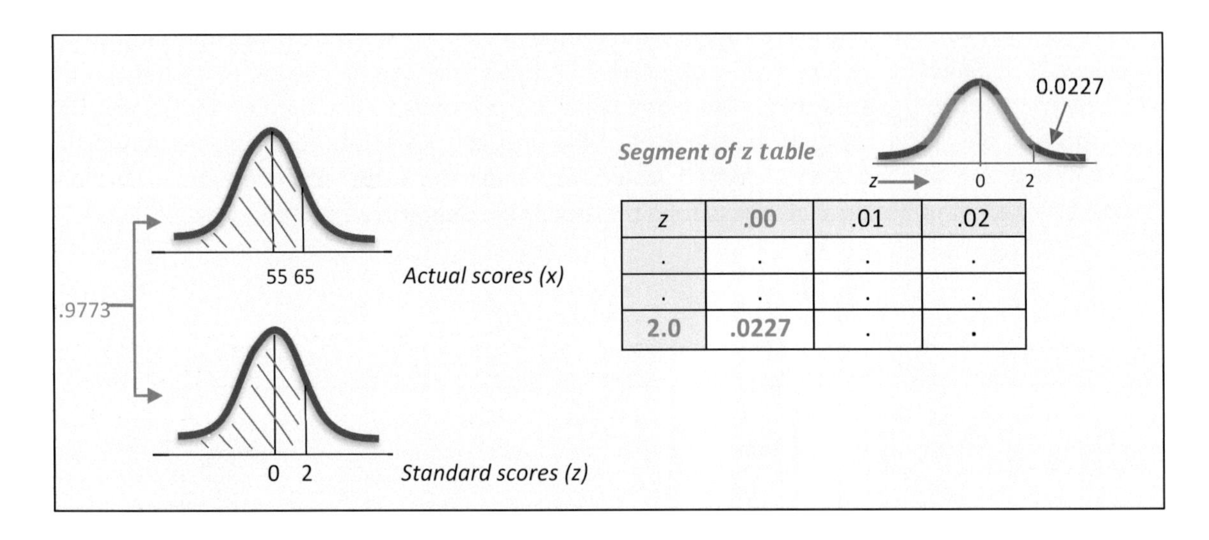

z	.00	.01	.02
.	.	.	.
.	.	.	.
2.0	.0227	.	.

3. What percentage of the population scored?

a. Between 80 and 90 in Mathematics

The approach to question 2 will be repeated here. Two bell curves are drawn as in previous answers and all the relevant information pertaining to this question is placed in these diagrams. The actual range of scores *(80 to 90)* is placed in the top diagram and their equivalent *z scores (Standardised range from* $z = \frac{80-85}{10}$ *= -0.5 to* $z = \frac{90-85}{10}$ *= 0.5)* are placed in the bottom diagram. The question *what percentage of the population scored between 80 and 90 in Mathematics* indicates that the area of interest and this area can be shaded in both diagrams. Using *the z table,* the area under the curve which corresponds to a *z score* of 0.5 is 0.3085. This proportion only refers to a tail area in 50% of the diagram. Therefore to derive the proportion of interest, we subtract 0.6170 *(2 x .3085)* from 1 *(total area under the curve)* to get 0.3830. Therefore, 38.30% of the population scored between 80 and 90 in Mathematics.

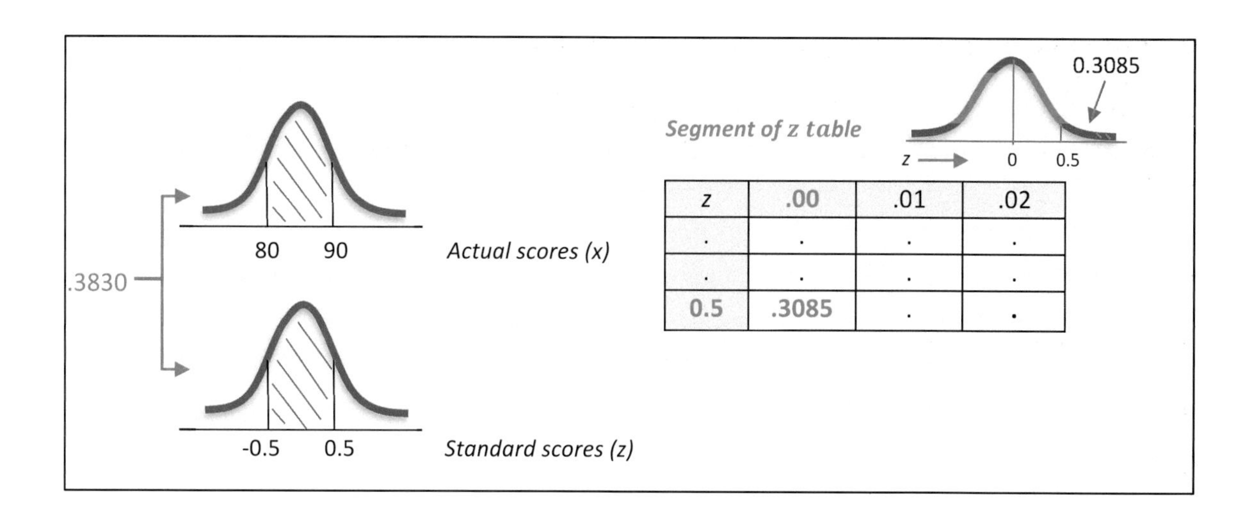

b. Below 45 in Geography

Two bell curves are drawn and all the relevant information pertaining to this question is placed in these diagrams *(Geography score = 45 and the average score = 55)*, and place their equivalent *z scores* into the bottom diagram *(Standardised Geography score z =* $\frac{45-55}{5}$ *= -2 and the standardised average z =* $\frac{55-55}{5}$ *= 0)*.

The question posed will help us to decide which portion or area under the curve is of interest. The question *what percentage of the population scored below 45 in Geography* indicates that the area below a score of 45 *(equivalent z score = -2)* is of interest and this area can be shaded in both diagrams. Using the *z table,* the area under the curve that corresponds to a *z score* of -2 is 0.0227 which tells us that 2.27% of the population scored below 45 in Geography.

When you look up a z score in the z table the proportion only refers to a tail area in 50% of the diagram

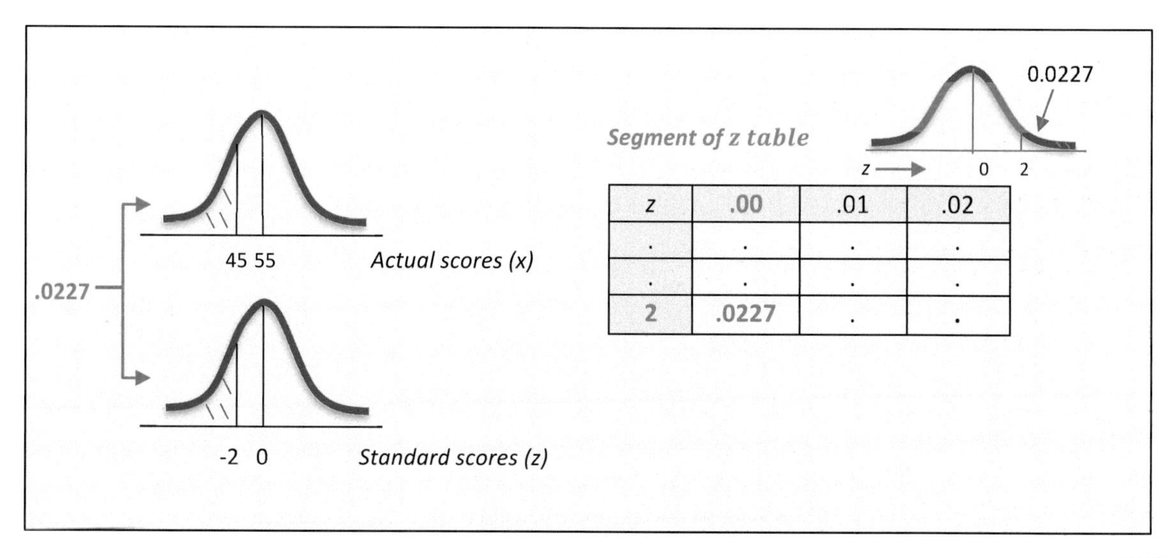

c. Above 80 in Chemistry

Two bell curves are drawn and all the relevant information pertaining to this question is placed in these diagrams *(Chemistry score = 80 and the average score = 60)*, and place their equivalent *z scores* into the bottom diagram *(Standardised Chemistry score* $z = \frac{80-60}{15} = 1.33$ *and the standardised average* $z = \frac{60-60}{15} = 0$*)*.

The question posed will help us to decide which portion or area under the curve is of interest. The question *what percentage of the population scored above 80 in Chemistry* indicates that the area above a score of 80 *(equivalent z score = 1.33)* is of interest and this area can be shaded in both diagrams. Using the *z table,* the area under the curve that corresponds to a *z score* of 1.33 is 0.0918 which tells us that 9.18% of the population scored above 80 in chemistry.

When you look up a z score in the z table the proportion only refers to a tail area in 50% of the diagram

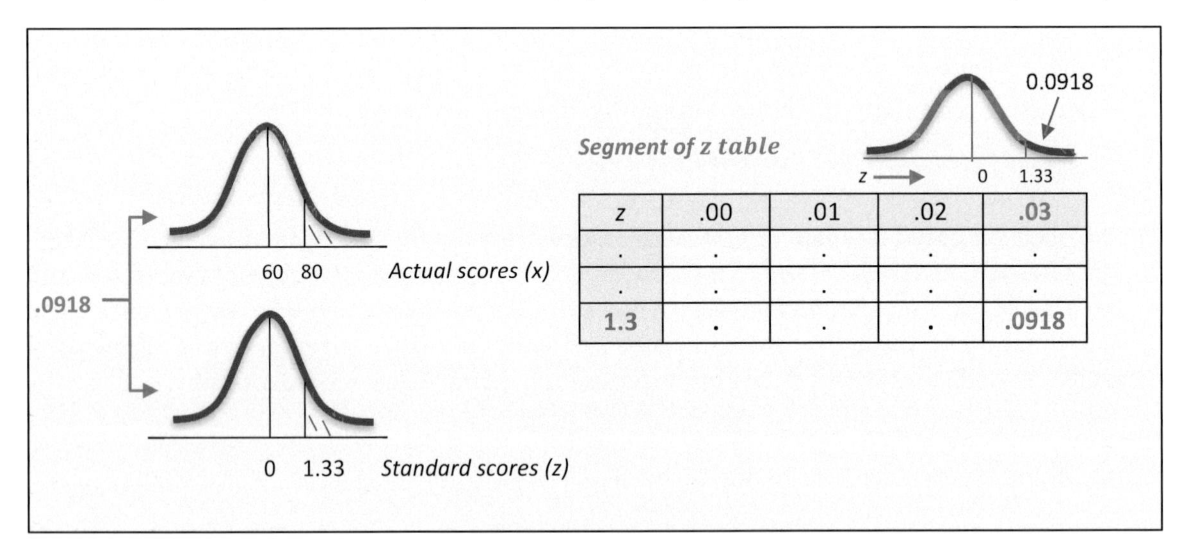

z	.00	.01	.02	.03
.	.	.	.	.
.	.	.	.	.
1.3	.	.	.	.0918

4. Between what two scores do the middle 60% of the scores lie in Mathematics?

Two bell curves are drawn and all the relevant information pertaining to this question is placed in these diagrams. In this type of question we are given the proportion and must work backwards until we arrive at actual scores *(in previous questions we started with the actual scores and worked until we arrived at a proportion)*. The proportion *(0.6000)* representing the shaded area is given and we are assume that this proportion is apportioned equally around the mean *(0.3000 is the shaded area either side of the mean)*. Since we know that the shaded area either side of the mean has a proportion equal to 0.3000, we look up 0.2000 *(0.5000 – 0.3000 which will give us the tail at one side of the normal curve)* and read the corresponding *z score*. We may need to settle for a proportion close to the value 0.2000 *(0.2005 is closest with a corresponding z score of 0.84)* as 0.2000 is not listed in the table. Since the normal curve is perfectly symmetrical, what we do for one side is equivalent to what we need to do on the other side. Since we have the *z scores* which enable us to interpolate the actual scores *(see calculations below)*. Therefore, the range of scores 76.6 to 93.4 contain 60% of the scores in mathematics.

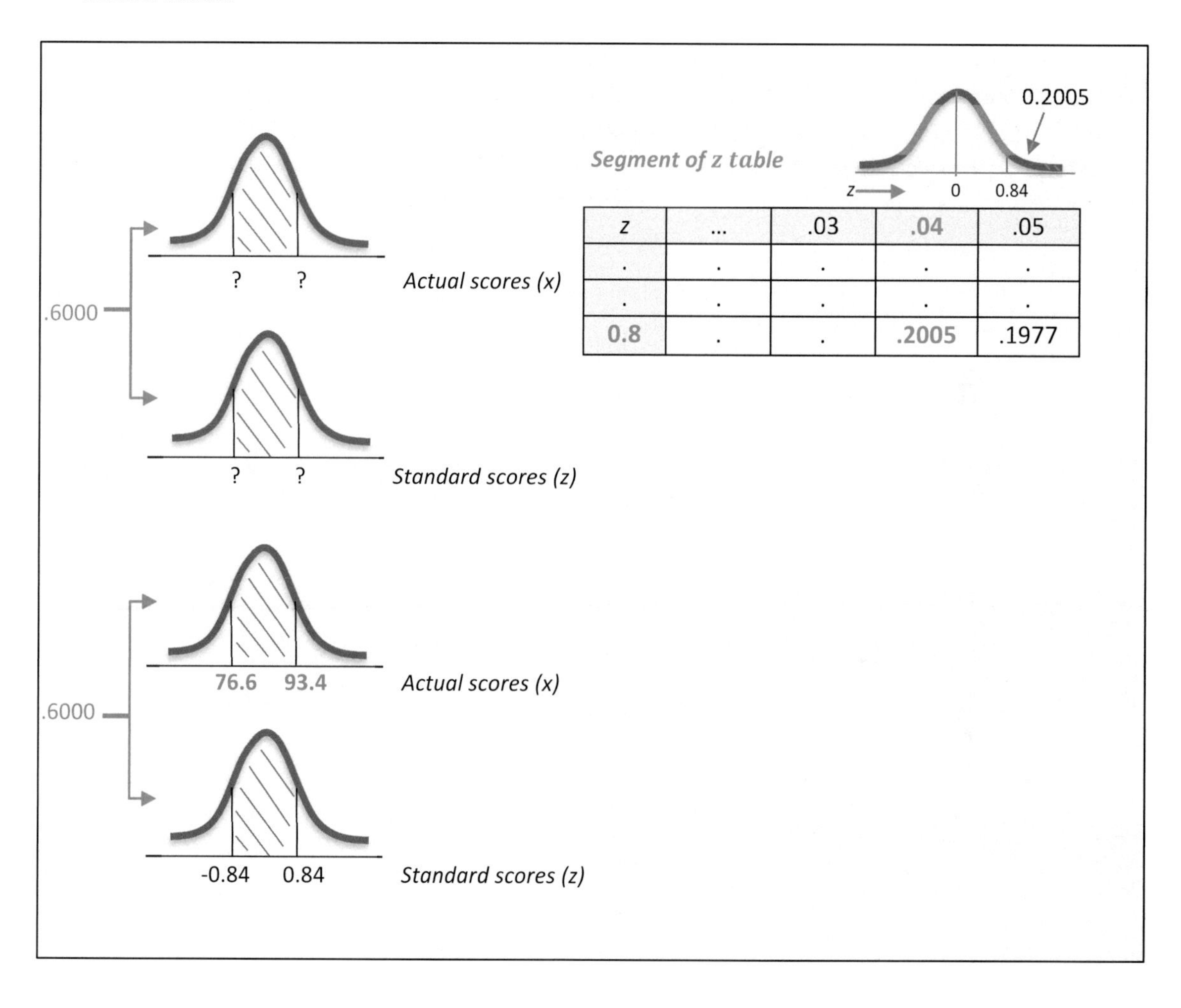

z	...	.03	.04	.05
.	.	.	.	.
.	.	.	.	.
0.8	.	.	.2005	.1977

Actual score (x) = $\left[-0.84 = \frac{?x-85}{10}\right] = \left[-0.84\ x\ 10 = \frac{?x-85}{10}\ x\ \frac{10}{1}\right]$ = *76.6*

Actual score (x) = $\left[+0.84 = \frac{?x-85}{10}\right] = \left[+0.84\ x\ 10 = \frac{?x-85}{10}\ x\ \frac{10}{1}\right]$ = *93.4*

5. The top 15% of students in Mathematics get additional bonus points in their application to the engineering faculty of a prestigious university. What minimum mark must be reached to achieve these bonus points?

   Two bell curves are drawn and all the relevant information pertaining to this question is placed in these diagrams. We include the average score *(85)* and its equivalent z score *(0)* as a reference point. As in the previous question, we are given the proportion and must work backwards until we arrive at an actual score. The proportion 0.1500 *(represents the shaded area in the upper tail)* is given so we can go directly to the *z table* and search for the proportion 0.1500 or some value close to it and read the corresponding *z score*. In this instance, the closest value to 0.1500 appears to be 0.1492 so the corresponding *z score* is 1.04. Since we have the *z score,* this enables us to interpolate the actual score *(see calculations below).* Therefore, the minimum mark that must be achieved to win the bonus points is 95.30.

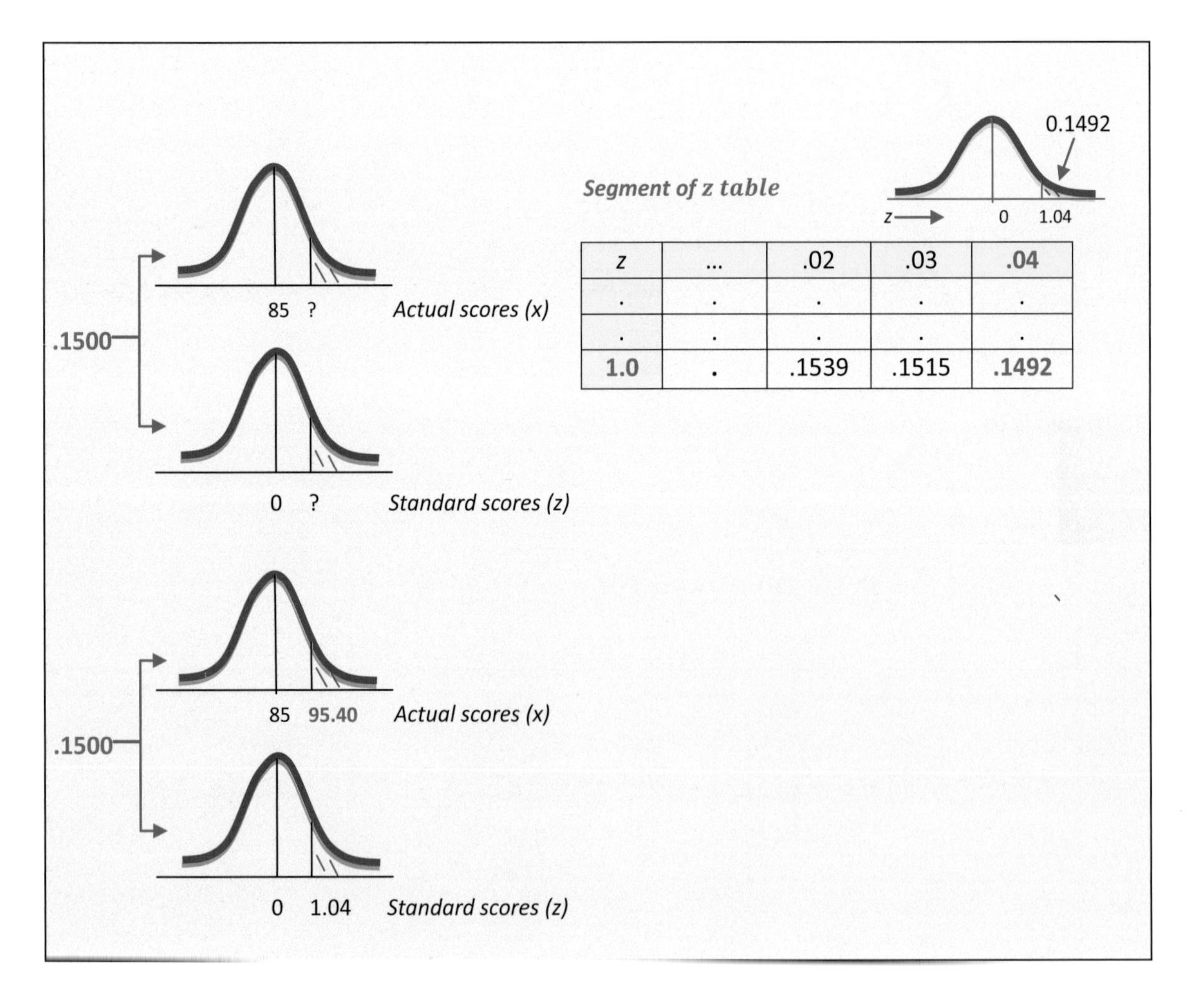

z	...	.02	.03	.04
.	.	.	.	.
.	.	.	.	.
1.0	.	.1539	.1515	.1492

Actual score (x) – $\left[1.04 = \frac{?x - 85}{10}\right] = \left[1.04\ x\ 10 = \frac{?x - 85}{10}\ x\ \frac{10}{1}\right]$ = *95.40*

4.5 Discrete Distributions – *Binomial Distribution*

The binomial distribution is a discrete probability distribution. The binomial distribution enables us to calculate probabilities with experiments which have the following properties or features:

a. *A number of repeated trials*
b. *Each trial has only two possible outcomes- Success or Failure*
c. *The probability of success on a trial is denoted by p and failure by 1-p*
d. *Each trial is independent from each other*

The following questions contain the features that are required to use the Binomial distribution.

Questions

1. A multiple choice exam has five answers to each question. If a student answers all questions randomly, what is the probability of getting four out of ten correct?

   a. *n = 10 repeated trials*
   b. *You guess a correct answer (success) versus an incorrect answer (failure)*
   c. *The probability of success on a single trial = p (success) =* $\frac{1}{5}$ *= 0.20 = p*
   d. *Your choice in one trial is not influenced by a previous decision i.e. each trial is independent*

2. A coin is tossed 10 times. Calculate the following probabilities:

(a) That 3 heads occur
(b) Less than 2 heads occur
(c) 4 or more heads occurring
(d) Mean for the experiment
(e) Standard deviation for the experiment

   a. *n = 10 repeated trials*
   b. *A head occurring (success) or a tail occurring (failure)*
   c. *The probability of success on a single trial = p(success) =* $\frac{1}{2}$ *= 0.50 = p*
   d. *Each trial is independent from each other*

Answers

1. The question being asked can be formally written as: *p(x successes in n trials)*

= $p(x = 4) = \binom{n}{x} . p^x . (1-p)^{n-x}$

$= {}^{n}C_{x} . p^x . (1-p)^{n-x}$ ⟶ ${}^{10}C_{4} = \frac{n!}{x!(n-x)!}$ = where n! is called *n* factorial *(3! = 3 x 2 x 1)*

$= \frac{n!}{x!(n-x)!} . p^x . (1-p)^{n-x}$

$= \frac{n!}{x!(n-x)!} = \frac{10!}{4!(10-4)!} = \frac{10 \times 9 \times 8 \times 7 \times \cancel{6 \times 5 \times 4 \times 3 \times 2 \times 1}}{4 \times 3 \times 2 \times 1(\cancel{6 \times 5 \times 4 \times 3 \times 2 \times 1})}$

$= \frac{10 \times 9 \times 8 \times 7}{4 \times 3 \times 2 \times 1} = 210$

$= 210 \times (0.20)^4 \times (1-0.20)^{10-4}$

$= 210 \times 0.0016 \times 0.262144$

= 0.0881 or 8.81%

2. A coin is tossed 10 times...

(a) The question being asked can be formally written as: *p(x successes in n trials)*

$p(x = 3) = \binom{n}{x} . p^x . (1-p)^{n-x}$

$= {}^{n}C_{x} . p^x . (1-p)^{n-x}$ ⟶ ${}^{10}C_{3} = \frac{n!}{x!(n-x)!}$

$= \frac{n!}{x!(n-x)!} . p^x . (1-p)^{n-x}$

$= \frac{n!}{x!(n-x)!} = \frac{10!}{3!(10-3)!} = \frac{10 \times 9 \times 8 \times \cancel{7 \times 6 \times 5 \times 4 \times 3 \times 2 \times 1}}{3 \times 2 \times 1(\cancel{7 \times 6 \times 5 \times 4 \times 3 \times 2 \times 1})}$

$= \frac{10 \times 9 \times 8}{3 \times 2 \times 1} = 120$

$= 120 \times 0.125 \times 0.0078125$

= 0.11718 or 11.72%

(b) The question being asked can be formally written as: *p(less than x successes in n trials)*

$p(x < 2) = p(x = 0) + p(x = 1)$

$= {}^{10}C_{0} . (0.5)^0 . (1-0.5)^{10-0} + {}^{10}C_{1} . (0.5)^1 . (1-0.5)^{10-1}$

= 0.0108

(c) The question being asked can be formally written as: *p(at least x successes in n trials)*

$p\ (x \geq 4) = p\ (x = 4) + p\ (x = 5) + p\ (x = 6) + p\ (x = 7) + p\ (x = 8) + p\ (x = 9) + p\ (x = 10)$

Or more conveniently:

$= 1 - p\ (x < 4) = 1 - [p\ (x = 0) + p\ (x = 1) + p\ (x = 2) + p\ (x = 3)]$

$= 1 - p\ (x < 4) = 1 - [.0010 + .0098 + .0439 + .1172]$

$= 1 - [0.1719]$ ⟶ *0.1719*   Binomial Table ⟶

$= 0.8281$ or 82.81%

			p	
n	x	.	.45	.50
	0	.	.	.0010
	1	.	.	.0098
n = 10	2	.	.	.0439
	3	.	.	.1172

(d) Mean = $\mu_X = np$

Mean = 10 x 0.5 = 5

(e) Standard deviation = $\sqrt{Variance} = \sqrt{\sigma_X^2} = \sqrt{np(1-p)} = \sqrt{np(1-p)} = \sqrt{10\ x\ 0.5\ (1-0.5)} =$ 1.58

4.6 **Discrete Distributions** – *Poisson Distribution*

The poisson distribution is a discrete probability distribution. This distribution enables us to calculate probabilities with the following features or properties:

a. *The mean number of occurrences/events per interval is known*
b. *The interval can be:*
    - *Time (per hour/per day/per week/per month/per week)*
    - *Length (per 100 meters/per 1km)*
    - *Area (per square feet)*
    - *Volume (per bucket/per glass/per cup)*
c. *Number of occurrences/events is infinite = countable infinite discrete random variable*
d. *The occurrences/events are independent*
e. *The probability of the occurrence/event is the same for any two intervals of equal length*

The following questions contain the features that are required to use the Poisson distribution.

Questions

1. A business receives on average 3 complaints per day, calculate the following probabilities:

    (a) The probability that the company will receive zero complaints tomorrow
    (b) The probability that the company will receive zero complaints over the next two days
    (c) The probability that the company will receive less than 2 complaints tomorrow

The mean = 3, the Interval = per day and the complaints are independent of each other

Answers

1. A business receives on average 3 complaints per day, calculate the following probabilities:

    (a) The probability that the company will receive zero complaints tomorrow i.e. *p(X = 0)*

Since we have one day *(one interval)* then the *mean* = $\lambda = 3$

$$p\ (X) = \frac{(\lambda^X)(e^{-\lambda})}{X!} = p\ (zero) = \frac{(\lambda^X)(e^{-\lambda})}{X!}$$

Where e = 2.71828... i.e. the base of Naperian Logarithms

Where $e^{-\lambda} = \frac{1}{e^3}$

$$p\ (0) = \frac{(3^0)(e^{-3})}{0!} = \frac{(0)(0.0498)}{0} = 0.0498$$

(b) The probability that the company will receive zero complaints over the next two days i.e. *p(X = 0)*

Now that we have two days then *mean* = λ = *6*

$p\ (0) = \frac{(6^0)(e^{-6})}{0!} = \frac{(0)(0.0025)}{0} = 0.0025$

(c) The probability that the company will receive less than 2 complaints tomorrow i.e. *p(X* < 2*)*

Since we have one day (one interval) then *mean* = λ = *3*

$p\ (x < 2) = p\ (0) + p\ (1) = \frac{(3^0)(e^{-3})}{0!} + \frac{(3^1)(e^{-1})}{1!}$

$= \frac{(0)(0.0498)}{0} + \frac{(3)(0.0498)}{1} = 0.0498 + 0.1494$

$= 0.1992$

4.7 Central Limit Theorem (CLT)

The reality of research is that we will be working with a single sample and an estimate *(e.g. sample mean)* that is calculated from that sample. This sample statistic *($\bar{x}$)* is an estimate of a possibly unknown population parameter *(μ)*. The question of how good this estimate is will always arise. Is the sample mean identical to the population mean or is there some degree of *sampling error*. The CLT will enable us to infer that if we base our estimate of the population mean on a single sample drawn from the population, then our estimate *($\bar{x}$)* of the true population parameter *(μ)* is likely to be closer as we increase the size of our sample. This inference is allowed since the dispersion of sample means will fall if we were to undertake repeated experiments with increasing sample sizes *(see example below)*. In addition, the CLT allows us to infer that, if we were to undertake repeated experiments with increasing sample sizes, the distribution of sample means approaches normality.

Consider a population of 4 numbers $[0, 3, 6, 9]$ from which we can easily calculate the true population parameters $[\mu = 4.5,\ \sigma = 3.94]$. The following table lists all the possible means that can be calculated from experiments which involve drawing varying sample sizes. Notice how the dispersion of sample means *(standard deviation of sample means)* falls as we undertake experiments with increasing sample sizes.

All possible means from varying sample sizes		
n = 2	*n = 3*	*n = 4*
$\bar{X}$	$\bar{X}$	$\bar{X}$
9	9	9
7.5	8	8.25
6	7	7.50
4.5	6	6.75
3	5	6
1.5	4	5.25
	3	4.5
	2	3.75
	1	3
	0	2.25
		1.5
		.75
		0
Mean $_{\text{sample means}}$ = 4.5	Mean $_{\text{sample means}}$ = 4.5	Mean $_{\text{sample means}}$ = 4.5
St. dev. $_{\text{Sample means}}$ = 2.7	St. dev. $_{\text{Sample means}}$ = 1.94	St. dev. $_{\text{Sample means}}$ = 1.68

The standard deviation of the sample means *(standard error)* diminishes as sample size increases. The standard error $\frac{\sigma}{\sqrt{n}}$ can be estimated from a single sample *(replacing σ with s)*.

Therefore, according to the CLT, the larger the sample size the closer our estimate will be to the true population parameter. However, even though a sample statistic *($\bar{x}$)* is a better estimate of the true population parameter *(μ)* as sample size increases, we must accept that such estimates are likely to be subject to error. It would be very useful if we could assert that the true population parameter lies within a range or interval with a high degree of probability. The CLT will assist us in this regard. The following properties of the CLT will enable us to construct such a range or interval:

a. The mean of the distribution of sample means *(Sampling distribution)* is equal to the mean of the population.
b. The standard error diminishes as sample size increases.
c. The distribution of sample means approaches normality in repeated experiments with increasing sample sizes.
d. An adjustment of the empirical rule reads as follows:

Empirical rule for a normally distributed population
1. 90% of the population of scores will fall within the interval $[\mu \pm 1.65\sigma]$
2. 95% of the population of scores will fall within the interval $[\mu \pm 1.96\sigma]$
3. 99% of the population of scores will fall within the interval $[\mu \pm 2.59\sigma]$

Thus we are now in a position to construct the range or interval within which the true population parameter lies with a high degree of probability. The following statements are possible:

1. We are 90% confident that the true population mean lies within the interval $\bar{x} \pm 1.65 \frac{\sigma}{\sqrt{n}}$
2. We are 95% confident that the true population mean lies within the interval $\bar{x} \pm 1.96 \frac{\sigma}{\sqrt{n}}$
3. We are 99% confident that the true population mean lies within the interval $\bar{x} \pm 2.58 \frac{\sigma}{\sqrt{n}}$

Strictly speaking, we are not stating that the probability is, say 95%, that our calculated interval contains the population mean *(even though many researchers take this liberty)*. What we are saying is that if we were to take repeated samples from the population, 95% of the constructed intervals will contain the population mean.

The CLT establishes the theoretical justification for the construction of confidence intervals which is a powerful alternative to the traditional parametric statistical tests

4.9 MCQs and Solutions

1. What is the z score for the following subjects?

   (a) 9 and 4
   (b) 7.11 and 11.25
   (c) 55 and 51
   (d) 1 and 1.25

	Sociology	*English Literature*
Score	64	45
Average = μ	55	40
Standard Deviation = σ	9	4

2. Assuming that the scores in the above table were 'normally distributed', what percentage of students scored less than the student in Sociology?

   (a) 34.13%
   (b) 84.13%
   (c) Cannot be determined
   (d) 50%

3. Assuming that the scores in the above table were 'normally distributed', what percentage of students scored more than the student in English Literature?

   (a) 50%
   (b) 39.44%
   (c) Cannot be determined
   (d) 10.56%

4. Assuming that the scores in the above table were 'normally distributed'. What percentage of students scored between 50% and 60% in Sociology?
   (a) 50%
   (b) 20.88%
   (c) Cannot be determined
   (d) 41.76%

5. Assuming that the scores in the above table were 'normally distributed'. The bottom 20% of students failed to progress to the higher course in English Literature. What was the cut off score for entry into the higher level course?

(a) 50%
(b) 36.64%
(c) Cannot be determined
(d) 43.36%

6. Assuming that the scores in the above table were 'normally distributed'. Between what two scores do the middle 30% of scores lie in Sociology?

(a) 50% and 60%
(b) 51.49% and 58.51%
(c) Cannot be determined
(d) 49.51% and 58.15%

7. A student sits a multiple choice exam in which there are 10 questions and 4 answers to each question. What is the probability of him getting 4 out of 10 correct, assuming that he guesses at random?

(a) 8.81%
(b) 50 – 50 chance
(c) Cannot be determined
(d) 14.60%%

8. A student sits a multiple choice exam in which there are 10 questions and 2 answers to each question. What is the probability of him getting 4 out of 10 correct, assuming that he guesses at random?

(a) 28.16%
(b) 50 – 50 chance
(c) Cannot be determined
(d) 20.51%%

9. A coin is tossed 5 times, what is the probability that you will get exactly 2 heads in this experiment?

(a) 31.25%
(b) 50 – 50 chance
(c) Cannot be determined
(d) 25%

10. A coin is tossed 5 times, what is the mean of this experiment?

(a) 5
(b) 2.5
(c) Cannot be determined
(d) zero

11. A receptionist receives on average 4 telephone enquiries per hour. What is the probability that he will get 5 calls in the next hour?

(a) 15.63%
(b) 25%
(c) Cannot be determined
(d) 0%

12. Which of the following distributions has the following population parameter values:
    a. Mean = 0
    b. Standard deviation = 1

(a) Binomial Distribution
(b) Standard Normal Distribution
(c) Poisson Distribution
(d) Exponential Distribution

13. Which of the following is the best estimate of the true population mean?

(a) Sample mean
(b) The mean of a large number of samples (each sample of size 10)
(c) The mean of a large number of samples (each sample of size 20)
(d) The mean of a large number of samples (each sample of size 30)

14. Given the following information for a data set (standard deviation 42 and a sample size of 16), what is the standard error?

(a) 2.625
(b) 0.380
(c) 26.00
(d) 10.50

15. If we take 400 samples and calculate the mean of each sample and then plot the means as a histogram, how might you describe that distribution?

(a) Sampling distribution of the mean
(b) Positively skewed distribution
(c) Negatively skewed distribution
(d) Exponential distribution

16. If the underlying population is skewed, then the sampling distribution of the mean derived from a large number of large samples (say with sample sizes ≥ 30) will take the following shape:

(a) Positively skewed
(b) Negatively skewed
(c) Bimodal
(d) Approximately normally distributed

17. Consider the experiments 'throwing a die' and 'tossing a coin'. What is the probability of getting a 6 and a tail?

(a) 8.3%
(b) 66.66%
(c) 0%
(d) 100%

18. A lottery drum contains a population of 7 balls (numbered 0 to 6). You must select one ball, record the number, and not return the ball. You must then select the second ball, record the number, and not return the ball. What is the probability of getting a 1 and a 7?

(a) 2.38%
(b) 30.8%
(c) 0%
(d) 100%

19. Consider the experiment 'Select a card from a shuffled pack'. What is the probability/ likelihood of getting a Queen or a Heart?

(a) 30.76%
(b) 32.69%
(c) 0%
(d) 100%

20. Consider the experiment 'throwing a die'. What is the probability of not getting a 1?

(a) 16.66%
(b) 83.33%
(c) 0%
(d) 100%

MCQ Solutions

1. (d)	6. (b)	11. (a)	16. (d)
2. (b)	7. (d)	12. (b)	17. (a)
3. (d)	8. (d)	13. (d)	18. (a)
4. (d)	9. (a)	14. (d)	19. (a)
5. (d)	10. (b)	15. (a)	20. (b)

The dog that did not bark

The space shuttle *Challenger (mission STS-51-L)* should not have exploded, but just 73 seconds after lift-off, at a height of 47,000 ft., it did. In 1986, the space shuttle *Challenger* was launched for the final time, killing seven people *(five men and two women)*. The launch of *Challenger* was meant to mark its 25th successful mission into outer space. This disaster could have and should have been avoided.

The shuttle was assisted by two booster rockets to lift it into orbit. Each booster rocket had 3 rubber seals *(O – rings)* which prevent the release of hot gases produced during combustion. After each flight these rubber seals are examined for damage. An examination of the data from *all* previous flights indicates that the subsequent explosion was not surprising. Unfortunately, consideration was given to only 7 out of the 23 previous flights. As the following scatterplot reveals, there is no apparent relationship between the ambient temperature at launch and the probability of O-ring damage *(higher damage occurred at both lower and higher temperatures).*

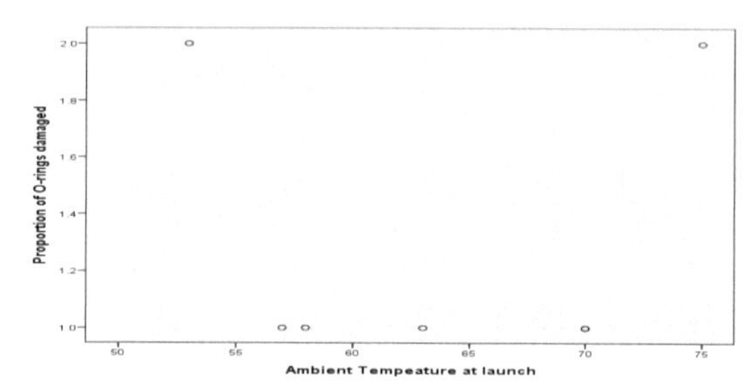

The information on the other *uneventful* 16 flights was disregarded *(the hardware of one flight was lost at sea).* There was no damage to the rubber seals on 16 flights, which, as it happens, all occurred at relatively higher ambient temperatures. A visual examination of what occurred on *all* previous flights would have revealed that on colder days, the chances of damage to the shuttles booster rockets increased. Except for one observation in the upper right of the scatterplot, there is a clear inverse relationship between the probability of O-ring damage and the ambient temperature.

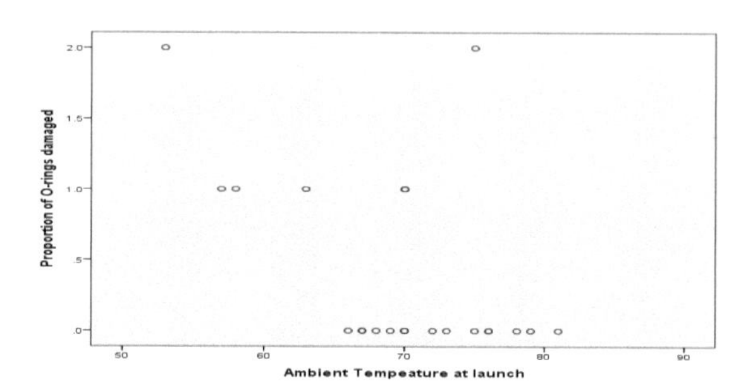

In fact, the chance of rubber seal damage on the day *Challenger* was launched was a staggering 96% *(derived from an advanced statistical technique – logistic regression)*. The exclusion of the information of 16 previous flights *(i.e. no damage to rubber seals at comparatively high temperatures)* proved to be catastrophic. There was as much to be inferred from these non-events, as in Sir Arthur Conan Doyle's 'Silver Blaze' *(Wikipedia 2012)*:

Holmes: *"To the curious incident of the dog in the night-time."*
Gregory: *"The dog did nothing in the night-time."*
Holme: *"That was the curious incident."*

Chapter 5 – Inferential Statistical Techniques

'Absence of evidence is not evidence of absence.'

Carl Edward Sagan (1934 – 96)

5.1 Hypothesis Testing

Hypothesis testing is an integral part of inferential statistical techniques. A hypothesis can be described as any one of the following: *theory, claim, question, belief, idea, assertion, suspicion, notion, hunch, belief/prediction, etc.* The researcher will attempt to test a hypothesis using gathered evidence *(sample data)*. To engage in hypothesis testing a *null and an alternative hypothesis* must be specified at the outset. The following distinguishes the *null and alternative* hypothesis.

1. The null hypothesis will:

a. *Be abbreviated as H_0 (i.e. H zero) or H_o (i.e. H nought).*
b. *Be the claim (implied or explicit) if a given statement specifies the equality operator ($=$ or $\leq$ or $\geq$) or if a given statement specifies no change from a given or accepted condition (not different from or no association between). The claim can be supported or otherwise after a decision is arrived at regarding the null hypothesis H_0.*
c. *Always contain the equality operator in some format (e.g. $=$ or $\geq$ or $\leq$) when a difference is being investigated.*
d. *Always contain the phrase 'is independent of' or 'no association with' when an association is being investigated.*
e. *Be adopted unless there is sufficient evidence (collected sample data) to warrant its rejection. The null hypothesis will get the 'benefit of doubt' unless the evidence against it is acceptable.*

2. The alternative hypothesis will:

a. *Be abbreviated as H_1 or H_A.*
b. *Be the claim (implied or explicit) if a given statement specifies the inequality operator ($\neq$ or $<$ or $>$) or if a given statement specifies a change from a given or accepted condition (is different from or is an association between). The claim can be supported or otherwise after a decision is arrived at regarding the null hypothesis H_0.*
c. *Always reflect an outcome other than that specified in the null hypothesis. when a difference is being investigated:*
   - ✓ *if the null hypothesis contains $=$ then the alternative will contain $\neq$*
   - ✓ *if the null hypothesis contains $\geq$ then the alternative will contain $<$*
   - ✓ *if the null hypothesis contains $\leq$ then the alternative will contain $>$*
d. *Always contain the phrase 'is dependent on' or 'is an association with' when an association is being investigated.*
e. *Often be referred to as the experimental or research or prediction hypothesis.*
f. *The alternative hypothesis will be set up to reflect 'an effect' which is usually in accordance with the researcher's prediction and intention to investigate (see chart below).*

The chart below will guide the construction of the *null and alternative* hypothesis. The *H_0 and H_1* for a given situation are matched *(colour coded)* in this chart. Using this chart, an experiment designed to test whether a new diet *has an effect* will be constructed as:

H_0: Diet has no effect
H_1: Diet has an effect

Option A		*Option B*		*Option C*
Null H_0	*Test*	*Null H_0*	*Test*	*Null H_0*
= *'no difference'* ≥ *'at least'* ≤ *'at most'*		*No effect/no change* *No effect/positive effect* *No effect/negative effect*		*No association/Independent* - -
Alternative H_1		*Alternative H_1*		*Alternative H_1*
≠ *'is different'* < *'lower than'* > *'higher than'*	*2-tail* *1-tail (left)* *1-tail (right)*	*An effect/change* *Negative effect* *Positive effect*	*2-tail* *1-left-tail* *1-right-tail*	*Is an association/Dependent* - -

1. Constructing H_0 and H_1 – Comparing two means *(Two sampled groups)*

Comparing the observed summary statistics for two groups

The following example investigates the weights of one week old babies in the south west region. A random sample of 48 male babies and 52 female babies were selected from the population of births (in the year 2012). The following table summarises the findings:

Male	$n_1 = 48$	$\bar{x}_1 = 4.7$	$s_1 = 0.52$
Female	$n_2 = 52$	$\bar{x}_2 = 4.41$	$s_2 = 0.60$

The *null (H_0) and an alternative hypothesis (H_1)* will be constructed for the following investigations: notice that each of the three hypotheses is phrased to investigate *a definite effect (one or two tail test)* i.e. *'is different from', 'is higher than' and 'is lower than'.*

Experimental/Research/Prediction hypotheses

1. To test whether the mean weight *(kg)* of one week old male babies *is different from* the mean weight *(kg)* of one week old female babies.
2. To test whether the mean weight *(kg)* of one week old male babies *is higher than* the mean weight *(kg)* of one week old female babies.
3. To test whether the mean weight *(kg)* of one week old male babies *is lower than* the mean weight *(kg)* of one week old female babies.

It is important to observe the key phrase in each of these research hypotheses: *('is different from', 'is higher than' or 'is lower than' or some variant of these phrases such as 'is not equal to', 'is more than', 'is less than', etc.)*. Once you have identified the key phrase, this will be your cue to set up the *alternative hypothesis (H_1)*. Once the *alternative hypothesis (H_1)* includes the key phrase, the *null hypothesis (H_0)* can be set up to include all other possible outcomes *(must include all other possible options for completeness)*.

1. Test whether the mean weight *(kg)* of one week old male babies *is different from* the mean weight *(kg)* of one week old female babies.

   The phrase *is different from* is a non-directional phrase *(i.e. the phrase makes no reference to either higher or lower)* and the *alternative hypothesis (H_1)* will reflect this non-direction by including the operator for non-equality i.e. ≠. The placing of the non-equality operator *(≠)* into the alternative hypothesis makes this a two tailed/sided or non-directional test. The null hypothesis will always contain some variant of the equality operator *(= or ≤ or ≥)*, therefore the null hypothesis will contain the = operator.

   H_0: $\mu_{male\ weights} = \mu_{female\ weights}$
   H_1: $\mu_{male\ weights} \neq \mu_{female\ weights}$
   Or
   H_0: $\mu_{male\ weights} - \mu_{female\ weights} = 0$
   H_1: $\mu_{male\ weights} - \mu_{female\ weights} \neq 0$
   Or
   H_0: The difference between the means of both groups is zero
   H_1: The difference between the means of both groups is not zero

2. Test whether the mean weight *(kg)* of one week old male babies *is higher than* the mean weight *(kg)* of one week old female babies.

   The phrase *is higher than* is a directional phrase *(i.e. the phrase does make reference to either higher or lower)* and the *alternative hypothesis (H_1)* will therefore include the operator for higher than i.e. >. The placing of a non-equality operator *(< or >)* into the alternative hypothesis makes this a one tailed/sided or directional test. The *null hypothesis (H_0)* must include the ≤ operator for completeness.

   H_0: $\mu_{male\ weights} \leq \mu_{female\ weights}$
   H_1: $\mu_{male\ weights} > \mu_{female\ weights}$
   Or
   H_0: $\mu_{male\ weights} - \mu_{female\ weights} \leq 0$
   H_1: $\mu_{male\ weights} - \mu_{female\ weights} > 0$
   Or
   H_0: The difference between the means of both groups is lower than or equal to zero
   H_1: The difference between the means of both groups is higher than zero

2. Constructing H_0 and H_1 – Comparing two means *(One sampled group)*

Comparing an observed summary statistic of one group (observed value) with some benchmark population value or known value (expected value)

The manufacturer of a popular perfume (the best-selling 50 ml bottle called 'Distracted') is being investigated. The manufacturer claims that the contents of 'Distracted' are known to be normally distributed with a mean of 50 ml (expected value) with a standard deviation of 1.50 ml. To test this claim a consumer watchdog group randomly sampled 35 bottles and recorded a mean of 50.75 ml (observed value).

Once again three possible test questions can be undertaken. The *null (H_0) and an alternative hypothesis (H_1)* will be constructed for the following investigations: notice that each of the three hypotheses is phrased to investigate *a definite effect (one or two tail test)* i.e. *'is different from', 'is higher than' and 'is lower than'.*

Experimental/Research/Prediction hypotheses

1. To test whether the mean contents *is different from* 50 ml.
2. Test whether the mean contents *is lower than* 50 ml.
3. Test whether the mean contents *is higher than* 50 ml.

It is important to observe the key phrase in each of these research hypotheses: *(is different from, is lower than or is higher than or some variant of these phrases)*. Once you have identified the key phrase, then this is your cue to set up the *alternative hypothesis (H_1)*. Once the *alternative hypothesis (H_1)* includes the key phrase, the *null hypothesis (H_0)* can be set up to include all other possible outcomes *(must include all other possible options for completeness)*.

1. Test whether the mean contents *is different from* 50 ml.

    The phrase *is different from* is a non-directional phrase and the *alternative hypothesis (H_1)* will therefore include the operator for non-equality i.e. ≠. The placing of the non-equality operator *(≠)* into the alternative hypothesis makes this a two tailed/sided or non-directional test. The null hypothesis will always contain some variant of the equality operator *(= or ≤ or ≥)*, therefore the null hypothesis will contain the = operator.

    H_0: $\mu = 50$
    H_1: $\mu \neq 50$
    Or
    H_0: Observed value – Expected value = 0
    H_1: Observed value – Expected value ≠ 0
    Or
    H_0: The difference between the observed sample mean and expected population mean is equal to zero
    H_1: The difference between the observed sample mean and expected population mean is not equal to zero

2. Test whether the mean contents *is lower than* 50ml.

   The phrase *is lower than* is a directional phrase and the *alternative hypothesis* (H_1) must therefore include the operator for lower than i.e. <. The placing of a non-equality operator (*< or >*) into the alternative hypothesis makes this a one tailed/sided or directional test. The *null hypothesis* (H_0) must include the ≥ operator for completeness.

   H_0: $\mu \geq 50$
   H_1: $\mu < 50$
   Or
   H_0: *Observed value – Expected value ≥ 0*
   H_1: *Observed value – Expected value < 0*
   Or
   H_0: *The difference between the observed sample mean and expected population mean is greater than or equal to zero*
   H_1: *The difference between the observed sample mean and expected population mean is less than zero*

3. Constructing H_0 and H_1 – Investigating associations

Test for association – between two qualitative/categorical variables

You have reason to believe that there is a relationship or association between exposure to parental smoke and the presence of Asthma (in children ages 8 – 11 years). The following contingency table summarises the results of a survey of 550 children.

	Asthma present	No Asthma Present	Total
Parent – Smoker	30	170	200
Parent – Non Smoker	35	315	350
Total	65	485	550

(Adapted from: Peat, Barton, Elliot, 2008)

To test whether incidence of asthma in young children *is associated with* exposure to parental smoking. In this test type, the *null hypothesis* will be set up to reflect no association between the categorical variables and the alternative hypothesis will reflect the only other outcome:

H_0: *There is no association between exposure to smoking and incidence of Asthma.*
H_1: *There is an association between exposure to smoking and incidence of Asthma.*
Or
H_0: *Exposure to smoking and incidence of Asthma are independent of each other.*
H_1: *Exposure to smoking and incidence of Asthma are dependent of each other.*

5.2 Appropriate *(required)* sample size

A lot of research involves the random selection of a *sample* of values from a *population* of values. The researcher must decide what constitutes an appropriate or *required* sample size. This decision must be made only after careful consideration of a number of important factors *(referred to as input parameters)*.

Sample Size Procedure – How do I select an appropriate or required sample size?

Adhering to the principles of simple random sampling *(SRS)* is essential to the conduct of proper statistical analysis. A simple random sample must include the following three elements *(elements 'a' and 'b' ensure that the sample is random whilst the final element guarantees a simple random sample SRS)*.

a. *Each member of the population has an equal chance or likelihood of selection*
b. *The selection of one member does not affect the selection of another member (independence)*
c. *Every possible sample of size n is equally likely*

The researcher must decide, in advance of a study, what constitutes an appropriate or required sample size. Intuitively, the researcher might well reason that a difference *(i.e. an effect)* between, say, the average weight of one week old male and female babies most likely does exist *(if only to some distant decimal place)* and that such a finding after employing an appropriate statistical test procedure should hardly be surprising *(although we can never be 100% certain that a difference actually exists)*. Therefore, the researcher ought to ponder one step further:

> *Since a difference (i.e. an effect) between two groups most likely does exist, perhaps I need to consider what size of difference (effect size) might be of practical importance.*

Selecting an appropriate sample size involves the researcher specifying the following considerations *(input parameters)* in advance of a study: The following *input parameters* will be considered in the context of a study designed to compare two independently sampled groups.

1. Power of the test – To detect statistical significance i.e. to detect a non-zero difference

The *statistical test procedure* being employed must have a strong capability or sufficient power to detect a *statistical significance (i.e. an effect or a non-zero difference)* between two means, if one exists i.e. the *statistical test procedure* should be sufficiently *powered up*. The *power* of a test *(denoted by 1 - β)* is its capacity to detect a non-zero difference *(statistical significance)* when it exists and the researcher can and should specify a minimum power level in advance of employing the test. The higher the power level *(1 - β)* specified by the researcher, then the bigger the sample size required. As Cohen wrote in 1992:

> *"Power is thus 1 - β, the probability of rejecting a false H_0. In this treatment, the only specification for power is .80 (so β = .20), a convention proposed for general use. A materially smaller value than .80 would incur too great a risk of a Type II error. A materially larger value*

would result in a demand for N that is likely to exceed the investigator's resources. Taken with the conventional α = .05, power of .80 results in a β:α ratio of 4:1 (.20 to .05) of the two kinds of risks"

2. Effect size – To reflect practical or meaningful significance

The researcher must be interested in discovering if a detected *effect (i.e. statistical significance)*, between say two means, has a meaningful or practical importance. The researcher must decide in advance of a study *(either from experience or from other similar studies or using Cohen's guidelines 1988)* what magnitude or size of difference *(effect size)* represents a meaningful or practical difference between the two groups. The lower the effect size specified by the researcher, then the bigger the sample size required. As Cohen wrote in 1992:

"Researchers find specifying the ES the most difficult part of power analysis. ... However, neither the determination of power or necessary sample size can proceed without the investigator having some idea about the degree to which the H_0 is believed to be false (i.e., the ES)."

3. Level of significance = α = Type 1 error

A statistical test procedure may allow the researcher to declare that *statistical significance (i.e. an effect or non-zero difference)* has been detected, but unfortunately, there is the risk that he may be wrong in arriving at this conclusion. Whilst it may seem intuitively logical that some difference exists to some decimal place, he cannot be 100% certain of this based on a sample. It could be the case that the observed difference *(as revealed from the collected sample data)* may have arisen due to chance/sampling error. The researcher can specify, in advance of employing a test, a cut-off tolerance limit *(referred to as the level of significance or α)* i.e. he can choose to live with a certain level of risk of incorrectly declaring a non-zero difference. The levels of risk can typically be: 10% *(α = 0.10)*, 5% *(α = 0.05)*, 1% *(α = 0.01)*. The lower the risk *(level of significance)* specified by the researcher, then the bigger the sample size required. As Cohen wrote in 1992:

"The risk of mistakenly rejecting the null hypothesis (H_0) and thus of committing a Type I error i.e. α, represents a policy: the maximum risk attending such a rejection. Unless otherwise stated (and it rarely is), it is taken to equal .05"

4. Other factors

The following table summarises additional factors which will influence the appropriate or required sample size. For example, selecting a parametric test procedure will require a smaller sample size compared to a non-parametric test procedure. These factors are summarised in the following table:

Factor		*Sample size required*
Parametric test procedure		*Smaller*
Non-parametric test procedure		*Bigger*
Matched/Paired t-test		*Smaller*
Independent samples t-test		*Bigger*
One – sided/tailed test		*Smaller*
Two – sided/tailed test		*Bigger*
Chi square Test	*Fewer degrees of freedom*	*Smaller*
	Fewer degrees of freedom	*Bigger*

Appropriate or required sample size – Statistical test procedures

The following input parameters were inputted into the software package *G*Power 3* which can be downloaded at zero cost, *courtesy of Erdfelder et al (1996) and Faul et al (2007).*

Independent samples t test = designed to compare two population means

For an *independent samples t test*, a sample size of 115 for each group is appropriate or required after each of the following input parameters were specified by the researcher.

1. *Power level for the test (1 - β) = 0.75 – This input specification implies that the statistical test procedure employed by the researcher will have a 75% chance of detecting statistical significance (i.e. an effect or non-zero difference) if one exists.*

2. *Desired effect size i.e. d = 0.35 (effect size value) - The researcher has decided, based on findings from similar studies that a meaningful effect size in this area of research is 0.35.*

3. *Significance level for the test i.e. α = 0.05 - The researcher is willing to tolerate incorrectly declaring an effect i.e. statistical significance, no more than 5 times in every 100.*

4. *Two tailed/sided test - The researcher has no prior indication that the mean of one group is higher or lower than the mean of the other group so he is content to simply test if a difference between the means exists.*

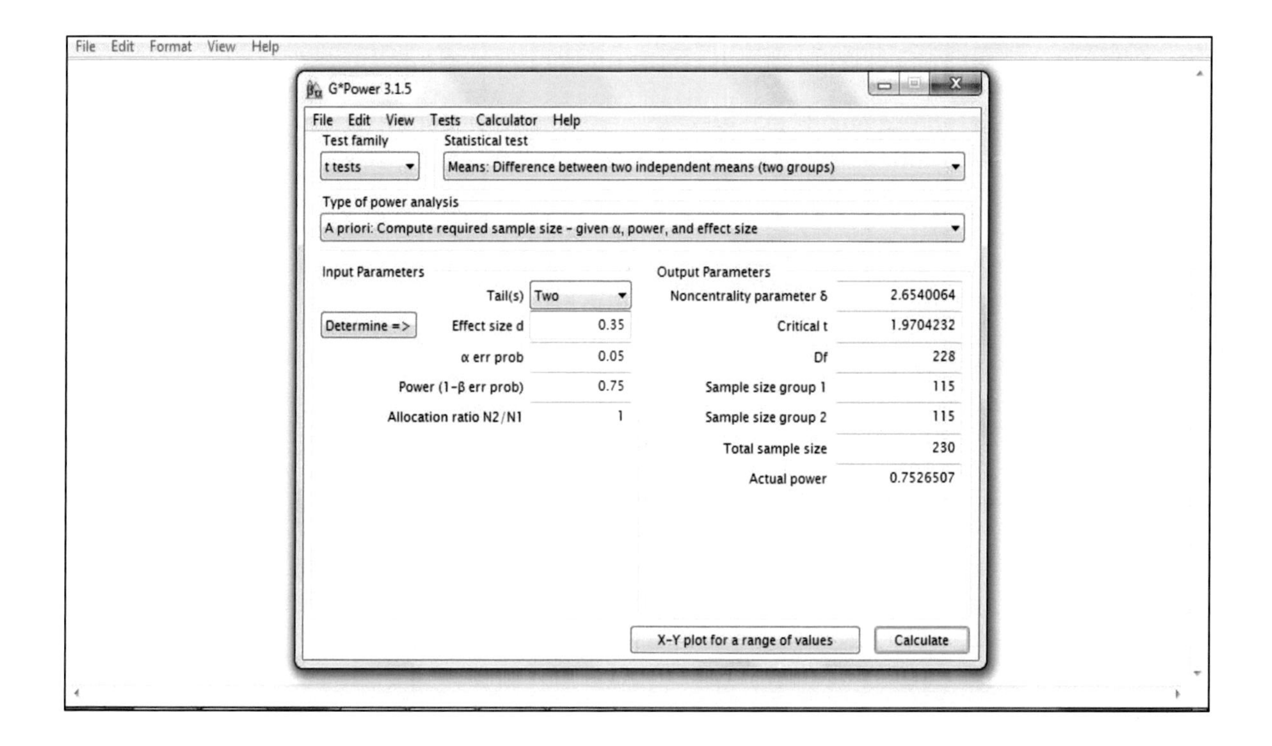

This approach to selecting an appropriate or required sample size accommodates all the concerns of the researcher, and tailors the statistical test procedure in accordance with the input parameters preferred by the researcher. The researcher is now armed with a sample size, which can be combined with an appropriate statistical test procedure to deliver a very high chance *(75% chance)* of detecting *statistical significance (i.e. an effect or non-zero difference)* with a *meaningful or practical difference (effect size of 3.5)* between the groups. If the researcher wished to increase the power *(1 – β)* of the statistical test procedure, or if he wishes to detect smaller differences *(effect size value below 0.35),* or if he simply wants to reduce the risk of incorrectly declaring a difference *(referred to as a type 1 error or α)*, then a higher sample size would be required and vice versa.

5.3 Procedures for statistical analysis

The following *procedures* will facilitate the subject matter of *statistical analysis* in later chapters:

1. *Statistical Test procedure*
2. *Confidence Intervals procedure*
3. *Effect Size procedure*

The following *procedures* will be considered in the context of a study designed to compare two independently sampled groups.

Statistical Test procedure – Is there a difference between the groups?

The statistical test procedure enables the researcher to generalise from the sample to the population. When sample statistics *(mean and standard deviation etc.)* for each group are calculated, some difference between the groups will most likely be observed. The statistical test procedure will provide the researcher with the probability *(p value)* that the observed difference arose by chance and can largely be explained by sampling error.

p value tells us how wrong we are likely to be if we reject H_0

The statistical test procedure will allow the researcher to infer if the observed mean difference between say, two groups is *statistically significant (i.e. that the true population mean difference is most likely to be non-zero or an effect is detected)* or if the observed difference between the two groups is *statistically not-significant (i.e. the collected sample evidence does not allow us to conclude that the true population difference is non-zero).* A *statistically non-significant* result only means that there is insufficient evidence to allow us to declare that there is a non-zero difference. However, this does not entitle us to declare that the difference is zero. The statistical test procedure ends there.

If the test allows us to declare that the difference between the means is *statistically significant*, we can only infer that the true population difference between the groups is not zero. If the test allows us to declare that the difference is *not-significant*, we can only infer that the evidence *(the collected sample data)* is insufficient to allow us to declare that there is a difference. Hence, the statistical test procedure provides the researcher with very limited conclusions since one is rarely only interested in whether the difference between two groups is not zero. The statistical test procedure does not allow us to select one of the following options (*Berry, 1986*):

a. *The difference is statistically significant and large enough to be of practical importance*
b. *The difference is statistically significant but too small to be of practical importance*
c. *The difference is not statistically significant but large enough to be of practical importance*
d. *The difference is not statistically significant and also not large enough to be of practical importance*

Option (c) is always a possibility and this is a concern that the researcher must attempt to minimise. This possibility may arise if the input parameters were not properly specified when deciding on the appropriate or required sample size or the researcher has been the victim of the 0.20 *(β)* risk of making a type II error *(assuming that the power of the test is specified at $1 - \beta = 0.80$)*. Options (b) and (d) may appear different but a closer inspection will reveal that they both amount to the same conclusion. A judgement on whether the difference between two groups is large enough to be of practical importance is a matter of opinion and not a statistical question. However, to assist in this regard, it is important to conduct both a *confidence interval procedure* and an *effect size procedure*.

Confidence Intervals procedure – Over what range of values will the true mean difference lie with a high degree of probability?

This procedure addresses the question: *Over what range of values might the true population mean difference (the parameter of interest) lie with a high degree of probability*. A confidence interval will give the researcher the range of possible values for the true mean difference. Arguments have been advanced to encourage less use of statistical test procedures *(significance tests)* towards an increased reliance on the confidence interval procedure *(Gardner and Altman, 1986)*.

An accurate interpretation of a 95% confidence interval is that 95% of the confidence intervals constructed from many repeated samples would include the true value of the parameter *(in this example the parameter is the true population mean difference)*. In practical terms, a convenient or manageable/intuitive interpretation of a 95% confidence interval is that we can be 95% confident that the constructed interval *(from a single sample)* contains the true value of the parameter. Confidence intervals can be used to make statistical inferences about populations parameters along with or instead of *significance tests*. The width of the confidence interval will guide the researcher in determining the relative importance of say, the population parameter under investigation *(true population mean difference in this example)*.

The statistical test procedure and confidence interval procedure will provide the researcher with an answer to the question *is there a difference between the groups (they will establish statistical significance or statistical non-significance)*. However the confidence interval procedure enables the researcher to make additional inferences. In simple terms, the statistical test procedure will only allow you to conclude either *yes (the difference is not zero)* or *no (the evidence collected is insufficient to suggest that the difference is other than zero)*. The confidence interval procedure will also allow you to conclude either *yes* to the question *(whether the calculated confidence interval does not contain zero which is equivalent to statistical significance)* or *no* to the question *(whether the calculated interval does contain zero which is equivalent to statistical non-significance)*.

However, the confidence interval procedure will also provide a range of values *(width of the confidence interval)* within which the true population mean difference might lie. Therefore, the confidence interval procedure answers the questions *is there a 'statistically significant' difference between the means of the two groups* and *what is the likely extent or range of the difference.*

Effect Size procedure – How large or important is size of the difference between the two groups?

Whilst the confidence interval will provide a range of values that may represent the true difference, the question will remain as to whether a *statistically significant* finding *(a non-zero difference or an effect)* has a practical or meaningful significance *(is the size of difference considered large enough to be considered important).* This requires a non-statistical judgement which can be made from experience or information derived from other similar studies which have contributed to identifying a possible benchmark value. An additional procedure to assist in this regard is the *effect size procedure*. This procedure provides the researcher with an *effect size* value which can be interpreted using general guidelines. The guidelines for interpreting these *effect size* values are only intended to be used when context-specific guidelines are unavailable in the researcher's particular research area. The effect size procedure addresses the question: *How large or important is the size of the difference*. Calculating an effect size helps the researcher to judge if a statistically significant finding is also large enough to be of practical importance. The calculation of effect size should, where possible, be compared to effect size calculations from other studies.

Deciding on appropriate sample size must involve consideration of a variety of input parameters in advance of the study

5.4 Understanding the significance level and the *p* value

Consider the following example in which we wish to compare the mean scores of males against the mean scores of females:

A random sample of 115 males and 115 females was selected and these two groups sat an IQ (intelligence quotient) test. The mean and standard deviations for each group was then calculated ($Mean_{males}$ = 105, $Standard\ Deviation_{males}$ = 3.5 and $Mean_{females}$ = 10.5, $Standard\ Deviation_{females}$ = 4.5). Use this information to test whether the mean IQ score of third level male students is different to the mean IQ score third level female students at the local institute at the 5% level of significance (α = 0.05).

The *null (H_0) and alternative hypothesis (H_1) may be written as:*

H_0: $\mu_{male\ IQ} = \mu_{female\ IQ}$ ⟶ *No effect present*
H_1: $\mu_{male\ IQ} \neq \mu_{female\ IQ}$ ⟶ *An effect is present*

The researcher must employ a parametric or non-parametric test procedure *(an issue for later chapters),* whichever is deemed appropriate, in order to arrive at a decision about the null hypothesis *(H_0)*. At the conclusion of the appropriate test procedure, the decision about the null hypothesis *(H_0)* will either be:

Reject the null hypothesis
Fail to reject the null hypothesis

1. *p* value

The *p value* is the probability that the differences or relationship observed in the sample data arose by chance and can be attributed to sampling error.

p value tells us how wrong we are likely to be if we reject H_0

The decision that the researcher makes will be based on the derived *p* value. The *p* value can be derived manually using statistical tables *(as demonstrated in Chapters 6, 7 and 8)* or can obtained as part of a statistical package output *(e.g. SPSS)* for whichever statistical test is selected.

2. Significance level *(α = 0.05)*

A Significance level is the cut-off point below which the researcher is willing to accept a level of risk of mistakenly rejecting the null hypothesis and thus committing a *type 1 error* i.e. if the *p* value is less than 0.05, this represents an acceptable tolerance of error. To undertake a test procedure *at the 5% level of significance (α = 0.05)* means that the researcher has set down a cut-off tolerance point. If he rejects the null hypothesis at the 0.05 level of significance, then he is willing to tolerate a likelihood of being wrong up to 5 times in 100 in rejecting.

5.5 The power of statistical tests $(1 - \beta)$ and inappropriate sample size

Consider the following example in which the researcher wishes to compare the mean scores of males against the mean scores of females. Suppose that he randomly selected 7 males and 9 females without any justification for selecting those sample sizes *(no prior specification of input parameters).*

A random sample of 7 males and 9 females was selected and these two groups sat a Statistics exam. The mean and standard deviations for each group was then calculated ($Mean_{males}$ = 79, $Standard\ Deviation_{males}$ = 6.88 and $Mean_{females}$ = 78, $Standard\ Deviation_{females}$ = 9.49). Use this information to test whether the mean score of male students is different to the mean score of female students at the 5% level of significance (α = 0.05).

$$H_0: \mu_{male\ IQ} = \mu_{female\ IQ}$$
$$H_1: \mu_{male\ IQ} \neq \mu_{female\ IQ}$$

A statistically significant *p* value arising out of the statistical test procedure simply means that the observed difference or observed relationship *(i.e. the collected sample data)* was unlikely to have occurred by chance alone *(i.e. unlikely to have occurred if the null hypothesis were in fact true).* If the researcher employs a statistical test procedure, without consideration to appropriate sample size*(s)*, the test may or may not detect a *statistical significance* or *effect*. Whilst your collected sample data is revealing some observed difference *(the difference may be large or small)*, a failure to arrive at *statistical significance* suggests that the observed differences in the collected sample data are most likely to be explained by *sampling error*.

In other words, the observed differences are not large enough to be considered *real* such that *sampling error* can be reasonably discounted. If the researcher does not arrive at *statistical significance* when a non-zero difference is highly likely to exist, then the statistical test procedure may not be adequately *powered up* or the researcher has been the victim of the 0.20 (β) risk of making a type II error (assuming that the power of the test is specified at $1 - \beta = 0.80$). If no consideration is given to what constitutes an appropriate sample size*(s)* then the researcher has not made sufficient provision to *power up* the test procedure.

G*Power 3, is a software package which, in addition to calculating the appropriate sample size, can also be used to check the post hoc power of completed statistical test procedures *[the power of a test $(1 - \beta)$ is the capacity of a test to detect statistical significance if it exists – a power value of 75% means that the statistical test procedure has a 75% chance of detecting statistical significance if it exists]*. The information in the example above is inputted into *G*Power 3* which will estimate the researchers chances of detecting a *statistical significance* if it exists *(the power of the test).*

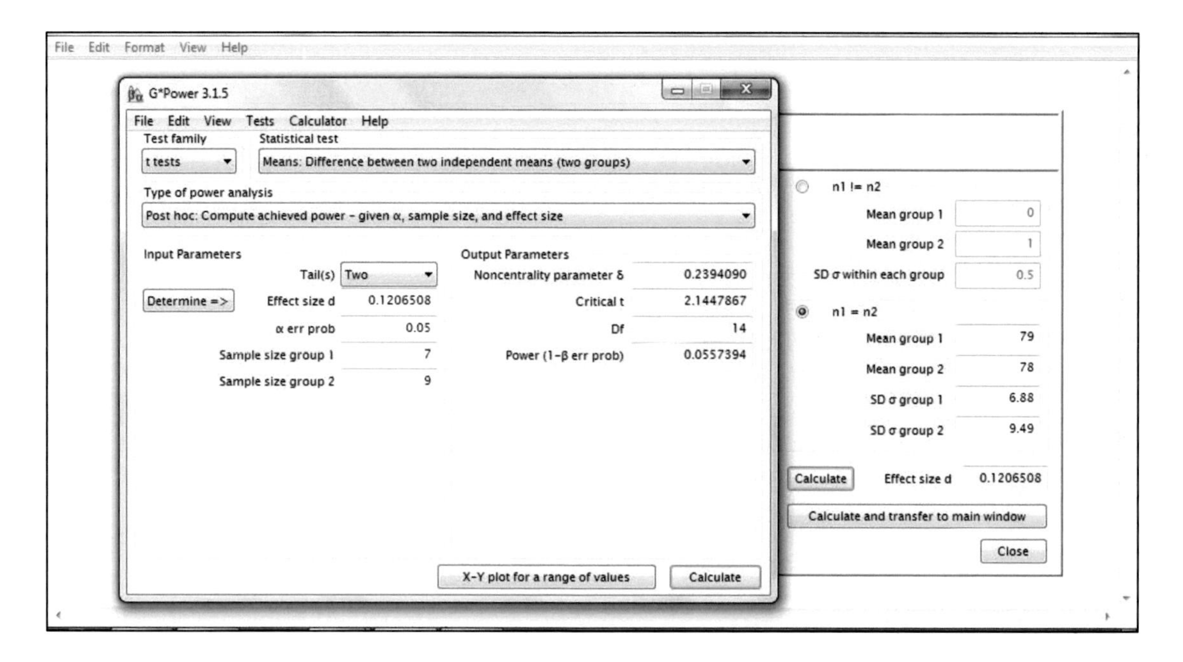

It appears that there was only a 5.57% chance of detecting significance if it exists. Therefore, before embarking on a piece of research, the researcher should make a decision on sample size*(s)*. To this end, *G*Power 3* can assist the researcher.

5.6 Using *G*Power 3* to decide appropriate *(required)* sample size

Independent Samples t test – Compares the means of two groups

The sample size deemed necessary for the *Independent Samples t test* is 57 per group given the following input parameters.

1. *Significance level for the test i.e. $\alpha = 0.05$*
2. *Desired effect size i.e. d = 0.50 (median effect size)*
3. *Power level for the test $(1 - \beta) = 0.75$*
4. *Two tailed/sided test*

*G*Power 3- Computing appropriate sample size(s)*

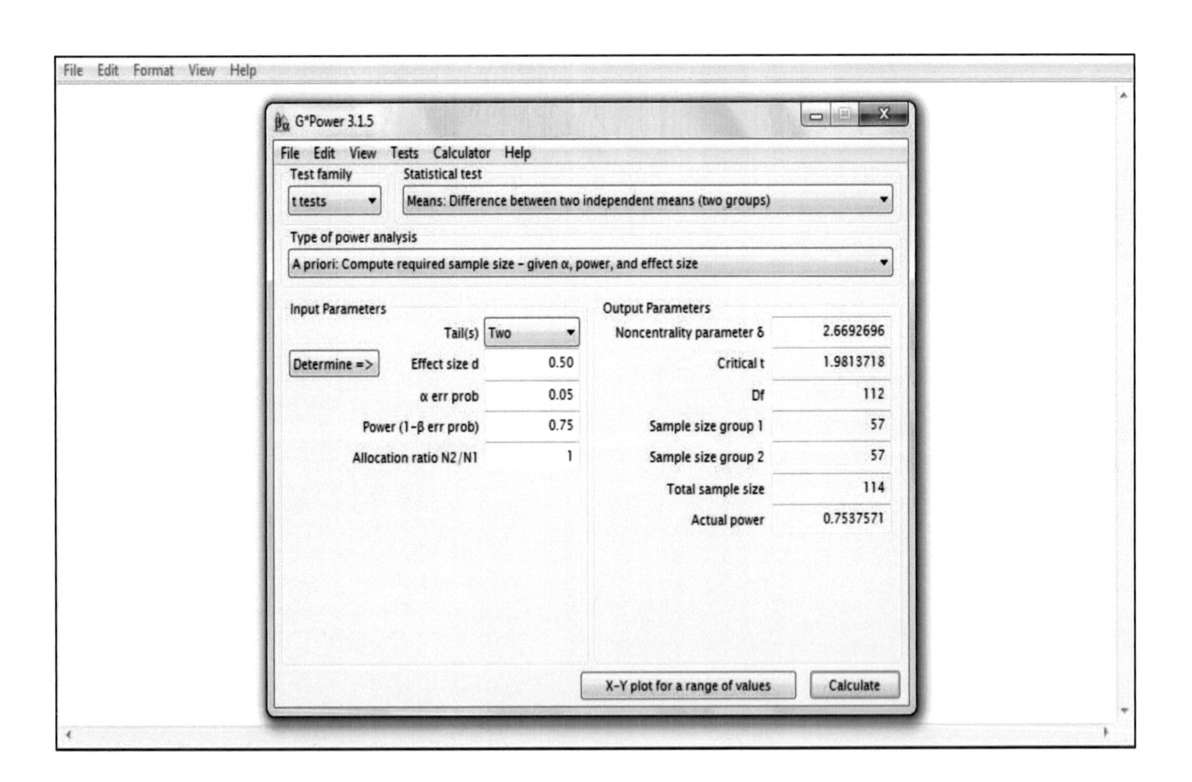

Chi-square test *(χ^2test)* – tests whether or not there is an association between two qualitative variables

The sample size deemed necessary for a *Chi-square test (χ^2test)* is 120 given the following input parameters.

1. *Significance level for the test i.e. α = 0.05*
2. *Desired effect size i.e. w = 0.30 (median effect size)*
3. *Power level for the test (1 - β) = 0.75*
4. *Degrees of freedom = For a 2 x 5 contingency table = (rows – 1) x (columns x 1) = (2 – 1) x (5 – 1) = 4.*

*G*Power 3- Computing appropriate sample size(s)*

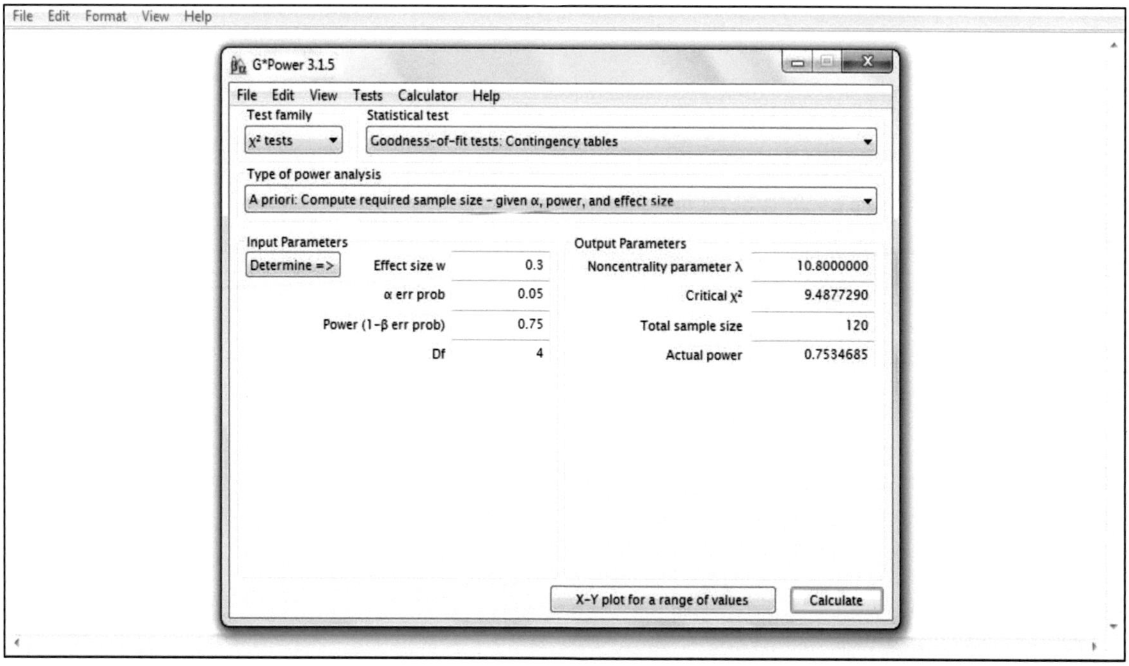

File Edit Format View Help

G*Power 3.1.5

File Edit View Tests Calculator Help

Test family: χ^2 tests

Statistical test: Goodness-of-fit tests: Contingency tables

Type of power analysis: A priori: Compute required sample size – given α, power, and effect size

Input Parameters		Output Parameters	
Effect size w	0.3	Noncentrality parameter λ	10.8000000
α err prob	0.05	Critical χ^2	9.4877290
Power (1-β err prob)	0.75	Total sample size	120
Df	4	Actual power	0.7534685

Determine =>

X-Y plot for a range of values

Calculate

Single Sample t test – tests the difference between an observed summary statistic of one group *(observed value)* with some benchmark population value *(expected value).*

The sample size deemed necessary for a *single sample t test (two tailed test)* is 30 given the following input parameters.

1. *Significance level for the test i.e. α = 0.05*
2. *Desired effect size i.e. d = 0.50 (median effect size)*
3. *Power level for the test (1 - β) = 0.75*
4. *Two tailed/sided test*

*G*Power 3- Computing appropriate sample size(s)*

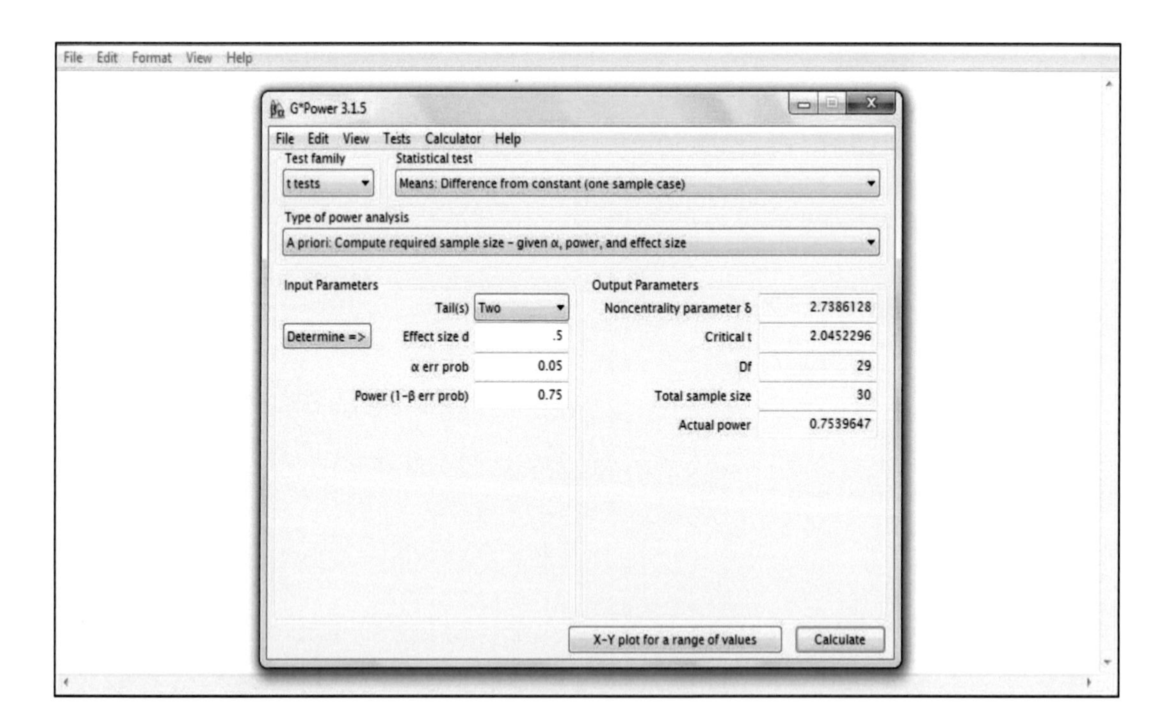

5.7 MCQs and Solutions

1. If we wish to investigate whether *a difference* exists between two means, then the H_0 is:

   (a) $H_0: \mu_1 - \mu_2 = 0$
   (b) $H_0: \mu_1 - \mu_2 \neq 0$
   (c) $H_0: \mu_1 - \mu_2 \leq 0$
   (d) $H_0: \mu_1 - \mu_2 \geq 0$

2. If we wish to investigate whether the first mean *is higher than* the second mean, then the H_0 is:

   (a) $H_0: \mu_1 - \mu_2 = 0$
   (b) $H_0: \mu_1 - \mu_2 \neq 0$
   (c) $H_0: \mu_1 - \mu_2 \leq 0$
   (d) $H_0: \mu_1 - \mu_2 \geq 0$

3. If we wish to investigate whether the first mean *is lower than* the second mean, then the H_0 is:

   (a) $H_0: \mu_1 - \mu_2 = 0$
   (b) $H_0: \mu_1 - \mu_2 \neq 0$
   (c) $H_0: \mu_1 - \mu_2 \leq 0$
   (d) $H_0: \mu_1 - \mu_2 \geq 0$

4. If we wish to investigate the assertion that the true population mean *is different from* 100, then the H_0 is:

   (a) $H_0: \mu = 100$
   (b) $H_0: \mu \leq 100$
   (c) $H_0: \mu \geq 100$
   (d) $H_0: \mu \neq 100$

5. If we wish to investigate the assertion that the true population mean *is lower than* 100, then the H_0 is:

   (a) $H_0: \mu = 100$
   (b) $H_0: \mu \leq 100$
   (c) $H_0: \mu \geq 100$
   (d) $H_0: \mu \neq 100$

6. If we wish to investigate the assertion that the true population mean *is higher than* 100, then the H_0 is:

   (a) $H_0: \mu = 100$
   (b) $H_0: \mu \leq 100$
   (c) $H_0: \mu \geq 100$
   (d) $H_0: \mu \neq 100$

7. If we wish to investigate if *a difference* between the means exists, then the test type is:

   (a) Two tailed
   (b) One tailed *(right-tail)*
   (c) One tailed *(left-tail)*
   (d) Both (b) and (c) above

8. If we wish to investigate if the first mean *is higher than* the second mean, then the test type is:

   (a) Two tailed test
   (b) One tailed *(right-tail)*
   (c) One tailed *(left-tail)*
   (d) Both (b) and (c) above

9. You are investigating the effects of a new employee assistance programme and that you believe one of the outcomes will be that there will be *less* employee absenteeism. Then H_1 will be:

   (a) H_1: As a result of the new employee assistance programme, there will be a *decrease* in employee absenteeism.
   (b) H_1: As a result of the new employee assistance programme, there will either be *no difference* in employee absenteeism or there will be *an increase*.
   (c) H_1: As a result of the new employee assistance programme, there will be a *difference* in employee absenteeism.
   (d) H_1: As a result of the new employee assistance programme, there will either be *no difference* in employee absenteeism.

10. Assume you are studying a new drug treatment for depression. The drug has gone through some initial animal trials, but has not yet been tested on humans. You believe *(based on theory and the previous research)* that the drug will have an effect, but you are not confident enough to hypothesize a direction and say the drug will reduce depression. Then H_1 will be:

(a) H_1: As a result of 300mg/day of the Zzz drug, there will be *no difference* in depression.
(b) H_1: As a result of 300mg/day of the Zzz drug, there will be a *difference* in depression.
(c) H_1: As a result of 300mg/day of the Zzz drug, there will be a *decrease* in depression.
(d) H_1: As a result of 300mg/day of the Zzz drug, there will be an *increase* in depression.

11. Assume that you are investigating the effectiveness of a new diet product called *New U Shape*. You wish to test if this new product reduces weight. Then H_1 will be:

(a) H_1: If you take *New U Shape* for a month, then you will either gain weight or stay the same.
(b) H_1: If you take *New U Shape* for a month, then you will either lose weight or stay the same
(c) H_1: If you take *New U Shape* for a month, then you will gain weight
(d) H_1: If you take *New U Shape* for a month, then you will lose weight

12. We denote a power value as:

(a) α
(b) β
(c) 1 - α
(d) $1 - \beta$

13. The power of a test is its ability

(a) To detect an effect when it actually exists
(b) To detect an effect when it doesn't exist
(c) To reject H_0 when it is false
(d) To reject H_0 when it is true

14. A power value of 0.8 means:

(a) 80% chance of detecting statistical significance when it exists
(b) 20% chance of detecting statistical significance when it exists
(c) Reject H_0 since $\alpha > 0.05$
(d) Accept H_0 since $\alpha > 0.05$

15. We denote the level of significance as:

(a) β
(b) $1-\alpha$
(c) α
(d) $1-\beta$

16. A type II error occurs when:

(a) The null hypothesis is rejected when it is false
(b) Fail to reject null hypothesis when it is true
(c) Fail to reject null hypothesis when it is false
(d) The null hypothesis is rejected when it is true

17. A type I error occurs when:

(a) The null hypothesis is rejected when it is false
(b) Fail to reject null hypothesis when it is true
(c) Fail to reject null hypothesis when it is false
(d) The null hypothesis is rejected when it is true

18. Which of the following is incorrect:

(a) The power of a test increases as sample size increases
(b) The power of a test increases as sample size decreases
(c) Sample size has no bearing on the power of a test
(d) The power of a test increases as if you change your level of significance from 0.05 to 0.01

19. Effect size can be described as:

(a) The strength of association or relationship between two variables
(b) The magnitude or size of the difference between two means
(c) Both (a) and (b) are correct
(d) None of the above is correct

20. Which of the following is correct:

(a) A power level of 0.8 means that an effect will be detected with 100% certainty
(b) An Independent sample t test is more powerful than a matched/paired sample t test
(c) Statistical significance implies practical significance
(d) The narrower the confidence intervals, the more confidence you can place in your results

MCQ Solutions

1. (a)	6. (b)	11. (d)	16. (c)
2. (c)	7. (a)	12. (d)	17. (d)
3. (d)	8. (b)	13. (a)	18. (b)
4. (a)	9. (a)	14. (a)	19. (c)
5. (c)	10. (b)	15. (c)	20. (d)

Chapter 6 – Inferential procedures for one population

'It is the mark of an instructed mind to rest assured with that degree of precision that the nature of the subject admits, and not to seek exactness when only an approximation of the truth is possible.'

Aristotle (BC 384 – BC 322)

6.1 Schematic Chart 1 - *Statistical tests for one population mean*

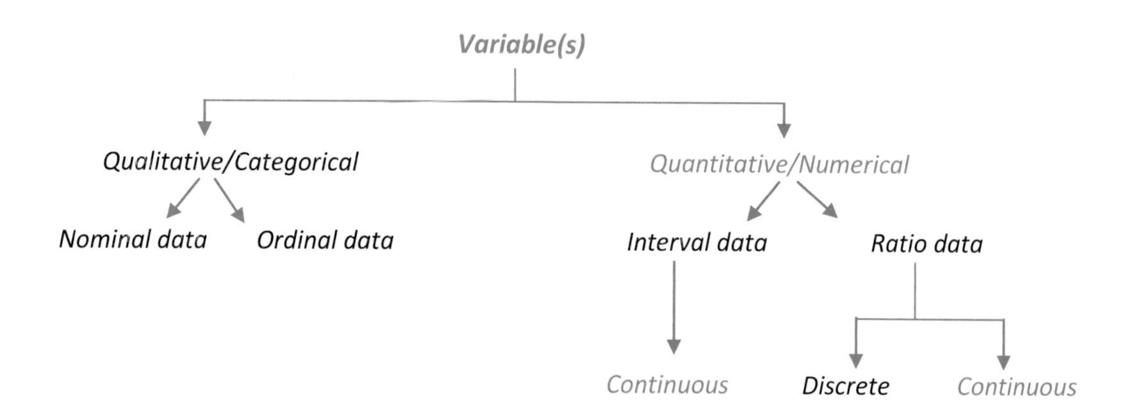

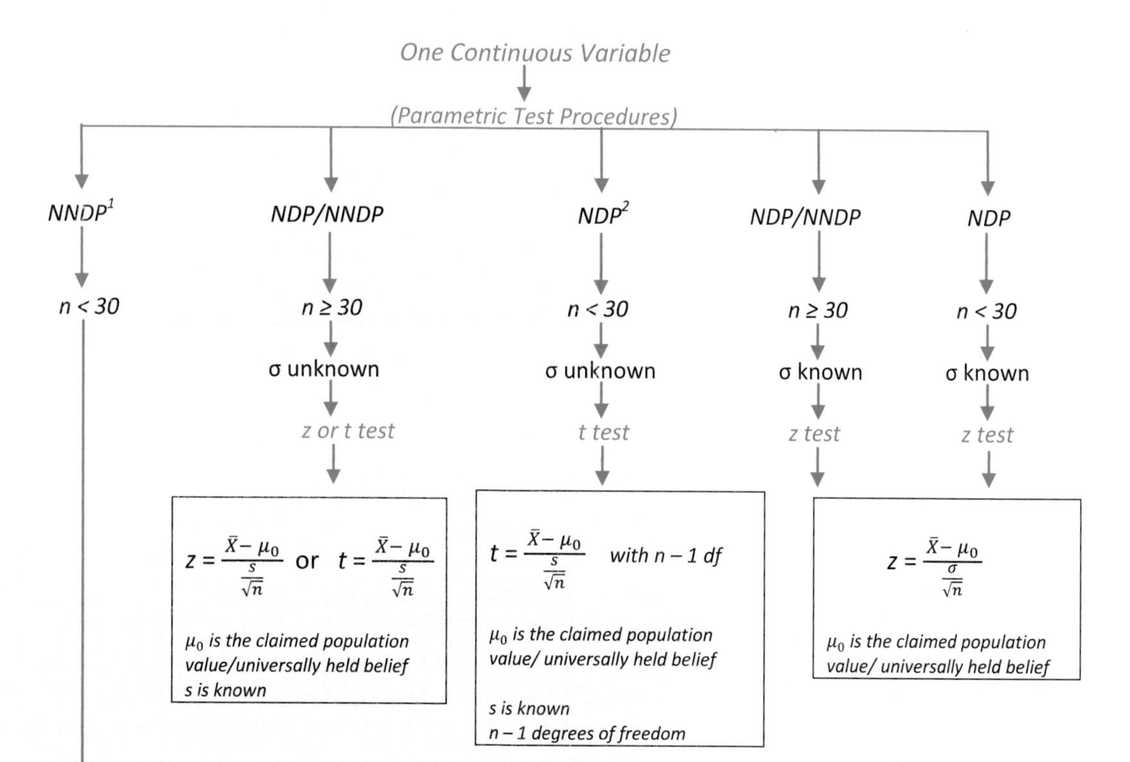

Use a non-parametric test or increase sample size to ≥ 30

Notes:

1. *NNDP = Not normally distributed population. The population from which the sample is drawn is not normally distributed*
2. *NDP = Normally distributed population. The population from which the sample is drawn is normally distributed*

6.2 Schematic Chart 2 – *Confidence intervals for the mean of one population*

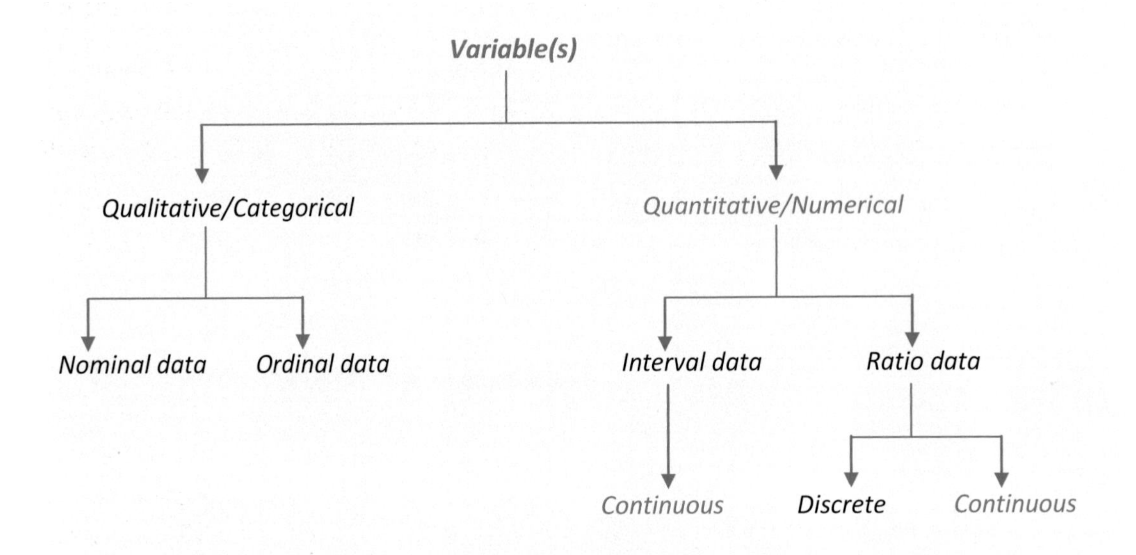

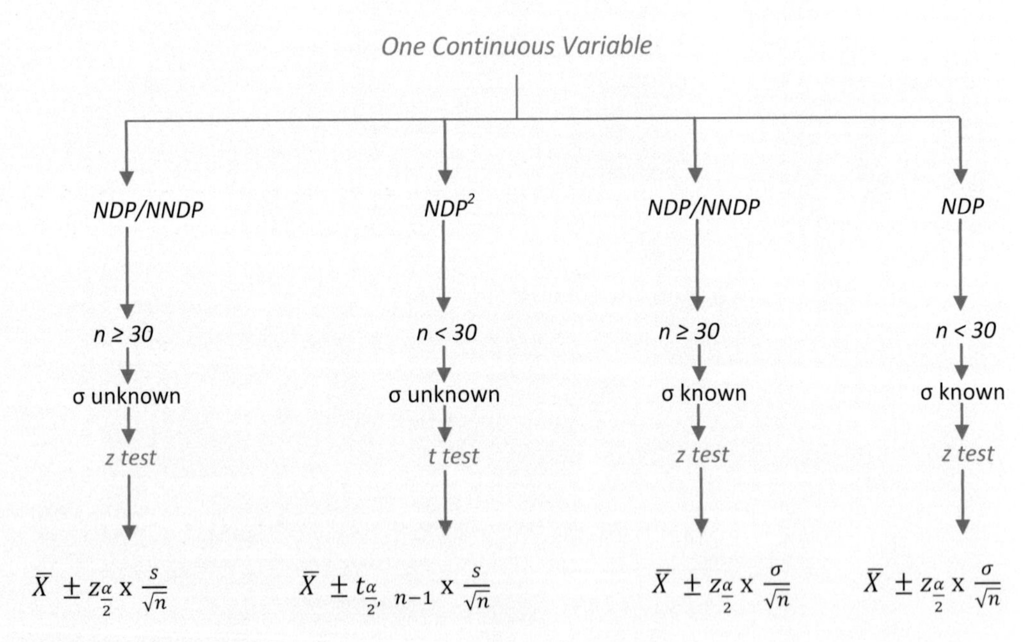

Notes:

1. *NNDP = Not normally distributed population. The population from which the sample is drawn is not normally distributed*
2. *NDP = Normally distributed population. The population from which the sample is drawn is normally distributed*

6.3 Introductory Comments

In this chapter we will explore test procedures which are appropriate for testing claims about the mean from one population.

A one-sample t-test compares the mean score of a sample to a known value, usually the population mean. The idea of the test is enable a comparison between sample average ($\bar{x}$) and the population average (μ).

The following is a summary of what is covered in this chapter:

1. One population mean – *σ known (z test) or unknown (z test/t test) – Two tailed tests*

a. A random sample from a population – Here we use the random sample to test whether or not the population mean has changed

The manufacturer of a popular perfume claims that the contents of its best-selling bottle are known to be normally distributed with a mean of 50 ml with a standard deviation of 1.50 ml. To test this claim the marketing department randomly sampled 35 bottles and recorded a mean of 50.75 ml. Use this information to test whether the mean contents is different to 50 ml at the 0.05 level of significance.

The claim in this example will be assigned to the null hypothesis since the statement of *explicit* claim in this example implies/contains the equality operator *(...with a mean of 50 ml...)*. Remember that the claim can be assigned to either the null or the alternative hypothesis as per page 175.

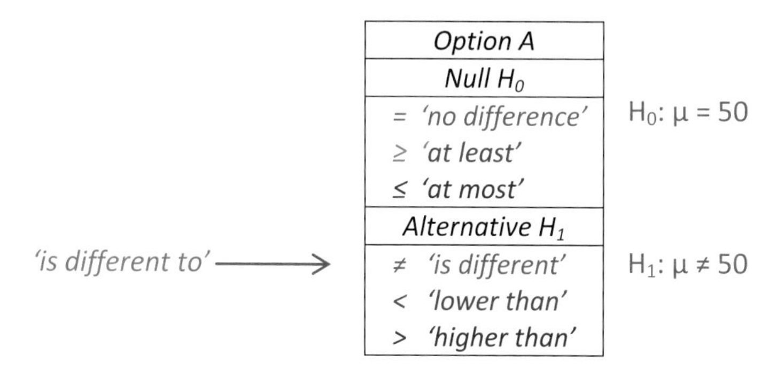

b. A random sample from a target population group selected from a larger population *(which is made up of a number of target populations or sub-groups)* – Here we use the random sample to test whether or not the population mean applies to a target population group *(sub-population)*. The sub-group/sub-population is our population of interest in this example.

A national students' survey claims that a typical student studies on average 18 hours per week outside of lectures with a standard deviation of 3.75 hours per week. A local institute does not believe that this finding applies to its students. A study was undertaken by the institute to reveal the truth. A random sample of 65 students from the local institute (the target population group/sub group) revealed an average study time of 16.75 hours per week. Test whether the mean study time of the target population group is different to 18 at the 0.05 level of significance.

The claim in this example will be assigned to the null hypothesis since the statement of *explicit* claim in this example implies/contains the equality operator *(...studies on average 18 hours...)*. Remember that the claim can be assigned to either the null or the alternative hypothesis as per page 175.

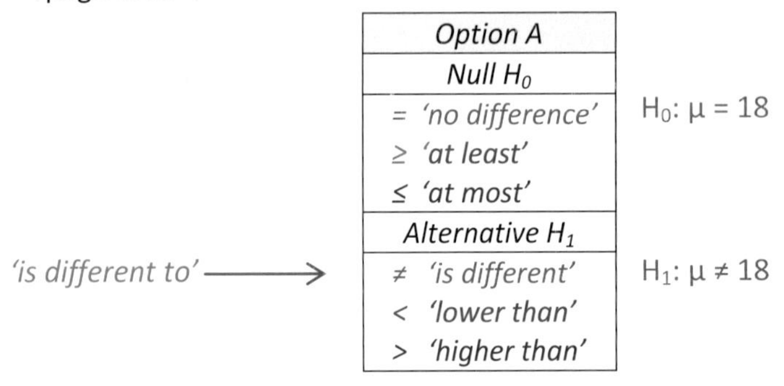

	Option A	
	Null H_0	
	= *'no difference'* ≥ *'at least'* ≤ *'at most'*	H_0: $\mu = 18$
	Alternative H_1	
'is different to' →	≠ *'is different'* < *'lower than'* > *'higher than'*	H_1: $\mu \neq 18$

c. A random sample from one population is selected and that random sample of people undergoes some treatment/training – Here we test whether the population mean could change if the entire population underwent the same treatment/training as the sample group.

The length of time it takes employees at a large hospital to prepare a hospital bed is known to be on average 140 seconds. A random sample of 35 employees undergo a new innovative training technique to improve the speed in preparing a hospital bed. The mean time to prepare a hospital bed for this sample group was recorded at 136 seconds with a standard deviation of 8 seconds. Test to see if the population mean is likely to change if the entire population underwent the same training at the 0.05 level of significance.

The claim in this example will be assigned to the null hypothesis since the statement of *implicit* claim in this example implies/contains the equality operator *(...is known to be on average 140 seconds...)*. Remember that the claim can be assigned to either the null or the alternative hypothesis as per page 175.

	Option A	*Option B*	
	Null H_0	*Null H_0*	
	= *'no difference'* ≥ *'at least'* ≤ *'at most'*	*No effect/no change* *No effect/positive effect* *No effect/negative effect*	H_0: $\mu = 140$
	Alternative H_1	*Alternative H_1*	
'change' →	≠ *'is different'* < *'lower than'* > *'higher than'*	*An effect/change* *Negative effect* *Positive effect*	H_1: $\mu \neq 140$

2. One population mean – *σ known (z test) or unknown (z test/t test) – One tailed tests*

The following situations are covered in this chapter:

a. A random sample from a population – Here we use the sample to test whether or not the population mean has increased or decreased

The manufacturer of a popular perfume claims that the contents of its best-selling bottle are known to be normally distributed with a mean of at least 50 ml with a standard deviation of 1.50 ml. A consumer interests group wishes to investigate their suspicion that the average contents are less than 50 ml. A random sample 35 bottles reveal a mean of 49.5 ml. Use this information to test whether the mean contents is lower than 50 ml at the 0.05 level of significance.

The claim in this example will be assigned to the null hypothesis since the statement of *explicit* claim in this example implies/contains the equality operator *(...with a mean of at least 50 ml...)*. Remember that the claim can be assigned to either the null or the alternative hypothesis as per page 175.

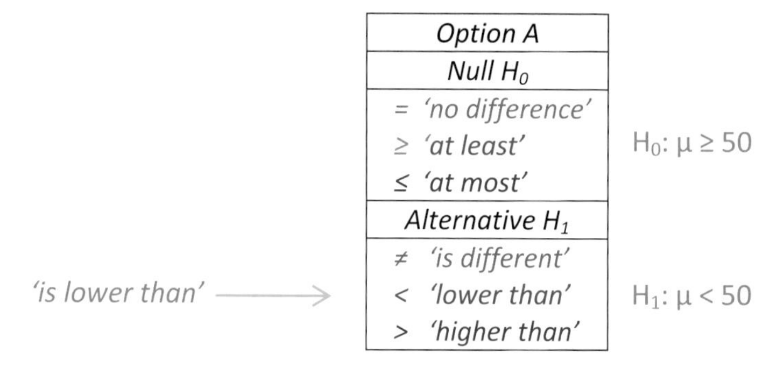

Option A	
Null H_0	
= *'no difference'* ≥ *'at least'* ≤ *'at most'*	H_0: $\mu \geq 50$
Alternative H_1	
≠ *'is different'* < *'lower than'* > *'higher than'*	H_1: $\mu < 50$

'is lower than' ⟶ < *'lower than'*

b. A random sample from a target group selected from a population – Here we test whether or not the target group mean is higher than or lower than the population mean

A national students' survey claims that a typical student studies on average 18 hours per week outside of lectures with a standard deviation of 3.75 hours per week. A local institute does not believe that this finding applies to its students and holds the belief that its students study less than the national average. A study was undertaken by the institute to reveal the truth. A random sample of 65 students from the local institute (the target group/sub group) revealed an average study time of 16.75 hours per week. Use this information to test whether mean study time of the target group is lower than 18 at the 0.05 level of significance.

The claim in this example will be assigned to the null hypothesis since the statement of *explicit* claim in this example implies/contains the equality operator *(...studies on average 18 hours per week...)*. Remember that the claim can be assigned to either the null or the alternative hypothesis as per page 175.

'is lower to' ⟶

Option A
Null H_0
= 'no difference' ≥ 'at least' ≤ 'at most'
Alternative H_1
≠ 'is different' < 'lower than' > 'higher than'

H_0: μ ≥ 50

H_1: μ < 50

c. A random sample from one population is selected and that sample undergoes some treatment/training – Here we test whether the population mean could increase or decrease if the entire population underwent the same treatment/training as the sample group.

The length of time it takes employees at a large hospital to dress a hospital bed is known to be on average 140 seconds. A random sample of 35 employees undergo a new innovative training technique to improve the speed in dressing a hospital bed. The mean time to dress a hospital bed for this sample group was recorded at 136 seconds with a standard deviation of 8 seconds. Test to see if the population mean is likely to decrease or positive change *if the entire population underwent the same training at the 0.05 level of significance.*

The claim in this example will be assigned to the null hypothesis since the statement of *explicit* claim in this example implies/contains the equality operator *(...is known to be on average 140 seconds...)*. Remember that the claim can be assigned to either the null or the alternative hypothesis as per page 175.

'decrease' ⟶

Option A	Option B
Null H_0	*Null H_0*
= 'no difference' ≥ 'at least' ≤ 'at most'	*No effect/no change* *No effect/positive effect* *No effect/negative effect*
Alternative H_1	*Alternative H_1*
≠ 'is different' < 'lower than' > 'higher than'	*An effect/change* *Negative effect* *Positive effect*

H_0: μ ≤ 140

H_1: μ > 140

6.4 **Template** –*Inference procedures for the mean of one population*

The following inference procedures should be following during the course of your statistical analysis:

1. *Statistical Test Procedure*
2. *Confidence Interval Procedure*
3. *Effect Size Procedure*

Statistical Test Procedure

1. State the necessary conditions required to validate the test
2. State the null hypothesis and alternative hypothesis
3. State the statistical decision rule given your selected level of significance
4. Select and calculate the appropriate test statistic
5. Compare the calculated test statistic with the critical value
6. Derive an approximate p value

Confidence Interval Procedure

1. Select a confidence interval and confidence level
2. Construct the selected confidence interval
3. State your inferences

Effect Size Procedure

1. Calculate the
2. 'measure of effect'
3. State your inferences

One-Sample t Test – Appropriate or required sample size for selected *input parameters*

*Using G*Power 3*

Sample Size Required			Effect Size		
α= 0.05			0.2	0.5	0.8
Power	0.75	1 - tail	136	23	10
		2 - tail	176	30	13
	0.80	1 - tail	156	27	12
		2 - tail	199	34	15
	0.85	1 - tail	182	31	13
		2 - tail	227	38	17

6.5 Statistical Inference: *One large sample/σ known – Two tailed z test*

Example 1 - A random sample from a population

*The manufacturer of a popular perfume claims that the contents of its best-selling bottle are known to be normally distributed with a mean of 50 ml with a standard deviation of 1.50 ml. To test this claim the marketing department randomly sampled 35 bottles and recorded a mean of 50.75 ml. Use this information to test whether the mean contents is different to 50 ml at the 0.05 level of significance ($\alpha = 0.05$). Use G*power 3 to calculate the post hoc power of the statistical test.*

Statistical Test Procedure

1. *State the assumptions required to validate this test*

   a. The measurement variable *Study time* is continuous.
   b. A random sample is selected from the population of interest *(The sub-group/sub-population is our population of interest).*
   c. I will assume that the population of *study times* is normally distributed. For sample size ≥ 30, the following statistical test procedure is robust even when this assumption is violated.

2. *State the null hypothesis and alternative hypothesis*

   H_0: $\mu_0 = 50$
   H_1: $\mu_0 \neq 50$ *Two-tailed test (determined by the operator ≠ in H_1)*
   Or
   H_0: *Observed mean of the sample – Expected mean of the population = 0*
   H_1: *Observed mean of the sample – Expected mean of the population ≠ 0*

3. *State the statistical decision rule for a selected level of significance*

   a. Appropriate test statistic is the z test since n ≥ 30 and σ is known and assumption 3 in part *(1)*
   b. The level of significance for this test: $\alpha = 0.05$.
   c. Identify the critical values in the diagram below *(A segment of the z tables is included here)*

      Identifying ± 1.96 in the diagram below requires 0.05 to be divided between both tails. Each tail has, therefore, an area equal to 0.025 each. Use the z tables to derive the critical values (z values) for an area equal to 0.025. Since the bell curve is symmetrical, the critical values are ± 1.96.

   d. Reject the null hypothesis *(H_0)* when the calculated test statistic (z test) from part 4 below > Critical value ± 1.96.

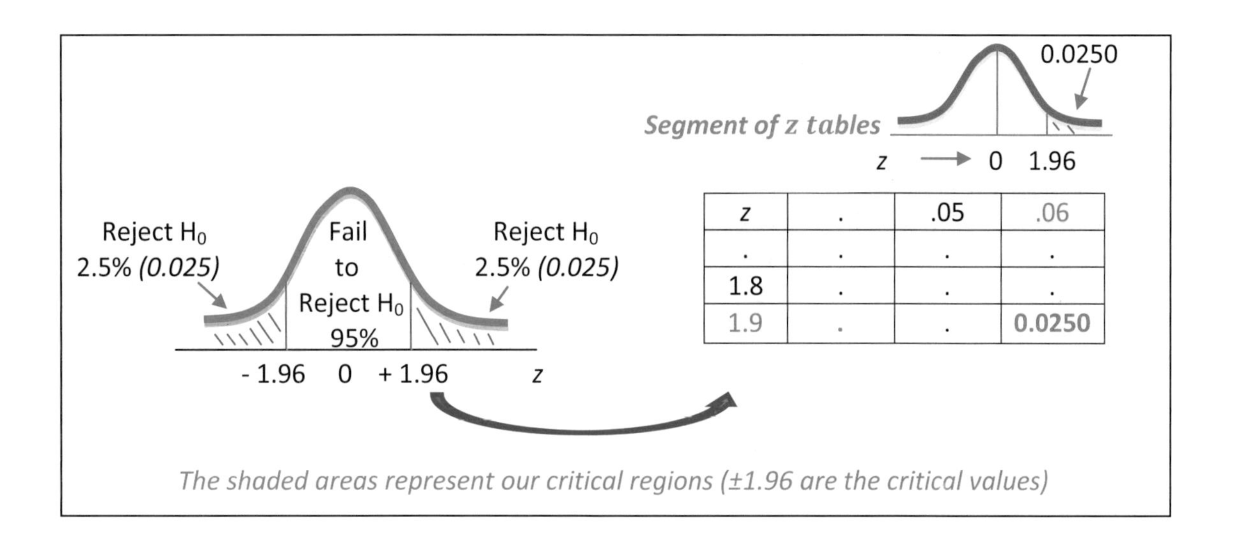

The shaded areas represent our critical regions (±1.96 are the critical values)

4. Select and calculate the appropriate test statistic

$$z \text{ test: } = \frac{\bar{X} - \mu_0}{\frac{\sigma}{\sqrt{n}}} = \frac{50.75-50}{\frac{1.50}{\sqrt{35}}} = 2.96$$

5. Compare the calculated test statistic with the critical value

The calculated *z test* statistic of 2.95 falls into the critical region *(to the right of 1.96),* where we reject H_0. In rejecting H_0, we are inferring that the mean study time for students at the local institute is different to the national average at the 0.05 level of significance.

6. Derive or locate an approximate p value using a segment of the z tables

The *p* value is the sum of the shaded areas under the curve defined by the calculated z value derived from the *z test* in Step 4.

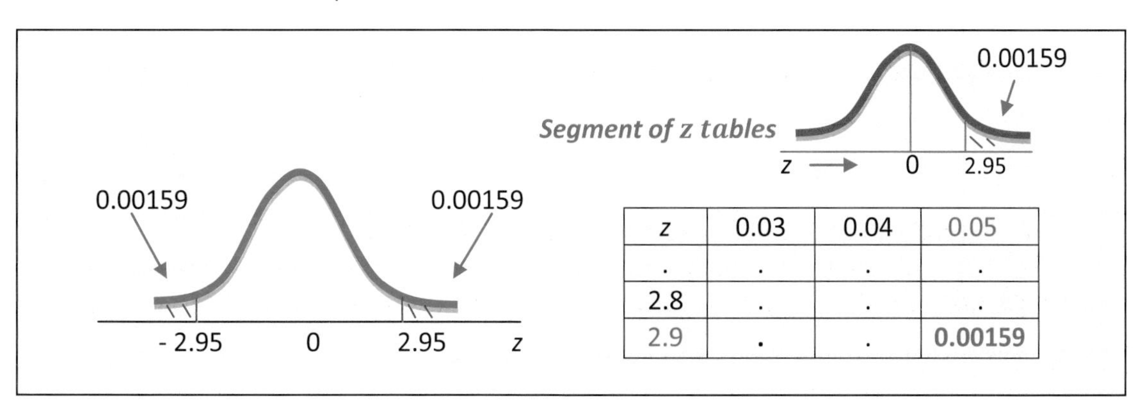

The sum of the shaded areas under the curve gives us a *p* value of 0.00318 *(2 x 0.00159 = 0.00318).*

Interpreting the p value

a. Traditional approach – explicit reference to a selected cut-off point of say $\alpha = 0.05$:

Since the p value of 0.00318 is below the 0.05 level of significance, we reject H_0 at the 0.05 level of significance (Applying the p value decision rule: If the p value < 0.05 we reject H_0). The difference between the observed mean from the sample and the expected mean of the population cannot be solely attributed to sampling error (chance).

b. Current approach – no explicit reference to a selected cut-off point of say $\alpha = 0.05$. The cut-off point is implicitly assumed as a guide value. The current practise is to report an exact *p* value *(included in the output of all statistical software packages).*

The p value reveals the likelihood of being wrong if we reject H_0 (the p value 0.00318 i.e. < 4 times in 1000).

Confidence Interval Procedure

Construct 95% confidence interval to estimate a range that includes the true population mean (for which our sample mean is a point estimate)

1. *Select a confidence interval and confidence level*

The appropriate confidence interval for $n \geq 30$ and σ known is:

$$\overline{X} \pm z_{\alpha/2}\, x\, \frac{\sigma}{\sqrt{n}}$$

2. *Construct the 95% confidence interval for the true population mean*

$$\overline{X} \pm z_{\alpha/2}\, x\, \frac{\sigma}{\sqrt{n}}$$

$$50.75 \pm 1.96\, x\, \frac{1.50}{\sqrt{35}} \rightarrow z_{\alpha/2} = z_{0.05/2} = z_{(0.025)} = 1.96$$

z	0.04	0.05	0.06
.	.	.	.
1.8	.	.	.
1.9	.	.	0.0250

$$50.75 \pm 1.96\, x\, 0.2535$$
$$50.75 \pm 0.4943$$

The 95% confidence interval is 50.25 to 51.24

3. *State your inferences*

Since the interval *(50.25 to 51.24)* does not contain the claimed population mean i.e. *(μ_0 = 50 ml)* then:

a. *The evidence available is compatible with a decision to reject the null hypothesis.*
b. *The probability that the calculated interval (50.25 to 51.24) contains the true population mean is 95%. This is an intuitive but not strictly a correct interpretation of a confidence interval.*

Effect Size Procedure

How large is the difference between the observed mean and the expected population mean?

1. *Identify the difference between the means*

Difference between the means: $(\bar{X} - \mu_0) = (50.75 - 50) = 0.75$

2. *Calculate the 'measure of effect'*

$$\text{Effect Size} = \frac{(\bar{X} - \mu_0)}{\sigma} = \frac{(50.75 - 50)}{1.5} = 0.5$$

3. *State your inferences*

To interpret this value, we refer to guidelines proposed by Cohen, 1988. The difference is of medium magnitude.

Effect Size *(d)*	Interpretation	% of overlap	
If d = 0	No effect	100%	
If d = 0.2	Small	85%	
If d = 0.5	Medium	67%	
If d = 0.8	Large	53%	

Reported results using the current approach (implicit cut-off guide point of $\alpha = 0.05$):

The observed mean contents ($\bar{x}_1 = 50.75$) is different to the expected population mean contents (μ = 50); p = 0.00318 (two-tailed). The mean difference ($\bar{X}$ - μ) of 0.75 is a medium effect size (d = 0.51). The 95% confidence interval for the true population mean is 50.25 and 51.24.

Power of the statistical test procedure using *G*power 3* software = 81.95%

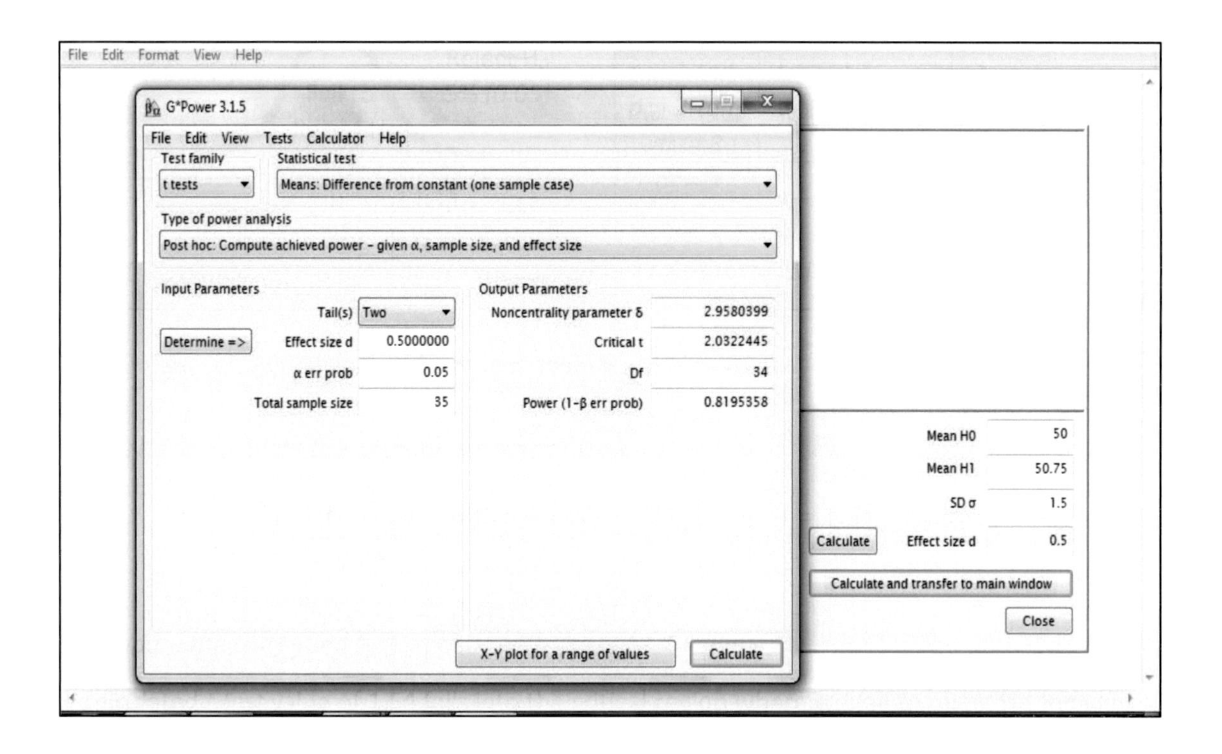

6.6 Statistical Inference: *One small sample/σ known – Two tailed z test*

Example 2 - A random sample from a target-group/sub-population selected from a population

*According to a national survey, the average IQ of primary school children is known to be 100 with a standard deviation of 8. A researcher suspects that students, whose parents give them a leading vitamin supplement, may have a different IQ. The researcher selected a random sample of 15 from this identified sub-group. These students scored on average 105 in an IQ test provided for them. Use this information to test the suspicion that the IQ scores of the sub-group are different from 100 at the 0.05 level of significance ($\alpha = 0.05$). Use G*power 3 to calculate the post hoc power of the statistical test.*

Statistical Test Procedure

1. *State the assumptions required to validate this test*

   As per Example 1

2. *State the null hypothesis and alternative hypothesis*

   H_0: $\mu_0 = 100$
   H_1: $\mu_0 \neq 100$ *Two-tailed test (as determined by the ≠ in H_1)*
   Or
   H_0: *Observed mean of the sample – Expected mean of the population = 0*
   H_1: *Observed mean of the sample – Expected mean of the population ≠ 0*

3. *State the statistical decision rule for a selected level of significance*

   a. Appropriate test statistic is the z test since σ is known and assumption 3 in part *(1)*
   b. The level of significance for this test: $\alpha = 0.05$
   c. Identify the critical values in the diagram below *(A segment of the z tables is included here)*

      Identifying ± 1.96 *in the diagram below requires 0.05 to be divided between both tails. Each tail has, therefore, an area equal to 0.025 each. Use the z tables to derive the critical values (z values) for an area equal to 0.025. Since the bell curve is symmetrical, the critical values are* ± 1.96.

   d. Reject the null hypothesis *(H_o)* when the calculated test statistic *(z test)* from part 4 below > Critical value ± 1.96.

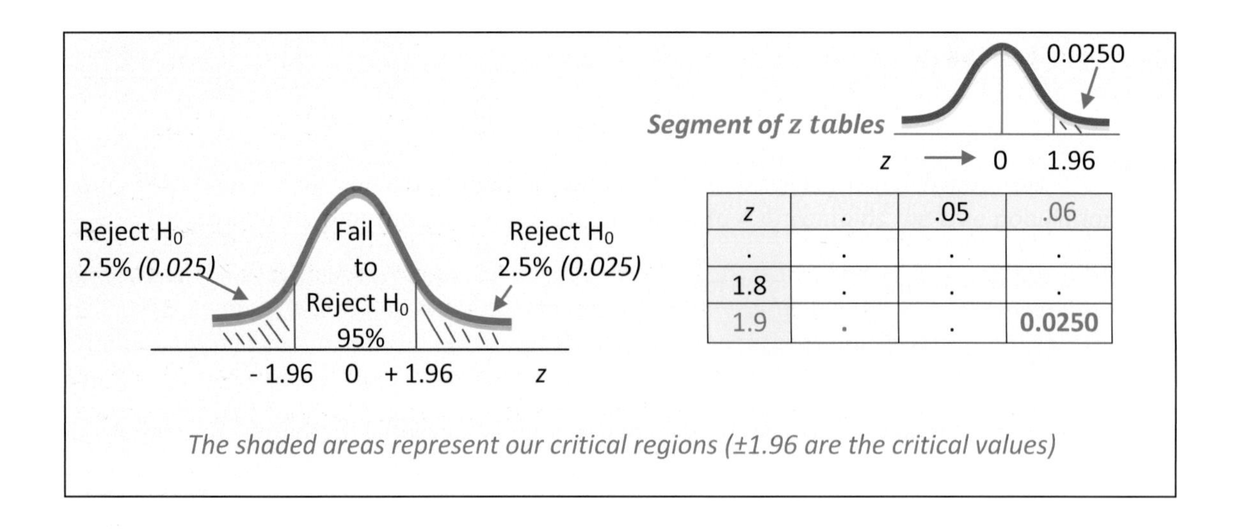

4. *Select and calculate the appropriate test statistic*

$$z\ test = \frac{\bar{X} - \mu_0}{\frac{\sigma}{\sqrt{n}}} = \frac{105 - 100}{\frac{8}{\sqrt{15}}} = 2.42$$

5. *Compare the calculated test statistic with the critical value*

The calculated *z test* statistic of 2.42 falls into the rightward critical region where we reject H_0. In rejecting H_0, we are inferring that the national mean IQ does not apply to the sub-group at the 0.05 level of significance.

6. *Derive or locate an approximate p value using a segment of the z tables*

The *p* value is the sum of the areas under the curve defined by the calculated z value derived from the *z test* in step 4.

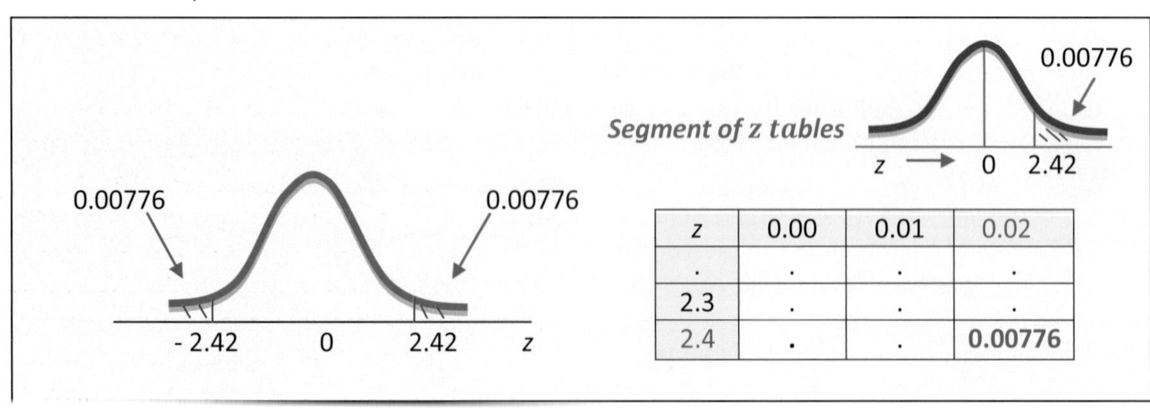

The sum of the shaded areas under the curve gives us a *p* value of 0.01552 *(2 x 0.00776 = 0.01552)*.

Interpreting the p value

a. Traditional approach – explicit reference to a selected cut-off point of say $\alpha = 0.05$:

Since the p value of 0.01552 is below the 0.05 level of significance, we reject H_0 at the 0.05 level of significance (Applying the p value decision rule: If the p value < 0.05 we reject H_0. The difference between the observed mean from the sample and the expected mean of the population cannot be solely attributed to sampling error (chance).

b. Current approach – no explicit reference to a selected cut-off point of say $\alpha = 0.05$. The cut-off point is implicitly assumed as a guide value. The current practise is to report an exact *p* value *(included in the output of all statistical software packages).*

The p value reveals the likelihood of being wrong if we reject H_0 (the p value 0.01552 i.e. < 2 times in 100).

Confidence Interval Procedure

Construct 95% confidence interval to estimate a range that includes the true population mean for the sub-group (for which the sample mean is a point estimate)

1. Select a confidence interval and confidence level

The appropriate confidence interval for n < 30 and σ known is:

$$\bar{X} \pm z_{\alpha/2} \times \frac{\sigma}{\sqrt{n}}.$$

2. Construct the 95% confidence interval for the true population mean

$$\bar{X} \pm z_{\alpha/2}\, x\, \frac{\sigma}{\sqrt{n}}$$

$$105 \pm 1.96\, x\, \frac{8}{\sqrt{15}} \longrightarrow z_{\alpha/2} = z_{0.05/2} = z_{(0.025)} = 1.96$$

$$108 \pm 1.96\, x\, 2.065$$
$$108 \pm 4.047$$

z	0.04	0.05	0.06
.	.	.	.
1.8	.	.	.
1.9	.	.	**0.0250**

The 95% confidence interval is 103.95 to 112.04

3. State your inferences

Since the interval *(103.95 to 112.04)* does not contain the claimed population mean i.e. *(μ_0 = 100)*:

a. *The evidence available is compatible with a decision to reject the null hypothesis.*
b. *The probability that the calculated interval (103.95 to 112.04) contains the true population mean is 95%. This is an intuitive and not strictly a correct interpretation of a confidence interval.*

Effect Size Procedure

How large is the difference between the observed mean and the expected population mean?

1. Identify the difference between the means

$$\text{Difference between the means: } (\bar{X} - \mu_0) = (105 - 100) = 5$$

2. Calculate the 'measure of effect'

$$\text{Effect Size} = \frac{(\bar{X} - \mu_0)}{\sigma} = \frac{(105-100)}{8} = 0.625$$

3. State your inferences

To interpret this value, we refer to guidelines proposed by Cohen, 1988. The difference is closer to medium magnitude.

Effect Size *(d)*	Interpretation	% of overlap	
If d = 0	No effect	100%	
If d = 0.2	Small	85%	
If d = 0.5	Medium	67%	
If d = 0.8	Large	53%	

Reported results using the current approach (implicit cut-off guide point of α = 0.05):

The observed mean ($\bar{x}_1$ = 105) is different to the expected population mean (μ = 100); p = 0.01552 (two-tailed). The mean difference ($\bar{X}$ - μ) of 5 is a medium effect size (d = 0.625). The 95% confidence interval for the true population mean is 103.95 to 112.04.

Power of the statistical test procedure using *G*power 3* software = 61.51%

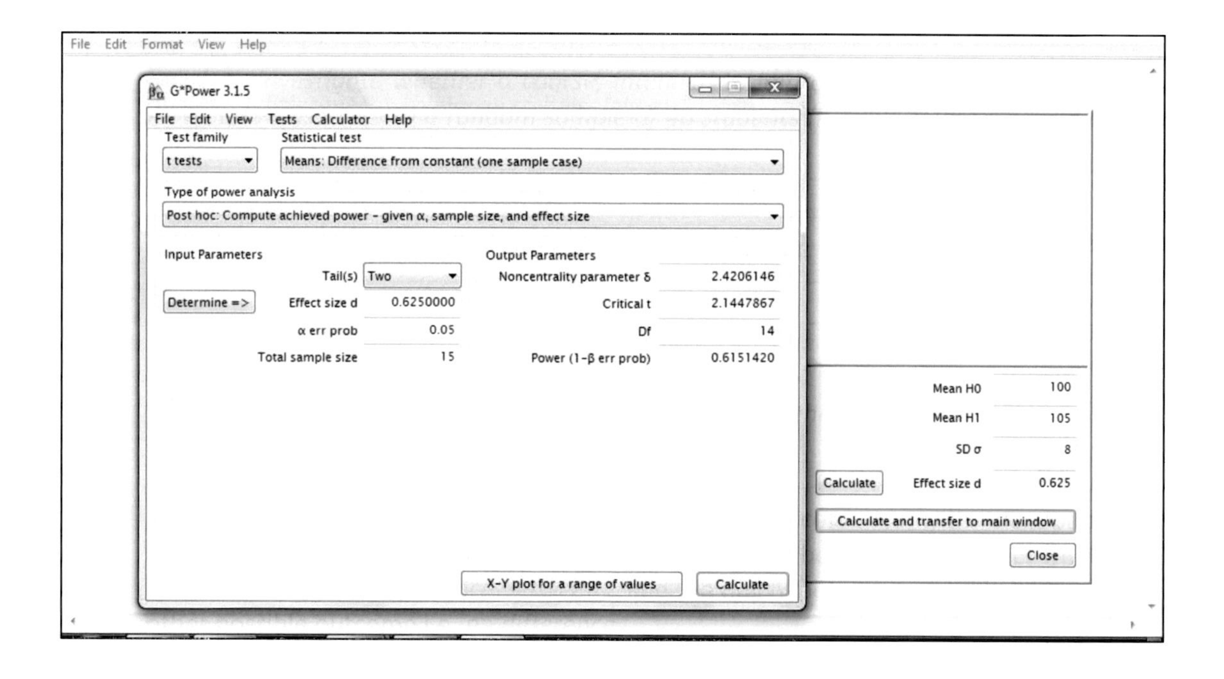

6.7 Statistical Inference: *One large sample/σ known – One tailed z test*

Example 3 - A random sample from a target-group/sub-population selected from a population

*A national students' survey claims that a typical student studies on average 18 hours per week outside of lectures with a standard deviation of 3.75 hours per week. A local institute does not believe that this finding applies to its students and holds the belief that its students study less than the national average. A study was undertaken by the institute to reveal the truth. A random sample of 65 students from the local institute (the target group/sub group) revealed an average study time of 16.75 hours per week. Use this information to test whether mean study time of the target group is less than 18 at the 0.05 level of significance ($\alpha = 0.05$). Use G*power 3 to calculate the post hoc power of the statistical test.*

Statistical Test Procedure

1. *State the assumptions required to validate this test*

   As per example 1

2. *State the null hypothesis and alternative hypothesis*

   H_0: $\mu_0 \geq 18$
   H_1: $\mu_0 < 18$ *One-tailed test (left tail as determined by the operator < in H_1)*
   Or
   H_0: *Observed mean of the sample – Expected mean of the population = 0*
   H_1: *Observed mean of the sample – Expected mean of the population ≠ 0*

3. *State the statistical decision rule for a selected level of significance*

   a. Appropriate test statistic is the z test since n ≥ 30 and σ is known and assumption 3 in part *(1)*
   b. The level of significance for this test: $\alpha = 0.05$
   c. Identify the critical values in the diagram below *(A segment of the z tables is included here)*

      Identifying -1.65 in the diagram below requires you to allocate 0.05 to the left tail. Use the z tables to derive the critical value (z value) for an area equal to 0.05.

   d. Reject the null hypothesis *(H_0)* when the calculated test statistic *($z\ test$)* from part 4 below > Critical value -1.65.

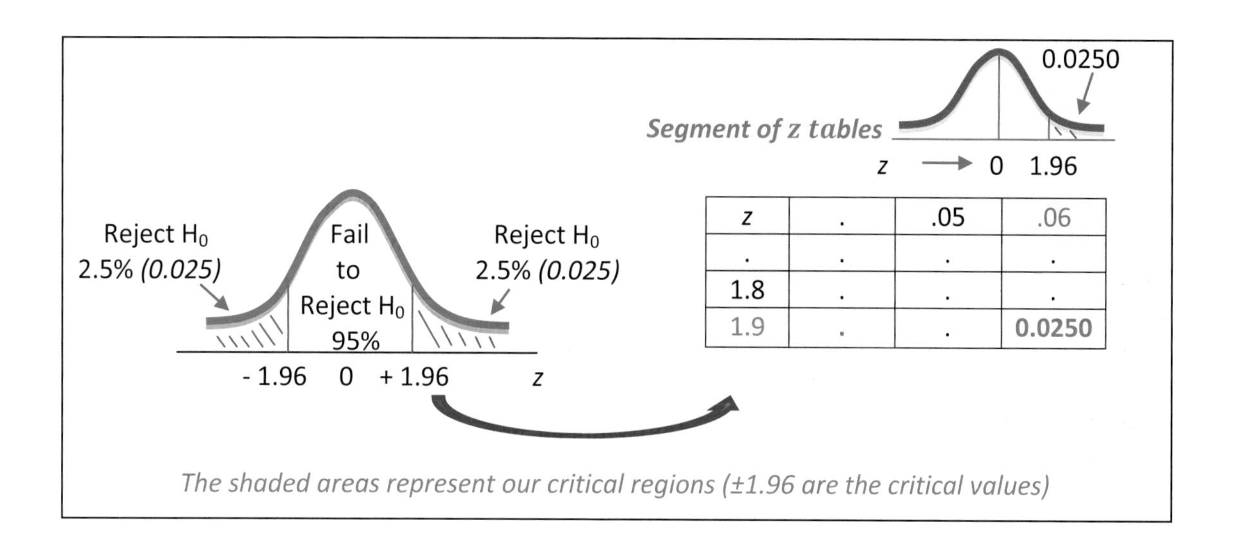

z	.	.05	.06
.	.	.	.
1.8	.	.	.
1.9	.	.	**0.0250**

4. Select and calculate the appropriate test statistic

$$z\ test: = \frac{\bar{X} - \mu_0}{\frac{\sigma}{\sqrt{n}}} = \frac{50.75 - 50}{\frac{1.50}{\sqrt{35}}} = 2.96$$

5. Compare the calculated test statistic with the critical value

The calculated *z test* statistic of 2.95 falls into the critical region *(to the right of 1.96),* where we reject H_0. In rejecting H_0, we are inferring that the mean study time for students at the local institute is different to the national average at the 0.05 level of significance.

6. Derive or locate an approximate p value using a segment of the z tables

The *p* value is the sum of the shaded areas under the curve defined by the calculated z value derived from the *z test* in Step 4.

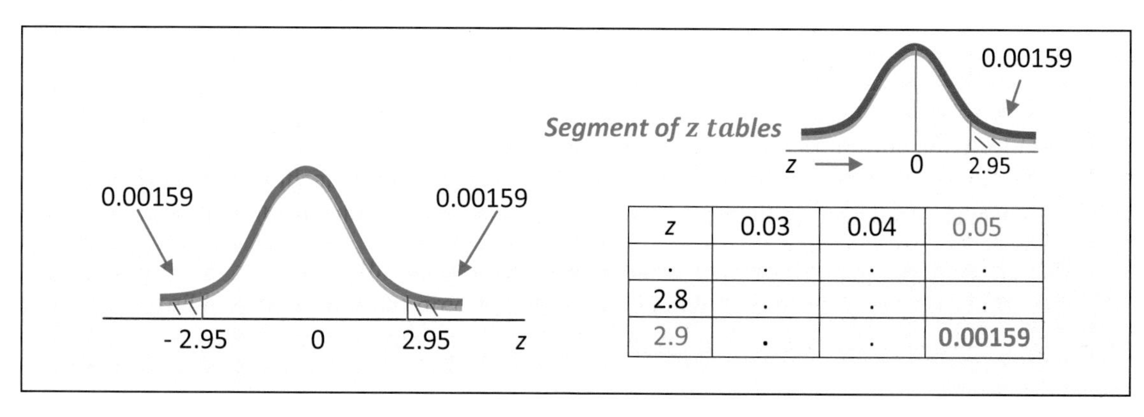

z	0.03	0.04	0.05
.	.	.	.
2.8	.	.	.
2.9	.	.	**0.00159**

The sum of the shaded areas under the curve gives us a *p* value of 0.00318 *(2 x 0.00159 = 0.00318).*

Since the p value of 0.00357 is below the 0.05 level of significance, we can reject H_0 at the 0.05 level of significance *(Applying the p value decision rule: If p value < 0.05 reject H_0).*

Interpreting the p value

a. Traditional approach – explicit reference to a selected cut-off point of say $\alpha = 0.05$:

   Since the p value of 0.00357 is below the 0.05 level of significance, we reject H_0 at the 0.05 level of significance (Applying the p value decision rule: If the p value < 0.05 we reject H_0. The difference between the observed mean from the sample and the expected mean of the population cannot be solely attributed to sampling error (chance).

b. Current approach – no explicit reference to a selected cut-off point of say $\alpha = 0.05$. The cut-off point is implicitly assumed as a guide value. The current practise is to report an exact p value *(included in the output of all statistical software packages).*

   The p value reveals the likelihood of being wrong if we reject H_0 (the p value 0.00357 i.e. < 4 times in 1000).

Confidence Interval Procedure

Construct 95% confidence interval to estimate a range that includes the true population mean μ_0

1. *Select a confidence interval and confidence level*

The appropriate confidence interval for n ≥ 30 and σ known is:

$$\bar{X} \pm z_{\alpha/2}\, x\, \frac{s}{\sqrt{n}}\,.$$

2. *Construct the 95% confidence interval for a population mean μ_0*

$$\bar{X} \pm z_{\alpha/2}\, x\, \frac{\sigma}{\sqrt{n}}$$

$$16.75 \pm 1.96\, x\, \frac{3.75}{\sqrt{65}} \rightarrow z_{\alpha/2} = z_{\alpha/2} = z_{(0.025)} = 1.96$$

z	0.04	0.05	0.06
.	.	.	.
1.8	.	.	.
1.9	.	.	0.0250

$$16.75 \pm 1.96\, x\, 0.465$$
$$16.75 \pm 0.911$$

The 95% confidence interval is therefore is 15.84 to 17.66

3. State your inferences

Since the interval *(15.84 to 17.66)* does not contain the national population mean then:

a. *The evidence available is not compatible with the null hypothesis being correct i.e. We reject H_0.*
b. *The probability that the calculated interval (15.84 to 17.66) contains the population mean for local institute students is 95%.*

Effect Size Procedure

How large is the difference between the observed mean and the expected population mean?

1. Identify the difference between the means

Difference between the means: $(\bar{X} - \mu_0)$ = $(16.75 - 18)$ = 1.25

2. Calculate the 'measure of effect'

$$\text{Effect Size} = \frac{(\bar{X} - \mu_0)}{\sigma} = \frac{(16.75 - 18)}{3.75} = -0.333$$

3. State your inferences

To interpret this value, we refer to guidelines proposed by Cohen, 1988. The difference is closer to small magnitude.

Effect Size (d)	Interpretation	% of overlap	
If d = 0	No effect	100%	
If d = 0.2	Small	85%	
If d = 0.5	Medium	67%	
If d = 0.8	Large	53%	

Reported results using the current approach (implicit cut-off guide point of α = 0.05):

The observed mean ($\bar{x}_1$ = 16.75) is lower than the expected population mean (μ = 18); p = 0.00357 (one-tailed). The mean difference ($\bar{X}$ - μ) of 1.25 is a small to medium effect size (d = -0.333). The 95% confidence interval for the true population mean is 15.84 to 17.66.

Power of the statistical test procedure using *G*power 3* software = 84.47%

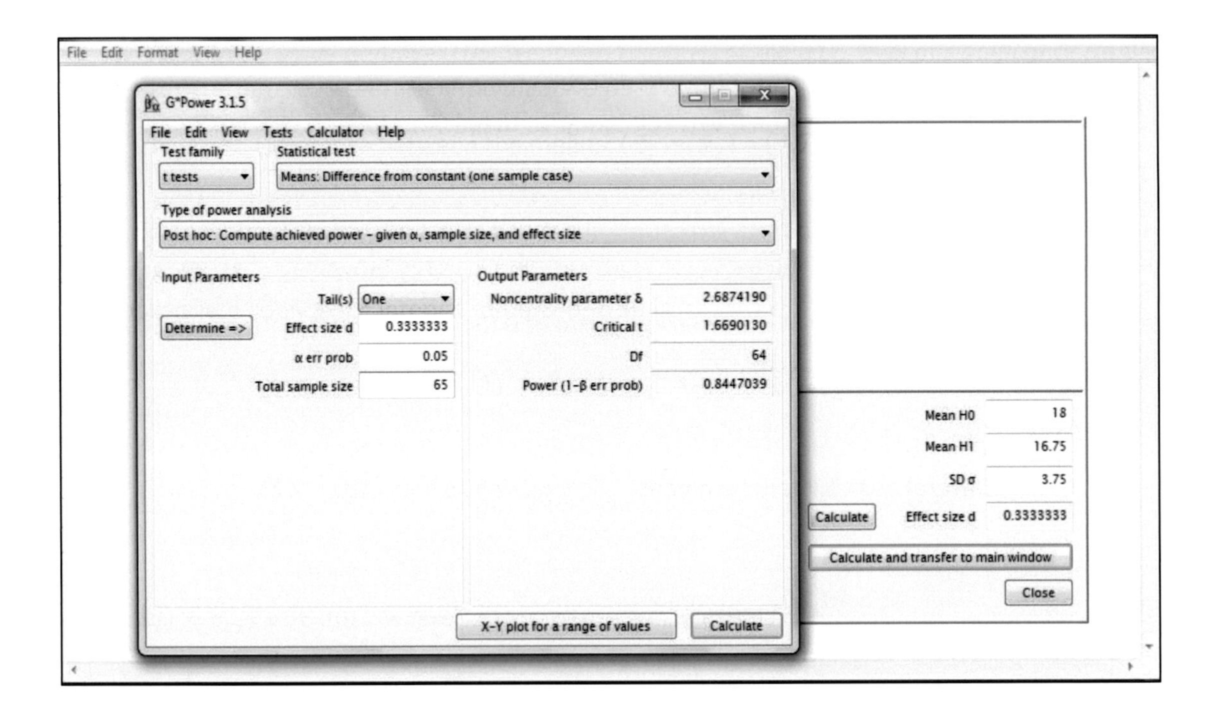

6.8 Statistical Inference: *One small sample/σ known – One tailed z test*

Example 4

*The average IQ of primary school children is known to be 100 with a standard deviation of 8. A researcher suspects that students, whose parents provide a leading supplement to their children, may have a higher IQ. The researcher identified these parents and selected a random sample of 15 students from this sub-group who take the supplement. These students scored on average 105 in an IQ test provided for them. Are the IQ scores of the population of primary students taking this supplement higher than 100 at the 0.05 level of significance (α = 0.05). Use G*power 3 to calculate the post hoc power of the statistical test.*

Statistical Test Procedure

1. *State the assumptions required to validate this test*

   As per example 1

2. *State the null hypothesis and alternative hypothesis*

   H_0: $\mu_0 \leq 100$
   H_1: $\mu_0 > 100$ *One-tailed test (right tail as determined by the operator > in H_1)*
   Or
   H_0: *Observed mean of the sample – Expected mean of the population* ≤ 0
   H_1: *Observed mean of the sample – Expected mean of the population* > 0

3. *State the statistical decision rule for a selected level of significance*

   a. Appropriate test statistic is the z test since n < 30 and σ is known and assumption 3 in part *(1)*
   b. The level of significance for this test: $\alpha = 0.05$
   c. Identify the critical value in the diagram below *(A segment of the z tables is included here)*

      Identifying 1.65 *in the diagram below requires you to allocate 0.05 to the right tail. Use the z tables to derive the critical value (z value) for an area equal to 0.05.*

   d. Reject the null hypothesis *(H_o)* when the calculated test statistic *(z test)* from part 4 below > Critical value 1.65.

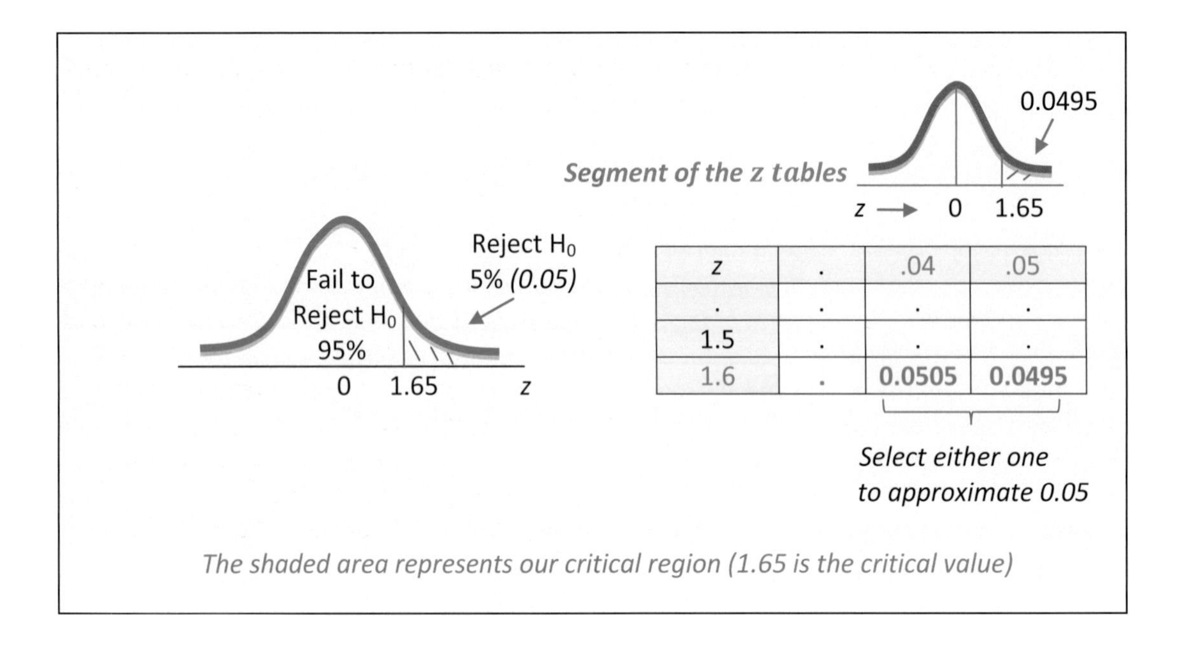

The shaded area represents our critical region (1.65 is the critical value)

4. *Select and calculate the appropriate test statistic*

$$z\ test = \frac{\bar{X} - \mu_0}{\frac{\sigma}{\sqrt{n}}} = \frac{105 - 100}{\frac{8}{\sqrt{15}}} = 2.41$$

5. *Compare the calculated test statistic with the critical value*

The calculated *z* test statistic of 2.41 falls into the critical region where we reject H_0. In rejecting H_0, we are inferring IQ scores of the population of primary students taking this supplement are higher than 100 at the 0.05 level of significance.

6. *Derive or locate an approximate p value using a segment of the z tables*

The *p* value is the area under the curve defined by the calculated z value derived from the *z test* in step 4.

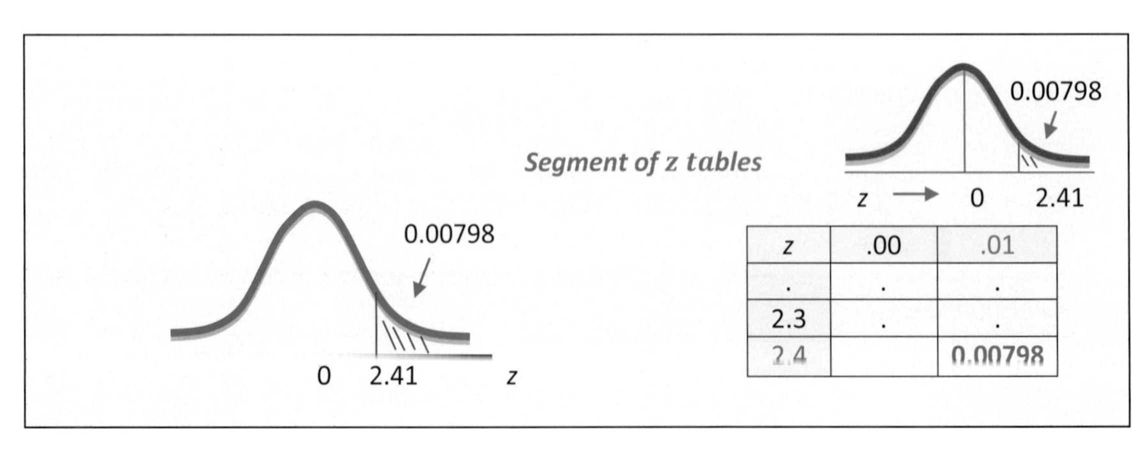

Since the *p* value of 0.00798 is below the 0.05 level of significance, we can reject H_0 at the 0.05 level of significance *(Applying the p value decision rule: If p value < 0.05 reject H_0).*

Interpreting the p value

a. Traditional approach – explicit reference to a selected cut-off point of say $\alpha = 0.05$:

   Since the p value of 0.00798 is below the 0.05 level of significance, we reject H_0 at the 0.05 level of significance (Applying the p value decision rule: If the p value < 0.05 we reject H_0. The difference between the observed mean from the sample and the expected mean of the population cannot be solely attributed to sampling error (chance).

b. Current approach – no explicit reference to a selected cut-off point of say $\alpha = 0.05$. The cut-off point is implicitly assumed as a guide value. The current practise is to report an exact *p* value *(included in the output of all statistical software packages).*

   The p value reveals the likelihood of being wrong if we reject H_0 (the p value 0.00798 i.e. < 1 time in 100).

Confidence Interval Procedure

Construct 95% confidence interval to estimate a range that includes the true population mean μ_0

1. *Select a confidence interval and confidence level*

The appropriate confidence interval for $n < 30$ and σ known is:

$$\bar{X} \pm z_{\alpha/2}\, x\, \frac{\sigma}{\sqrt{n}}$$

2. *Construct the 95% confidence interval for a population mean μ_0*

$$\bar{X} \pm z_{\alpha/2}\, x\, \frac{\sigma}{\sqrt{n}}$$

$$105 \pm 1.96\, x\, \frac{8}{\sqrt{15}} \rightarrow z_{\alpha/2} = z_{\alpha/2} = z_{(0.025)} = 1.96$$

z	0.04	0.05	0.06
.	.	.	.
1.8	.	.	.
1.9	.	.	**0.0250**

$$105 \pm 1.96\, x\, 2.067$$
$$105 \pm 4.05$$

The 95% confidence interval is 100.95 to 109.05

3. State your inferences

Since the interval *(100.95 to 109.05)* does not contain the population mean 100 then:

a. *The evidence available is not compatible with the null hypothesis being correct i.e. we reject H_0.*
b. *The probability that the calculated interval (100.95 to 109.05) contains the true population mean is 95%.*

Effect Size Procedure

How large is the difference between the observed mean and the expected population mean μ_0?

1. Identify the difference between the means

$$\text{Difference between the means: } (\bar{X} - \mu_0) = (105 - 100) = 5$$

2. Calculate the 'measure of effect'

$$\text{Effect Size} = \frac{(\bar{X} - \mu_0)}{\sigma} = \frac{(105-100)}{8} = 0.625$$

3. State your inferences

To interpret this value, we refer to guidelines proposed by Cohen, 1988. The difference is closer to medium magnitude.

Effect Size (d)	Interpretation	% of overlap	
If d = 0	No effect	100%	
If d = 0.2	Small	85%	
If d = 0.5	Medium	67%	
If d = 0.8	Large	53%	

Reported results using the current approach (implicit cut-off guide point of α = 0.05):

The observed mean ($\bar{x}_1$ = 105) is higher than the expected population mean (μ = 100); p = 0.00798 (one-tailed). The mean difference ($\bar{X}$ - μ) of 5 is a medium effect size (d = 0.625). The 95% confidence interval for the true population mean is 100.95 to 109.05.

Power of the statistical test procedure using *G*power 3* software = 74.41%

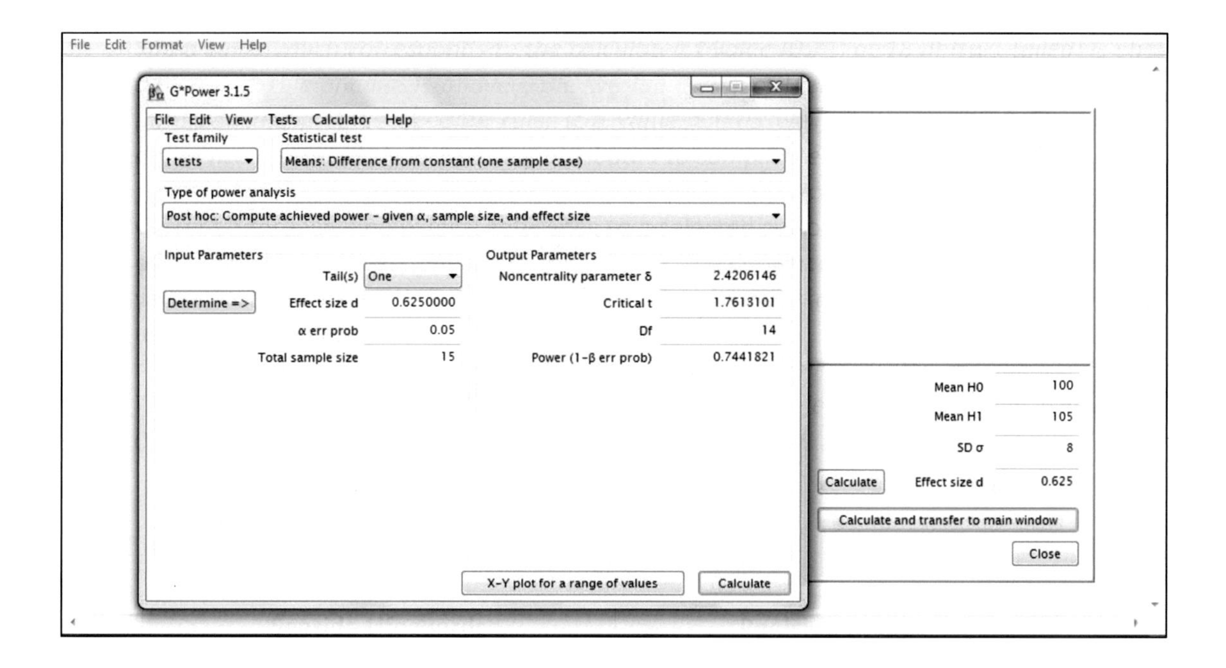

6.9 Statistical Inference: *One large sample/σ unknown – Two tailed z test*

Example 5 - A random sample from one population is selected and that sample undergoes some treatment/training

*The length of time it takes employees at a large hospital to dress a hospital bed is known to be on average 140 seconds. A random sample of 35 employees undergo a new innovative training technique to improve the speed in dressing a hospital bed. The mean time to dress a hospital bed for this sample group was recorded at 136 seconds with a standard deviation of 8 seconds. Test to see if the population mean is likely to change (from 140) if the entire population underwent the same training at the 0.05 level of significance (α = 0.05). Use G*power 3 to calculate the post hoc power of the statistical test.*

Statistical Test Procedure

1. *State the assumptions required to validate this test*

   As per example 1

2. *State the null hypothesis and alternative hypothesis*

   H_0: $\mu_0 = 140$
   H_1: $\mu_0 \neq 140$ *Two-tail test (determined by ≠ in H_1)*
   Or
   H_0: *Observed mean of the sample – Expected mean of the population = 0*
   H_1: *Observed mean of the sample – Expected mean of the population ≠ 0*

3. *State the statistical decision rule for a selected level of significance*

   a. Appropriate test statistic is the z test since n ≥ 30 and assumption 3 in part *(1)*
   b. The level of significance for this test : $\alpha = 0.05$.
   c. Identify the critical values in the diagram below *(A segment of the z tables is included here)*

   Identifying ± 1.96 in the diagram below requires you to split 0.05 between both tails. Each tail has, therefore, an area equal to 0.025 each. Use the z tables to derive the critical values (z values) for an area equal to 0.025. Since the bell curve is symmetrical, the critical values are ± 1.96.

   d. Reject the null hypothesis *(H_o)* when the calculated test statistic *(z test)* from part 4 below > Critical value ± 1.96.

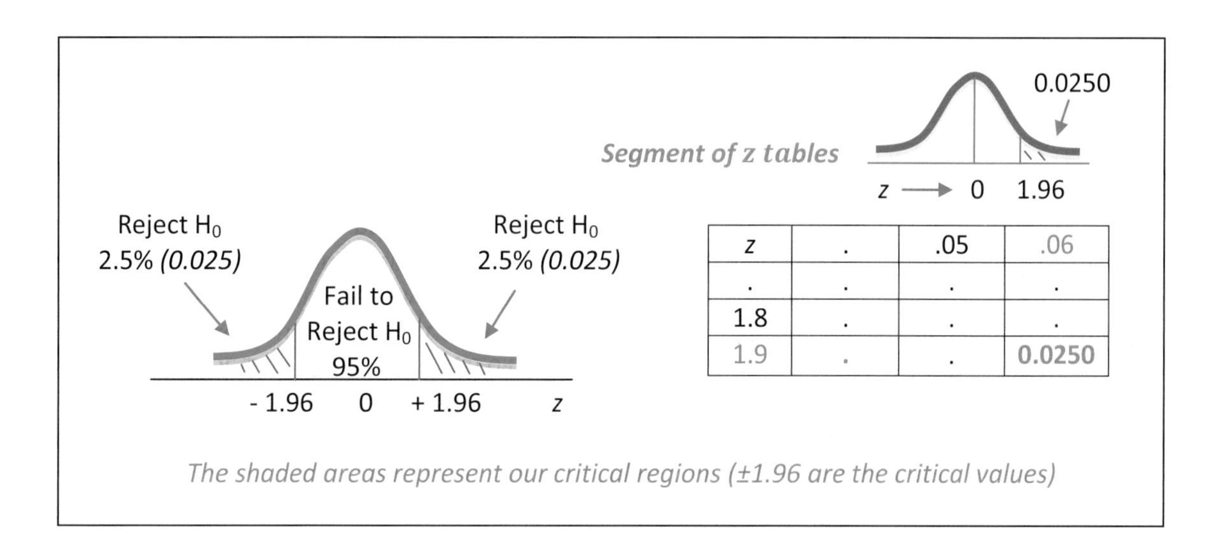

z	.	.05	.06
.	.	.	.
1.8	.	.	.
1.9	.	.	0.0250

4. Select and calculate the appropriate test statistic

$$z = \frac{\bar{X} - \mu_0}{\frac{s}{\sqrt{n}}} = \frac{136 - 140}{\frac{8}{\sqrt{35}}} = -2.96$$

5. Compare the calculated test statistic with the critical value

The calculated z test value *(-2.96)* falls into the region where we reject H_0. In rejecting H_0, we are inferring that the population mean is likely to change *(from 140)* if the entire population underwent the same training at the 0.05 level of significance.

6. Derive or locate an approximate p value using a segment of the z tables

The *p* value is the sum of the areas under the curve defined by the calculated z value derived from the *z test* in step 4.

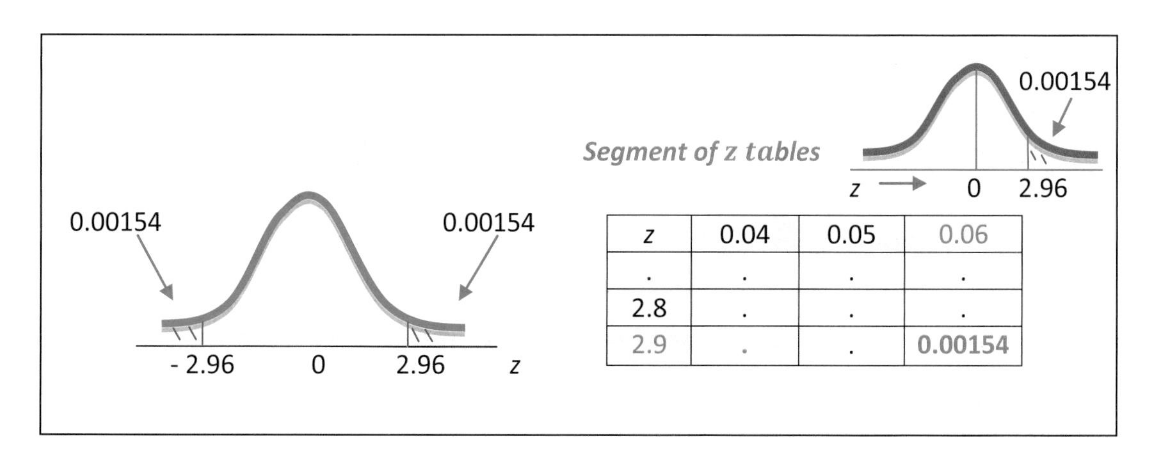

z	0.04	0.05	0.06
.	.	.	.
2.8	.	.	.
2.9	.	.	0.00154

The sum of the shaded areas under the curve gives us a p value of 0.00308 *(2 x 0.00154 = 0.00154)*. Since the p value of 0.00308 is below the 0.05 level of significance, we reject H_0 at the 0.05 level of significance *(Applying the p value decision rule: If p value < 0.05 we reject H_0*.

Interpreting the p value

a. Traditional approach – explicit reference to a selected cut-off point of say $\alpha = 0.05$:

   Since the p value of 0.00308 is below the 0.05 level of significance, we reject H_0 at the 0.05 level of significance (Applying the p value decision rule: If the p value < 0.05 we reject H_0. The difference between the observed mean from the sample and the expected mean of the population cannot be solely attributed to sampling error (chance).

b. Current approach – no explicit reference to a selected cut-off point of say $\alpha = 0.05$. The cut-off point is implicitly assumed as a guide value. The current practise is to report an exact p value *(included in the output of all statistical software packages)*.

   The p value reveals the likelihood of being wrong if we reject H_0 (the p value 0.00308 i.e. < 4 times in 1000).

Confidence Interval Procedure

Construct 95% confidence interval to estimate a range that includes the true population mean μ_0

1. *Select a confidence interval and confidence level*

The appropriate confidence interval for $n \geq 30$ and σ known is:

$$\overline{X} \pm z_{\alpha/2}\, x\, \frac{s}{\sqrt{n}}$$

2. *Construct the 95% confidence interval for a population mean μ*

$$\overline{X} \pm z_{\alpha/2}\, x\, \frac{s}{\sqrt{n}}$$

$136 \pm 1.96\, x\, \frac{8}{\sqrt{35}}$ → $z_{\alpha/2} = z_{\alpha/2} = z_{(0.025)} = 1.96$

z	0.04	0.05	0.06
.	.	.	.
1.8	.	.	.
1.9	.	.	0.0250

$136 \pm 1.96\, x\, 1.35$

136 ± 2.65

The 95% confidence interval is 133.35 to 138.65

3. *State your inferences*

Since the interval *(133.35 to 138.65)* does not contain the population mean 140 then:

a. The evidence available is not compatible with the null hypothesis being correct i.e. we reject H_0.
b. The probability that the calculated interval (133.35 to 138.65) contains the population mean for the trained sub-group is 95%.

Effect Size Procedure

How large is the difference between the observed mean and the expected population mean μ_0?

1. *Identify the difference between the means*

$$\text{Difference between the means: } (\bar{X} - \mu_0) = (136 - 140) = -4$$

2. *Calculate the 'measure of effect'*

$$\text{Effect Size} = \frac{(\bar{X} - \mu_0)}{\sigma} = \frac{(136-140)}{8} = -0.5$$

(s is used for the unknown σ)

3. *State your inferences*

To interpret this value, we refer to guidelines proposed by Cohen, 1988. The difference is of medium magnitude.

Effect Size (d)	Interpretation	% of overlap	
If d = 0	No effect	100%	
If d = 0.2	Small	85%	
If d = 0.5	Medium	67%	
If d = 0.8	Large	53%	

Reported results using the current approach (implicit cut-off guide point of α = 0.05):

The observed mean ($\bar{x}_1 = 136$) is different to the expected population mean (μ = 140); p = 0.00308 (one-tailed). The mean difference ($\bar{X}$ - μ) of -4 is a medium effect size (d = -0.5). The 95% confidence interval for the true population mean is 133.35 to 138.65.

Power of the statistical test procedure using *G*power 3* software = 81.95%

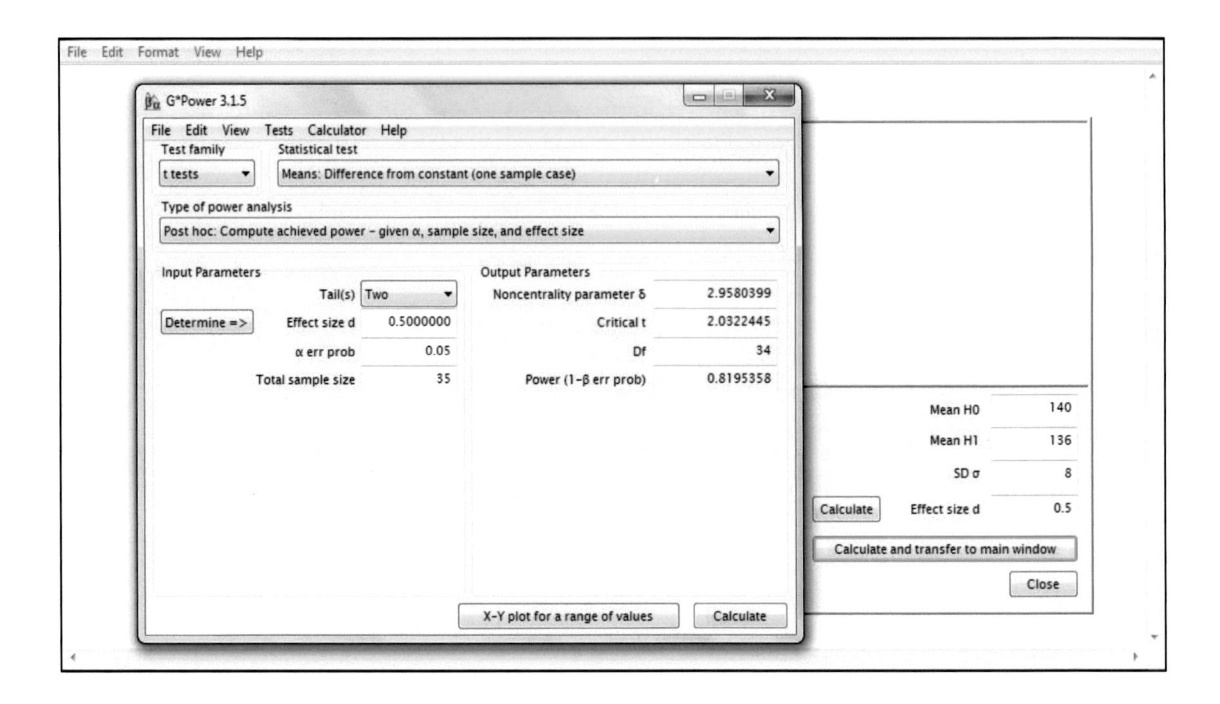

6.10 Statistical Inference: *One small sample/σ unknown – Two tailed t test*

Example 6 - A random sample from a population

*A pouch of 'cat snack' claims to contain 85 g e of food in it. A random sample of 15 pouches revealed contents which, on average, weighed 86.5 g e with a standard deviation of 1.8 g e. I wish to test whether the mean contents is different to 85 g e at the 0.05 level of significance (α = 0.05). Use G*power 3 to calculate the post hoc power of the statistical test.*

Statistical Test Procedure

1. *State the assumptions required to validate this test*

   As per Example 1

2. *State the null hypothesis and alternative hypothesis*

   H_0: $\mu_0 = 85$
   H_1: $\mu_0 \neq 85$ *Two-tail test (determined by ≠ in H_1)*
   Or
   H_0: *Observed mean of the sample – Expected mean of the population = 0*
   H_1: *Observed mean of the sample – Expected mean of the population ≠ 0*

3. *State the statistical decision rule given your selected level of significance*

   a. Appropriate test statistic is the *t* test since σ is unknown and assumption 3 in part *(1)*
   b. The level of significance for this test : $\alpha = 0.05$
   c. Identify the critical values in the diagram below *(A segment of the t tables is included here)*

      Identifying ± 2.145 *in the diagram below requires 0.05 to be divided between both tails. Each tail has, therefore, an area equal to 0.025 each. Use the t tables to derive the critical values (t values) for an area equal to 0.025 @ n–1 degrees of freedom. Since the bell curve is symmetrical, the critical values are* ± 2.145.

   d. Reject the null hypothesis *(H_o)* when the calculated test statistic *(z test)* from part 4 below > Critical value ± 2.145.

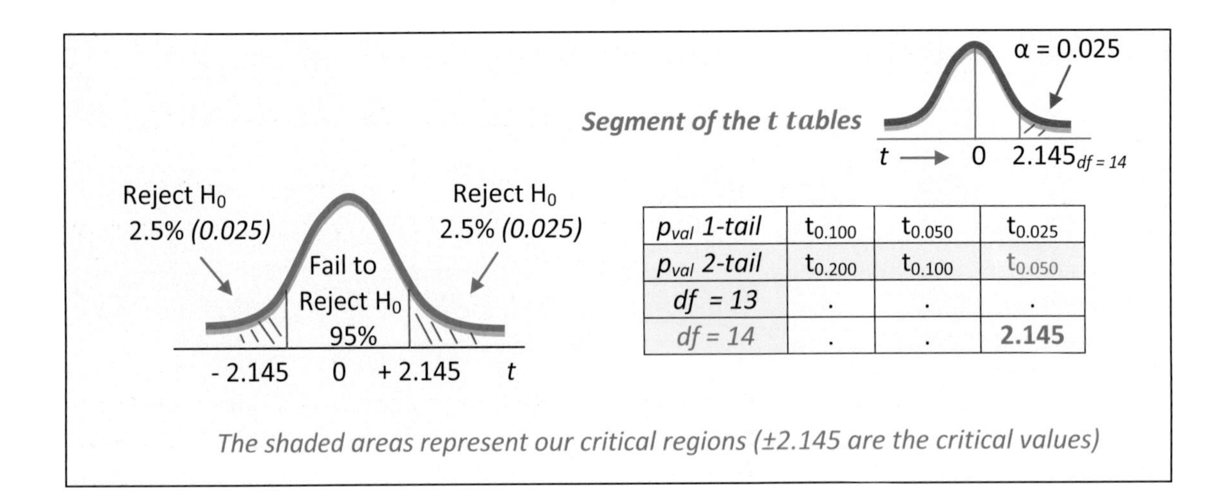

p_{val} 1-tail	$t_{0.100}$	$t_{0.050}$	$t_{0.025}$
p_{val} 2-tail	$t_{0.200}$	$t_{0.100}$	$t_{0.050}$
df = 13	.	.	.
df = 14	.	.	**2.145**

The shaded areas represent our critical regions (±2.145 are the critical values)

4. *Select and calculate the appropriate test statistic*

$$t = \frac{\bar{X} - \mu_0}{\frac{s}{\sqrt{n}}} \text{ with } n - 1 \; df \qquad t = \frac{86.5 - 85}{\frac{1.8}{\sqrt{15}}} = 3.4$$

5. *Compare the calculated test statistic with the critical value*

The calculated t test statistics of 3.4 falls into the rightward critical region where we reject H_0. In rejecting H_0, we are inferring that there is that mean contents is not equal to 85 g e at the 0.05 level of significance.

6. *Derive or locate an approximate p value using a segment of t tables*

Segment of t tables

p_{val} 1-tail	$t_{0.100}$	$t_{0.050}$	$t_{0.025}$	$t_{0.010}$	$t_{0.005}$	$t_{0.0005}$
p_{val} 2-tail	$t_{0.200}$	$t_{0.100}$	$t_{0.050}$	$t_{0.02}$	$t_{0.01}$	$t_{0.001}$
			→	→	*below 0.05*	
df = 13	.	.	.	.	.	.
df = 14	1.345	1.761	2.145	2.624	**2.997**	**4.140**

We search the t table for a value which comes nearest to our calculated t test value *(3.4)* at 14 degrees of freedom for a two tailed test *(it falls in the range 2.997 to 4.140 corresponding to p values 0.01 to 0.001)*. Since the p value is well below 0.05, we reject H_0 *(Applying the p value decision rule: If p value < 0.05 we reject H_0)*.

Interpreting the p value

a. Traditional approach – explicit reference to a selected cut-off point of say $\alpha = 0.05$:

Since the p value is within the range 0.01 to 0.001 which is below the 0.05 level of significance, we reject H_0 at the 0.05 level of significance (Applying the p value decision rule: If the p value < 0.05 we reject H_0. The difference between the observed mean from the sample and the expected mean of the population cannot be solely attributed to sampling error (chance).

b. Current approach – no explicit reference to a selected cut-off point of say $\alpha = 0.05$. The cut-off point is implicitly assumed as a guide value. The current practise is to report an exact *p* value *(included in the output of all statistical software packages)*. Using tables will only give us approximations.

The p value reveals the likelihood of being wrong if we reject H_0 (the p value is in the range 0.01 to 0.001).

Confidence Interval Procedure

Construct 95% confidence interval to estimate a range that includes the true population mean μ_0

1. Select a confidence interval and confidence level

The appropriate confidence interval for n < 30 and σ unknown is:

$$\bar{X} \pm t_{\alpha/2,\ n-1} \times \frac{s}{\sqrt{n}}.$$

2. Construct the 95% confidence interval for a population mean μ_0

$$\bar{X} \pm t_{\alpha/2,\ n-1} \times \frac{s}{\sqrt{n}}$$

$$86.5 \pm 2.145\ x\ \frac{1.8}{\sqrt{15}}$$

$t_{\alpha/2,\ n-1} = t_{0.05/2,\ 15-1} = t_{(0.025,\ 14)}$
$= 2.145$

p_{val} 1-tail	$t_{0.100}$	$t_{0.050}$	$t_{0.025}$
p_{val} 2-tail	$t_{0.200}$	$t_{0.100}$	$t_{0.050}$
df = 13	.	.	.
df = 14	.	.	**2.145**

$$86.5 \pm 2.145\ x\ 0.47$$
$$86.5 \pm 1$$

The 95% confidence interval is 85.5 to 87.5

3. State your inferences

Since the interval *(85.5 to 87.5)* does not contain the true population mean i.e. manufacturers claim then *(85 g e)*:

a. *The evidence available is not compatible with the null hypothesis being correct i.e. reject H_0.*
b. *The probability that the calculated interval (85.5 to 87.5) contains the true population mean is 95%.*

Effect Size Procedure

How large is the difference between the observed mean and the expected population mean μ_0?

1. Identify the difference between the means

Difference between the means: $(\bar{X} - \mu_0) = (86.5 - 85) = 1.5$

2. Calculate the 'measure of effect'

Effect Size = $\frac{(\bar{X} - \mu_0)}{\sigma} = \frac{(86.5 - 85)}{1.8} = 0.83$ *(s is used for the unknown σ)*

3. State your inferences

To interpret this value, we refer to guidelines proposed by Cohen, 1988. The difference is large in magnitude.

Effect Size *(d)*	Interpretation	% of overlap	
If d = 0	No effect	100%	
If d = 0.2	Small	85%	
If d = 0.5	Medium	67%	
If d = 0.8	Large	53%	

Reported results using the current approach (implicit cut-off guide point of α = 0.05):

The observed mean ($\bar{x}_1 = 86.5$) is different to the expected population mean (μ = 85); p < 0.01 (two-tailed). The mean difference ($\bar{X}$ - μ) of 1.5 is a large effect size (d = 0.83). The 95% confidence interval for the true population mean is 85.5 to 87.5.

Power of the statistical test procedure using *G*power 3* software = 85.07%

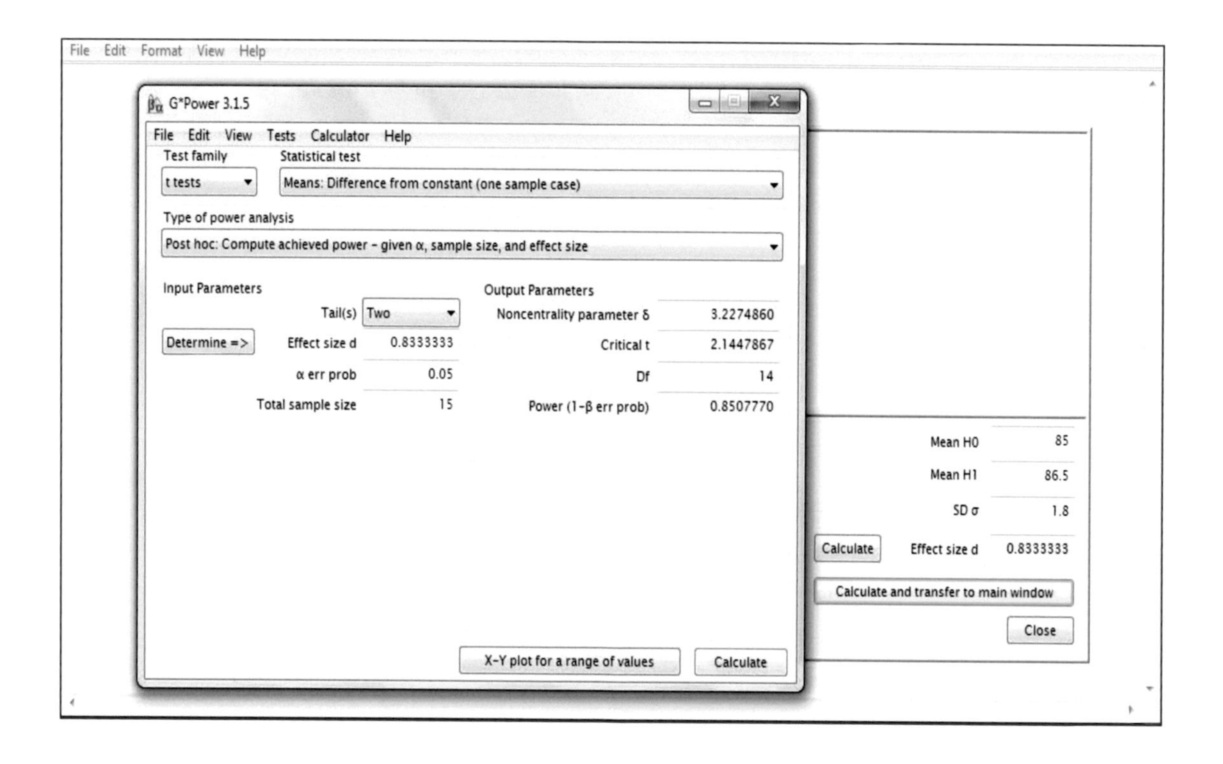

Example 7 - A random sample from a population

*Lloyd worked as a tour guide at the wax museum last year. He held a belief (as told by the job placement company) that he would could earn, on average, €20 per day in tips. Lloyd recorded the tips he received each day. At the end of the year Lloyd sampled 35 days from which he estimated mean tips of €21.50 per day, with a standard deviation of €4.25. Is the average 'tips per day' higher than €20 at the 0.05 level of significance (α = 0.05). Use G*power 3 to calculate the post hoc power of the statistical test.*

Statistical Test Procedure

1. *State the assumptions required to validate this test*

   As per example 1

2. *State the null hypothesis and alternative hypothesis*

   H_0: $\mu_0 \leq 20$
   H_1: $\mu_0 > 20$ *One-tail test (right tail as determined by the > in H_1)*
   Or
   H_0: *Observed mean of the sample – Expected mean of the population* ≤ 0
   H_1: *Observed mean of the sample – Expected mean of the population* > 0

3. *State the statistical decision rule for a selected level of significance*

a. Appropriate test statistic is the *z* test since n ≥ 30 and assumption 3 in part *(1)*
b. The level of significance for this test : $\alpha = 0.05$
c. Identify the critical values in the diagram below *(A segment of the t tables is included here)*

   Identifying 1.65 *in the diagram below requires you to allocate 0.05 to the right tail. Use the z tables to derive the critical value (z value) for an area equal to 0.05.*

d. Reject the null hypothesis *(H_o)* when the calculated test statistic *(z test)* from part 4 below > Critical value 1.65.

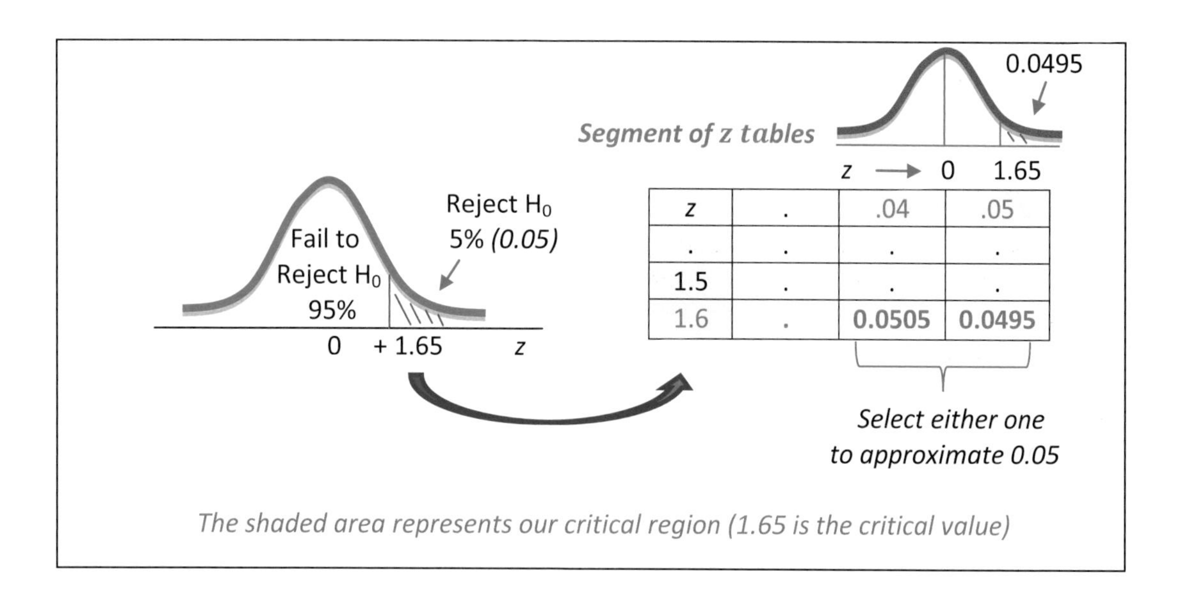

z	.	.04	.05
.	.	.	.
1.5	.	.	.
1.6	.	0.0505	0.0495

4. *Select and calculate the appropriate test statistic*

$$z = \frac{\bar{X} - \mu_0}{\frac{s}{\sqrt{n}}} = \frac{21.50 - 20}{\frac{4.25}{\sqrt{35}}} = 2.09$$

5. *Compare the calculated test statistic with the critical value*

The calculated *z* test value of 2.09 falls into the critical region where we reject H_0. In rejecting H_0, we are inferring that the claim that the mean tip earned *is more than* €20 is correct at the 0.05 level of significance.

6. *Derive or locate an approximate p value using a segment of the z tables*

The *p* value is the area under the curve defined by the calculated z value derived from the *z test* in step 4.

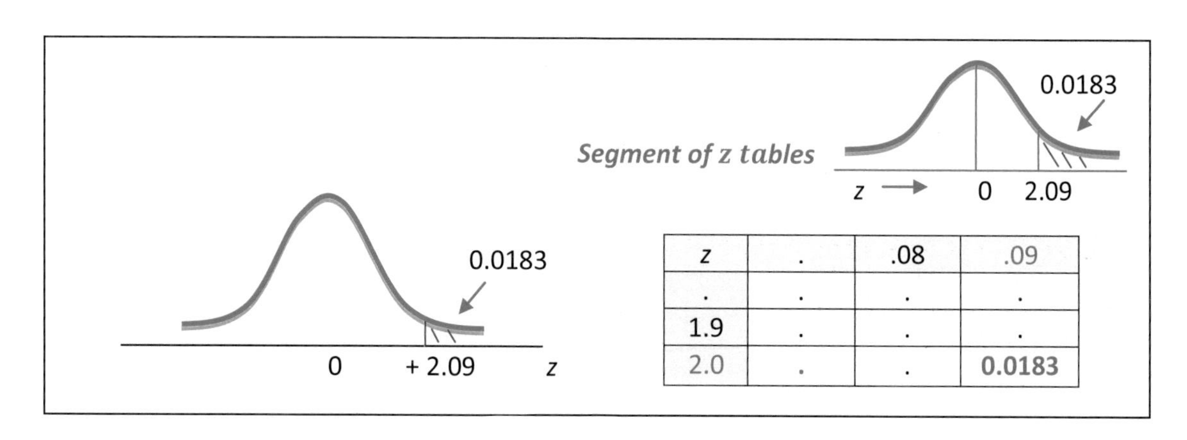

z	.	.08	.09
.	.	.	.
1.9	.	.	.
2.0	.	.	0.0183

Since the *p* value of 0.0183 is below the 0.05 level of significance, we can reject H_0 at the 0.05 level of significance *(Applying the p value decision rule: If p value < 0.05 reject H_0).*

Interpreting the p value

a. Traditional approach – explicit reference to a selected cut-off point of say $\alpha = 0.05$:

   Since the p value is 0.0183 *which is below the 0.05 level of significance, we reject H_0 at the 0.05 level of significance (Applying the p value decision rule: If the p value < 0.05 we reject H_0. The difference between the observed mean from the sample and the expected mean of the population cannot be solely attributed to sampling error (chance).*

b. Current approach – no explicit reference to a selected cut-off point of say $\alpha = 0.05$. The cut-off point is implicitly assumed as a guide value. The current practise is to report an exact *p* value *(included in the output of all statistical software packages)*. Using tables will only give us approximations.

   The p value reveals the likelihood of being wrong if we reject H_0 (the p value is 0.0183).

Confidence Interval Procedure

Construct 95% confidence interval to estimate a range that includes the true population mean μ_0

1. *Select a confidence interval and confidence level*

The appropriate confidence interval for $n \geq 30$ is:

$$\bar{X} \pm z_{\alpha/2}\, x\, \frac{s}{\sqrt{n}}$$

2. *Construct the 95% confidence interval for a population mean μ_0*

$\bar{X} \pm z_{\alpha/2}\, x\, \frac{s}{\sqrt{n}}$

$21.5 \pm 1.96\, x\, \frac{4.25}{\sqrt{35}}$ $\qquad z_{\alpha/2} = z_{\alpha/2} = z_{(0.025)} = 1.96$

z	0.04	0.05	0.06
.	.	.	.
1.8	.	.	.
1.9	.	.	0.0250

$21.5 \pm 1.96\, x\, 0.7183$
21.5 ± 1.408

The 95% confidence interval is 20.09 to 22.90

3. State your inferences

Since the interval *(20.09 to 22.90)* does not contain the true population mean then:

a. *The evidence available is not compatible with the null hypothesis being correct i.e. we reject H_0.*
b. *The probability that the calculated interval (20.09 to 22.90) contains the true population mean is 95%.*

Effect Size Procedure

How large is the difference between the observed mean and the expected population mean μ_0?

1. Identify the difference between the means

$$\text{Difference between the means: } (\bar{x} - \mu) = (21.5 - 20) = 1.5$$

2. Calculate the 'measure of effect'

$$\text{Effect Size} = \frac{(\bar{x} - \mu)}{\sigma} = \frac{(21.5 - 20)}{4.25} = 0.35$$ *(s is used for the unknown σ)*

3. State your inferences

To interpret this value, we refer to guidelines proposed by Cohen, 1988. The difference is between small to medium in magnitude.

Effect Size (d)	Interpretation	% of overlap	
If d = 0	No effect	100%	
If d = 0.2	Small	85%	
If d = 0.5	Medium	67%	
If d = 0.8	Large	53%	

Reported results using the current approach (implicit cut-off guide point of α = 0.05):

The observed mean ($\bar{x}_1$ = 21.5) is higher than the expected population mean (μ = 20); p < 0.0183 (one-tailed). The mean difference ($\bar{X}$ - μ) of 1.5 is a small to medium effect size (d = 0.35). The 95% confidence interval for the true population mean is 20.09 to 22.90.

Power of the statistical test procedure using *G*power 3* software = 65.59%

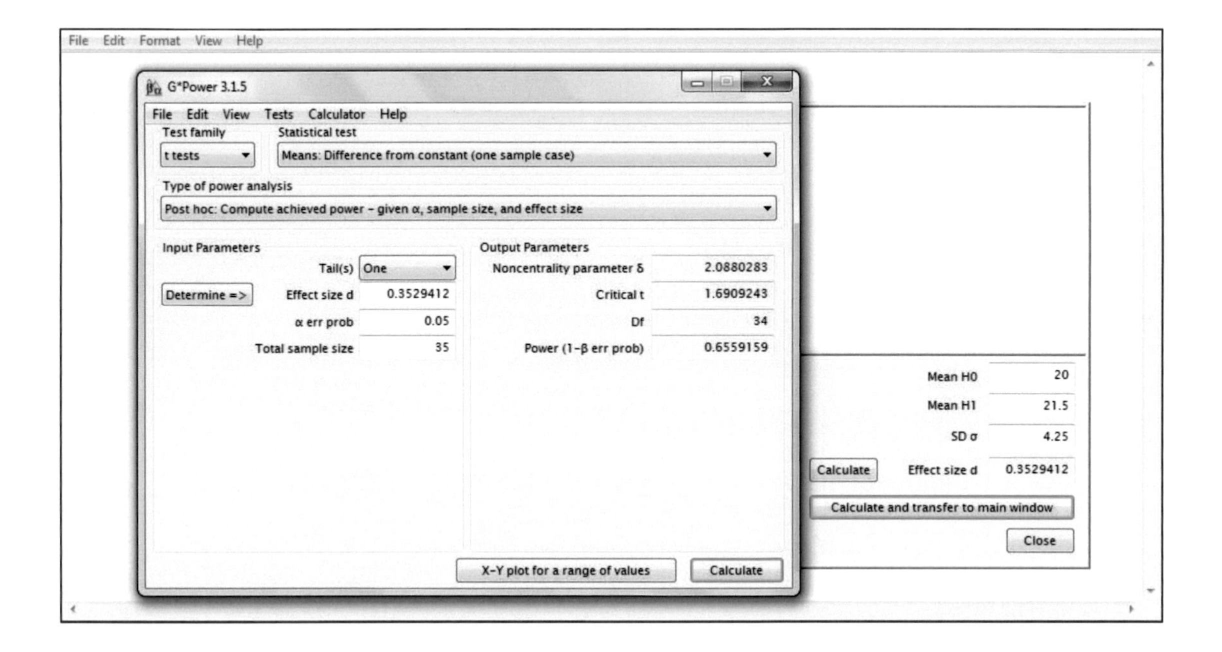

6.12 Statistical Inference: *One Small sample/σ unknown – One tailed t test*

Example 8 - A random sample from a population

*Past experience in raising turkeys revealed a mean weight at 2 months is 4.35 lbs. To increase their weight, an extra ingredient is added to their feed. A sample of 10 turkeys and a mean weight of 4.37 lbs with a standard deviation of 0.04 lbs was recorded. Is the mean weight higher than 4.35lbs at the 0.05 level of significance (α = 0.05). The researcher gave no consideration to what would constitute an appropriate sample size. Use G*power 3 to calculate the post hoc power of the statistical test. If the statistical test procedure fails to detect statistical significance, use G*power 3 to calculated the appropriate sample size.*

Statistical Test Procedure

1. *State the assumptions required to validate this test*

   As per example 1

2. *State the null hypothesis and alternative hypothesis*

   H_0: $\mu_0 \leq 4.35$
   H_1: $\mu_0 > 4.35$ *One-tail test (right tail as determined by the > in H_1)*
   Or
   H_0: *Observed mean of the sample – Expected mean of the population* ≤ 0
   H_1: *Observed mean of the sample – Expected mean of the population* > 0

3. *State the statistical decision rule for a selected level of significance*

   a. Appropriate test statistic is the *t* test since n < 30 and σ unknown and assumption 3 in part *(1)*
   b. The level of significance for this test : $\alpha = 0.05$
   c. Identify the critical values in the diagram below *(A segment of the t tables is included here)*

      Identifying 1.833 *in the diagram below requires you to allocate 0.05 to the right tail. Use the t tables to derive the critical value (t value) for an area equal to 0.05 @ n–1 degrees of freedom.*

   d. Reject the null hypothesis *(H_o)* when the calculated test statistic *(z test)* from part 4 below > Critical value 1.833.

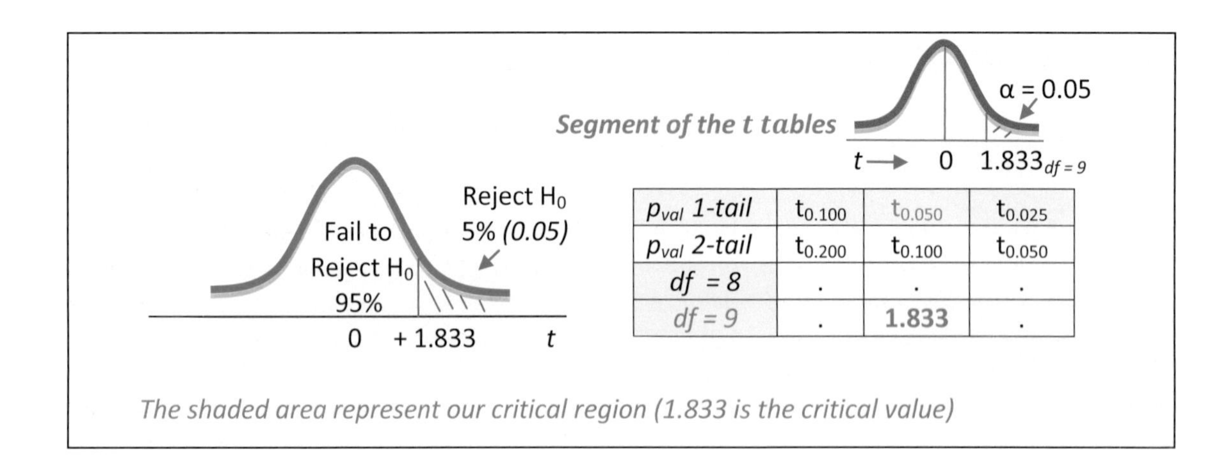

4. *Select and calculate the appropriate test statistic*

$$t = \frac{\bar{X} - \mu_0}{\frac{s}{\sqrt{n}}} \quad \text{with } n - 1 \; df \qquad t = \frac{4.37 - 4.35}{\frac{0.04}{\sqrt{10}}} = 1.54$$

5. *Compare the calculated test statistic with the critical value*

The calculated *t test* value of 1.54 falls into the critical region where we fail to reject H_0. In failing to reject H_0, we are inferring that the mean weight is not greater than 4.35 at the 0.05 level of significance i.e. that he extra ingredient did not increase the mean weight of chickens.

6. *Derive or locate an approximate p value using a segment of the t tables*

Segment of t tables

p_{val} 1-tail	$t_{0.100}$	$t_{0.050}$	$t_{0.025}$
p_{val} 2-tail	$t_{0.200}$	$t_{0.100}$	$t_{0.050}$
Above 0.05 ⟸			
df = 8	.	.	.
df = 9	1.383	1.833	2.262

We search the t table for a value which comes nearest to our calculated *t* test value *(1.54)* at 9 degrees of freedom for a one tailed test *(it falls in the range 1.383 to 1.833 corresponding to p values 0.100 to 0.050)*. Since the *p* value is well above 0.05, we fail to H_0 *(Applying the p value decision rule: If p value* > 0.05 *we fail to reject* H_0*)*.

Interpreting the p value

a. Traditional approach – explicit reference to a selected cut-off point of say $\alpha = 0.05$:

   Since the p value is within the range 0.100 to 0.050 which is above the 0.05 level of significance, we fail to reject H_0 at the 0.05 level of significance (Applying the p value decision rule: If the p value > 0.05 we fail to reject H_0. The difference between the observed mean from the sample and the expected mean of the population can be attributed to sampling error (chance).

b. Current approach – no explicit reference to a selected cut-off point of say $\alpha = 0.05$. The cut-off point is implicitly assumed as a guide value. The current practise is to report an exact *p* value *(included in the output of all statistical software packages)*. Using tables will only give us approximations.

   The p value reveals the likelihood of being wrong if we reject H_0 (the p value is in the range 0.100 to 0.050).

Confidence Interval Procedure

Construct 95% confidence interval to estimate a range that includes the true population mean μ_0

1. *Select a confidence interval and confidence level*

The appropriate confidence interval for n < 30 is:

$$\overline{X} \pm t_{\alpha/2,\ n-1} \times \frac{s}{\sqrt{n}}.$$

2. *Construct the 95% confidence interval for a population mean μ_0*

$$\overline{X} \pm t_{\alpha/2,\ n-1} \times \frac{s}{\sqrt{n}}$$

$t_{\alpha/2,\ n-1} = t_{0.05/2,\ 10-1} = t_{(0.025,\ 9)} = 2.262$

p_{val} *1-tail*	$t_{0.100}$	$t_{0.050}$	$t_{0.025}$
p_{val} *2-tail*	$t_{0.200}$	$t_{0.100}$	$t_{0.050}$
df = 8	.	.	.
df = 9	.	.	**2.262**

$$4.37 \pm 2.262\ x\ \frac{0.04}{\sqrt{10}}$$
$$4.37 \pm 2.262\ x\ 0.013$$
$$4.37 \pm 0.0294$$

The 95% confidence interval is 4.34 to 4.4

3. State your inferences

Since the interval *(4.34 to 4.4)* does contain the true population mean then:

a. *The evidence available is compatible with us failing to reject the null hypothesis.*
b. *The probability that the calculated interval (4.34 to 4.4) contains the true population mean is 95%.*

Effect Size Procedure = Not applicable since statistical significance was not declared

How large is the difference between the observed mean and the expected population mean μ_0?

Effect Size (d)	Interpretation	% of overlap	
If d = 0	No effect	100%	
If d = 0.2	Small	85%	
If d = 0.5	Medium	67%	
If d = 0.8	Large	53%	

Reported results using the current approach (implicit cut-off guide point of $\alpha = 0.05$):

The observed mean ($\bar{x}_1 = 4.37$) is not higher than the expected population mean ($\mu = 4.35$); $p > 0.05$ (one-tailed). The 95% confidence interval for the true population mean is 20.09 to 22.90.

Power of the statistical test procedure using *G*power 3* software = 42.72%

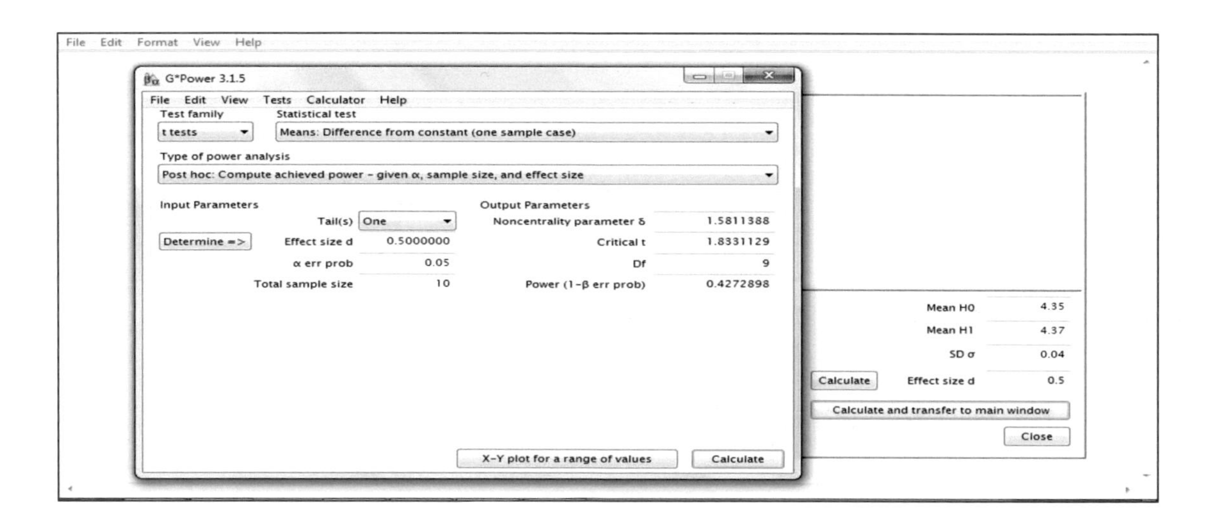

Appropriate sample size using *G*power 3* software

The appropriate sample size for the following input parameters is 62:

a. *α = 0.05*
b. *Desire effect size i.e. d = 0.30 (this value is derived from experience or from past studies)*
c. *Power level for the test = 0.75*
d. *One-sided test*

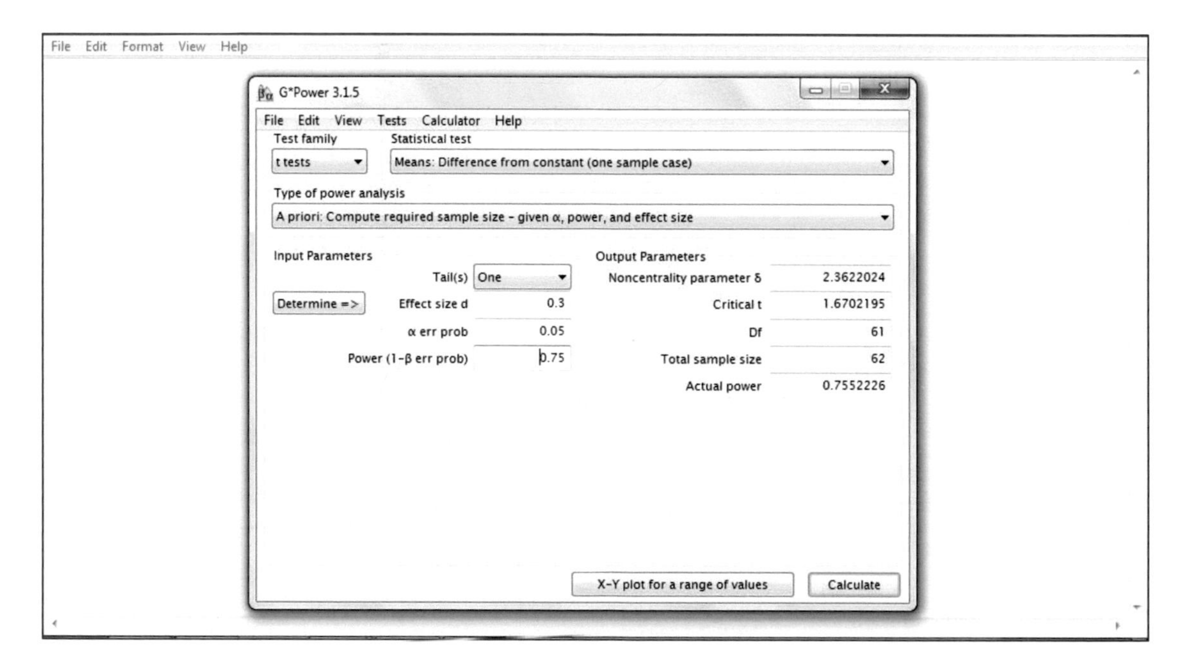

6.13 Statistical Inference: *MCQs and solutions*

Question 1 and 2 refer to the following problem:

The management at the local cinema complex are concerned about an automatic mineral dispensing machine that was recently purchased. The machine dispenses exactly 500 cm^2 of cola per single usage which is in accordance with the manufacturers claim. The management doubt that this is so and wish to test whether the reality is different to this claim. A random sample of 40 drinks was dispensed over the course of the day and the exact contents were recorded. The sample mean was 515 cm^2. The population standard deviation is known from past experience to be 0.80 cm^2.

1. Which of the following represents the correct null and alternative hypothesis?

   (a) H_0: $\mu = 500$
   H_1: $\mu \neq 500$
   (b) H_0: $\mu \geq 500$
   H_1: $\mu < 500$
   (c) H_0: $\mu \leq 500$
   H_1: $\mu > 500$
   (d) H_0: $\mu = 500$
   H_1: $\mu > 500$

2. This appropriate test procedure for this problem is a:

   (a) One-tailed test
   (b) Two-tailed test
   (c) One and two-tailed test
   (d) None of the above

Question 3 and 4 refer to the following problem:

A national students' survey, conducted by the head office of the national students union during Ireland's Celtic Tiger, claimed that the average weekly spend by third level students on social activities was at least €85 with a standard deviation of €3.50. The head office officials now believe that students spend less in these recessionary times. A random sample of 65 students reveals an average weekly spend of €78.

3. Which of the following represents the correct null and alternative hypothesis?

(a) $H_0: \mu = 85$
    $H_1: \mu \neq 85$
(b) $H_0: \mu \geq 85$
    $H_1: \mu < 85$
(c) $H_0: \mu \leq 85$
    $H_1: \mu > 85$
(d) $H_0: \mu = 85$
    $H_1: \mu > 85$

4. This appropriate test procedure for this problem is a:

(a) One-tailed test
(b) Two-tailed test
(c) One and two-tailed test
(d) None of the above

5. Consider the following *SPSS* output:

The average sleep time is assumed to be 8 hours. The students union in the local 3rd level college believes that their students sleeping habits are different. A random sample of 10 students is selected and their sleep times are recorded.

One-Sample Statistics

	n	*Mean*	*Standard Deviation*	*Std. Error Mean*
Sleep Time for College	*10*	*5.20*	*1.135*	*0.359*

One Sample Test

	Test Value = 8						
	t	*df*	*Sig. (2 tailed)*	*Mean Diff.*	*Std. Error Difference*	*95% Confidence Interval Of the difference*	
						Lower	*Upper*
Sleep Time for College	*-7.799*	*9*	*0.000*	*-2.8*	*1.898*	*-3.61*	*-1.99*

Which of the following is a correct interpretation of this output?

(a) Since the *p* value is significant at the 1% level of significance then we can state that the sleeping habits of the local 3rd level students is in keeping with the population average *(μ = 8)*
(b) Since the *p* value is significant at the 1% level of significance then we can state that the sleeping habits of the local 3rd level students is different to the population average *(μ = 8)*
(c) We cannot determine if the sleeping habits of local 3rd level students is different to the population average *(μ = 8)* until we conduct an effect size procedure
(d) None of the above is correct

6. In the one sample test *(about a population mean)*, the null hypothesis will always represent:

(a) The claim or status quo about the population mean
(b) The challenge to the claim or status quo about the population mean
(c) Is also known as the alternative hypothesis
(d) Will contain one of the following ($\neq$ or $>$ or $<$)

7. In the one sample test *(about a population mean)*, the alternative hypothesis will always represent:

(a) The claim or status quo about the population mean
(b) The challenge to the claim or status quo about the population mean
(c) Is also known as the null hypothesis
(d) Will contain one of the following ($=$ or $\geq$ or $\leq$)

8. To conduct a one sample test *(about a population mean)*, it is essential to have which one of the following:

(a) σ *(population standard deviation)*
(b) $n < 30$ *(n = sample size)*
(c) $n \geq 30$
(d) μ *(population mean)*

9. Which of the following best justifies the researcher decision to employ a one sample test *(about a population mean)*

(a) The measurement variable is continuous
(b) The population of values *(of the measurement variable)* is assumed to be normally distributed or failing the normality assumption, that the sample size $\geq$ 30
(c) That a random sample is selected from the population of interest
(d) All of the above

10. Which of the following would justify my employment of a one sample t-test *(about the population mean)* assuming that the population of values *(of the measurement variable)* is assumed to be normally distributed.

(a) σ is known and $n < 30$
(b) σ is known and $n \geq 30$
(c) σ is unknown and $n \geq 30$
(d) σ is unknown and $n < 30$

11. The one sample test *(about a population mean)* can only be employed when the variable/data type is:
(a) Nominal scaled
(b) Ordinal scaled
(c) Quantitative *discrete* variable
(d) Quantitative *continuous* variable

Question 12 through to 16 refers to the following case study:

An indicator of health of new born babies is their weight at birth. Birth weight is influenced by the circumstances expectant mothers experience during pregnancy. In the US, mother who experience poverty generally have lighter babies than their more affluent counterparts. The average birth weight in the US is approximately 116.4 ounces, whereas the average birth weight of babies whose mothers experience poverty is 98.77 ounces. A local hospital introduced a prenatal care programme to reverse the low birth weights experienced by mothers living in poverty. A random sample of 25 mothers who experienced poverty during pregnancy, participated in the programme and the average birth weight of their babies was 108.47 ounces with a standard deviation of 17.64 ounces.

12. Which of the following is not given in the case study:

(a) n = sample size
(b) $\mu_{\text{poverty weights}}$ = population mean weight *(For babies born to mothers experiencing poverty)*
(c) $\bar{x}$ and s = sample mean and standard deviation
(d) $\sigma_{\text{poverty weights}}$ = population standard deviation weight *(For babies born to mothers experiencing poverty)*

13. What is the appropriate null and alternative hypothesis when we wish to test if the prenatal care programme made *a difference (Hint: what we wish to test is non-directional)*?

(a) H_0: $\mu = 98.77$
H_1: $\mu \neq 98.77$
(b) H_0: $\mu \geq 98.77$
H_1: $\mu < 98.77$
(c) H_0: $\mu \leq 98.77$
H_1: $\mu > 98.77$
(d) H_0: $\mu = 98.77$
H_1: $\mu > 98.77$

14. What is the appropriate null and alternative hypothesis when we wish to test if the prenatal care programme *increased* the average birth weight of babies for mothers who participated in the programme *(Hint: What we wish to test is directional)*?

(a) H_0: $\mu = 98.77$
H_1: $\mu \neq 98.77$
(b) H_0: $\mu \geq 98.77$
H_1: $\mu < 98.77$
(c) H_0: $\mu \leq 98.77$
H_1: $\mu > 98.77$
(d) H_0: $\mu = 98.77$
H_1: $\mu > 98.77$

15. Applying the appropriate one sample statistical test gives the following results:

One Sample Test

	Test Value = 98.77						
	t	*df*	*Sig. (2 tailed)*	*Mean Diff.*	*Std. Error Difference*	*95% Confidence Interval Of the difference*	
						Lower	*Upper*
Birth Weights For women In prenatal programme	*2.7494*	*24*	*0.0112*	*9.7*	*3.528*	*2.4168*	*16.9814*

Which of the following is correct?

(a) There is a difference between the sample average and the population average at the 0.05 level of significance
(b) There is no difference between the sample average and the population average at the 0.05 level of significance
(c) Information on effect size is required before we can make an inference
(d) None of the above

16. How can we interpret the 95% confidence interval of the difference:

(a) Since the interval does not contains zero we reject H_0
(b) Since the interval does not contain zero we fail to reject H_0
(c) If we repeat this exercise a large number of times 95% of the constructed confidence intervals will contain the true population mean difference
(d) If we repeat this exercise a large number of times 5% of the constructed confidence intervals will not contain the true population mean difference

MCQ Solutions

1. (a)
2. (b)
3. (b)
4. (a)
5. (b)
6. (a)
7. (b)
8. (d)
9. (d)
10. (d)
11. (d)
12. (d)
13. (a)
14. (c)
15. (a)
16. (c)

Individuals	*Sample 1* *3rd level students*	*Sample 2* *2nd level students*
	$\mu = 8$	*$\mu = 8$*
1	6	8
2	5	7
3	4	7
4	3	8
5	7	7
6	5	8
7	5	9
8	5	7
9	6	7
10	6	6.5

Exercise 1

The average sleep time is assumed to be 8 hours. The students union in the local 3rd level college believes that their students sleeping habits are different. A random sample of 10 students is selected and their sleep times are recorded. Test whether a mean sleep time of 8 hours *is different to* the local population of 3rd level college students at the 0.05 level of significance. No Consideration was given to appropriate sample size. Use G*Power to calculate the *post hoc* power for the one sample t test.

Exercise 2

The average sleep time is assumed to be 8 hours. The principal in the local 2nd level school believes that his students sleeping habits are different. A random sample of 10 students is selected and their sleep times are recorded. Test whether a mean sleep time of 8 hours *is different* to the local population of 2nd level students at the 0.05 level of significance. No Consideration was given to appropriate sample size. Use G*Power to calculate the *post hoc* power for the one sample t test.

IBM SPSS Statistics 20 Instructions

Step 1 – Open *IBM SPSS Statistics 20* select *Type in data* and click *OK*. Click *Variable View* at the bottom left corner and enter the variable*(s)*.

Variable View Editor

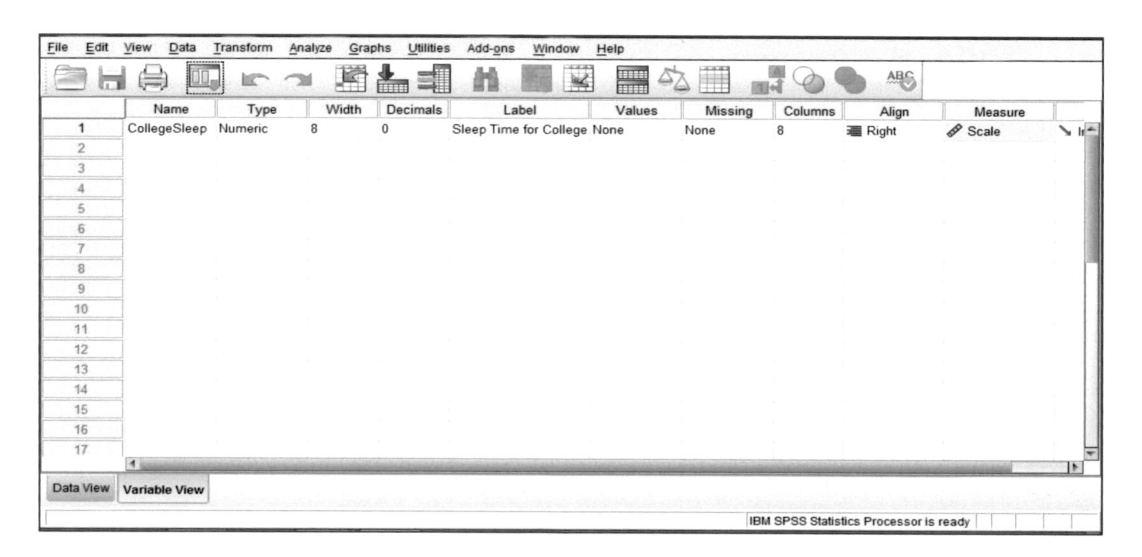

Step 2 – Click *Data View* at the bottom left corner and enter the data.

Data View Editor

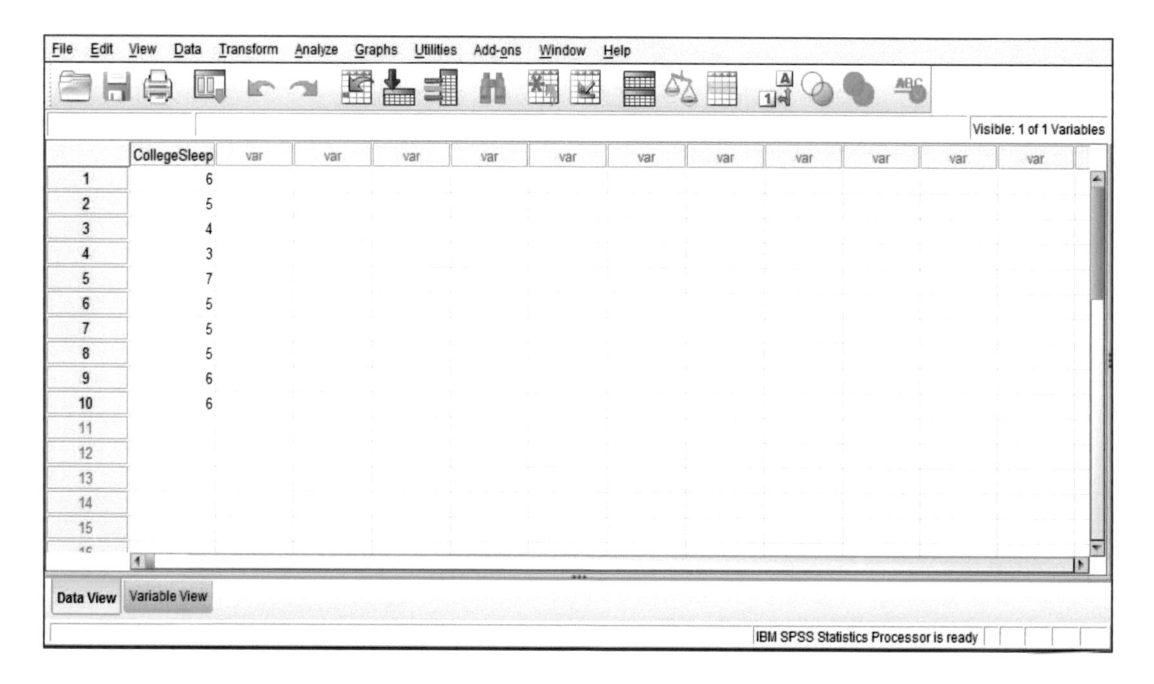

Step 3 – Click *Analyse* and select *Compare Means* and then select *One-Sample T Test*.

Data View Editor

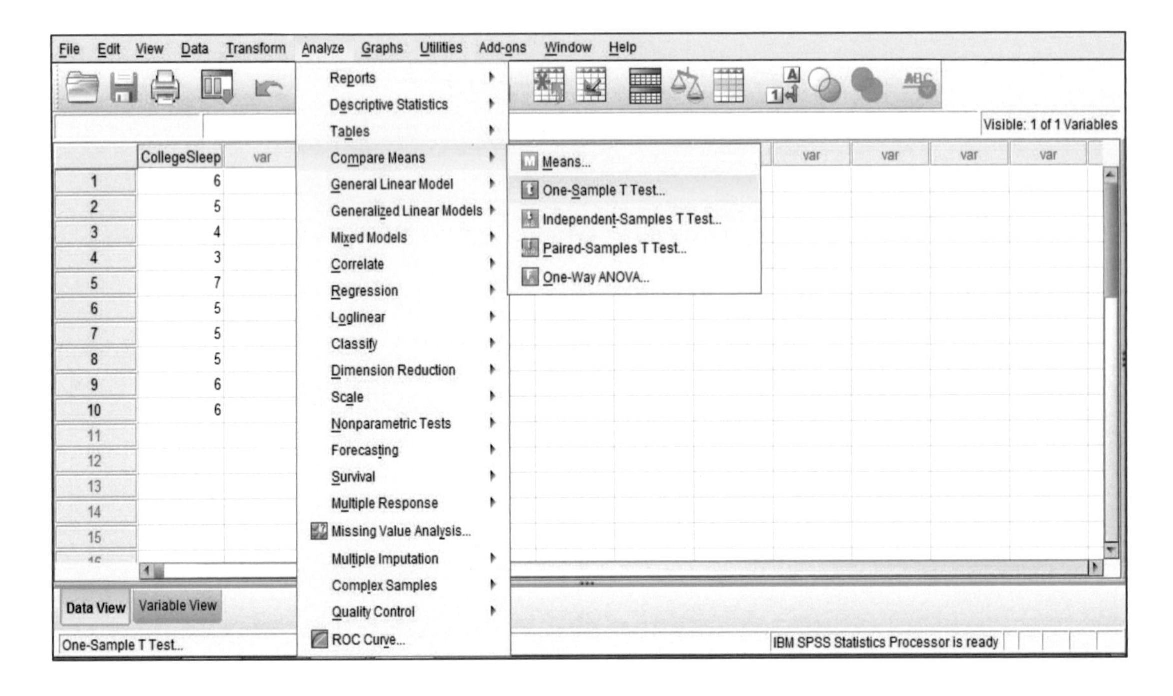

Step 4 – Move *Sleep Time for College* into *Test Variable(s)* place 8 *(the claimed or universally held belief)* into *Test Value*. Then click *OK*

Data View Editor

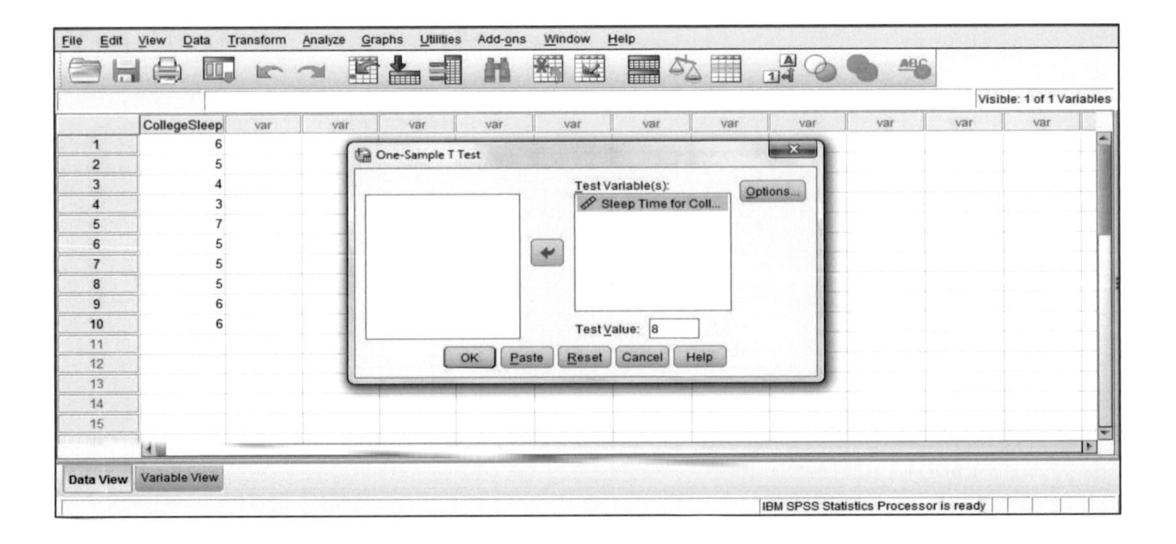

IBM SPSS Statistics 20 Output

One-Sample Statistics

	n	*Mean*	*Standard Deviation*	*Std. Error Mean*
Sleep Time for College	*10*	*5.20*	*1.135*	*0.359*

One Sample Test

	Test Value = 8						
	t	*df*	*Sig. (2 tailed)*	*Mean Diff.*	*Std. Error Difference*	*95% Confidence Interval Of the difference*	
						Lower	*Upper*
Sleep Time for College	*-7.799*	*9*	*0.000*	*-2.8*	*1.898*	*-3.61*	*-1.99*

Power of the one sample t test = 94.49%

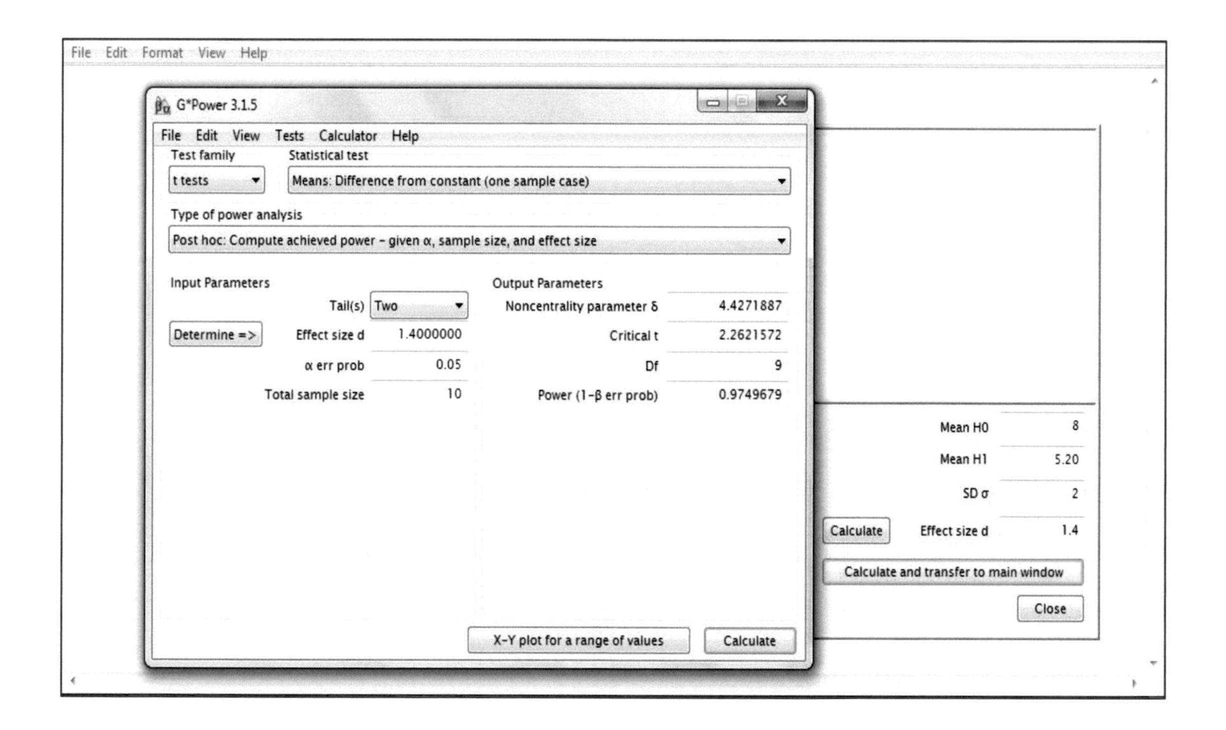

Chapter 7 – Inferential procedures for two populations

'But the fact that some geniuses were laughed at does not imply that all who are laughed at are geniuses. They laughed at Fulton, they laughed at the Wright brothers. But they also laughed at Bozo the Clown.'

Carl Edward Sagan (1934 – 96)

7.1 Schematic Chart – *Statistical tests to compare two population means*

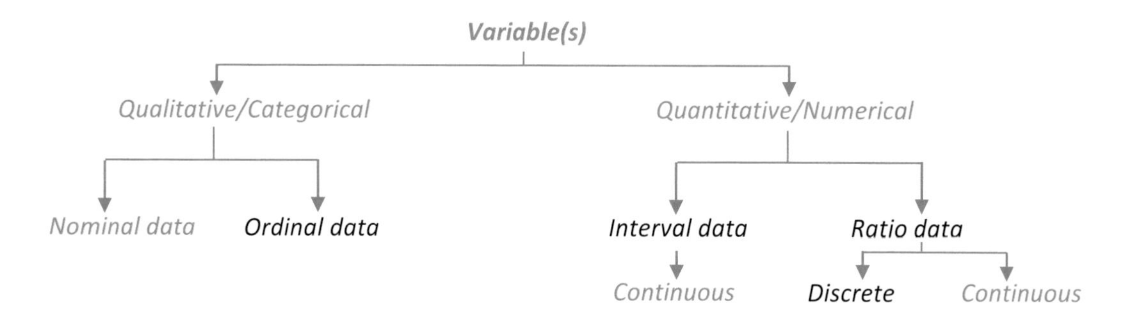

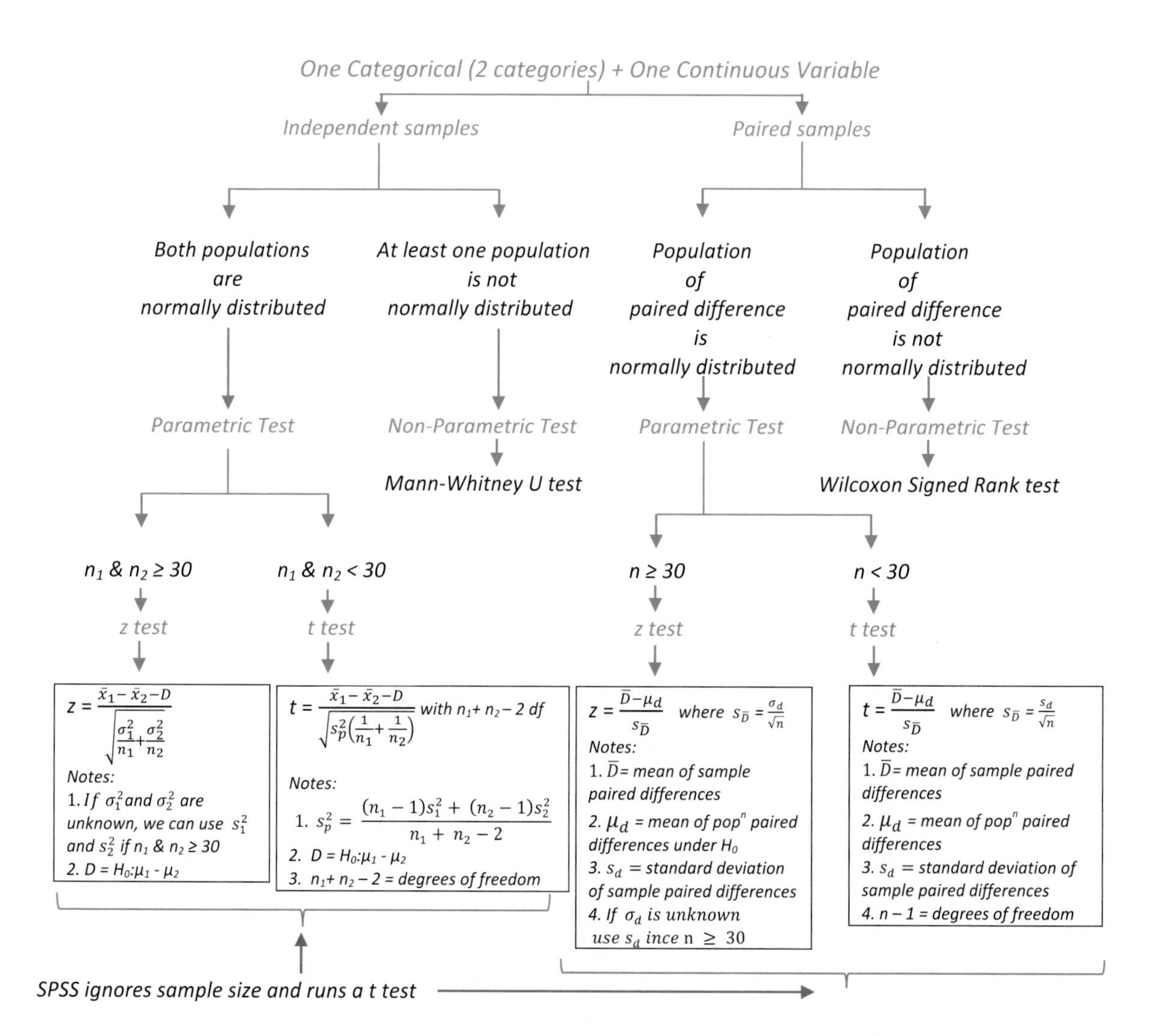

7.2 Schematic Chart 2 – *Confidence intervals for the mean difference of two populations*

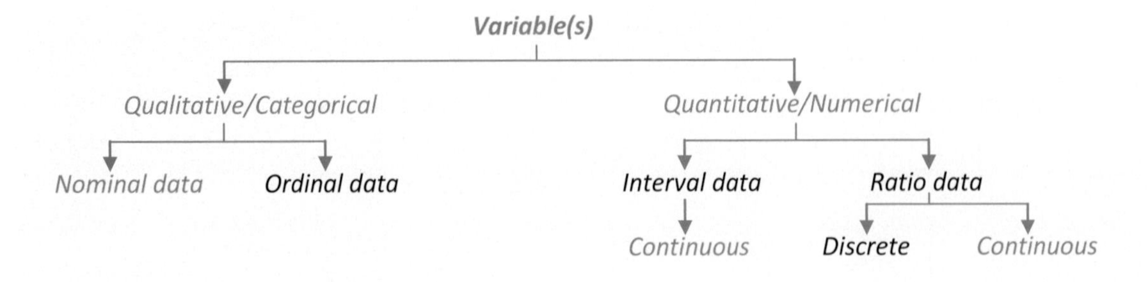

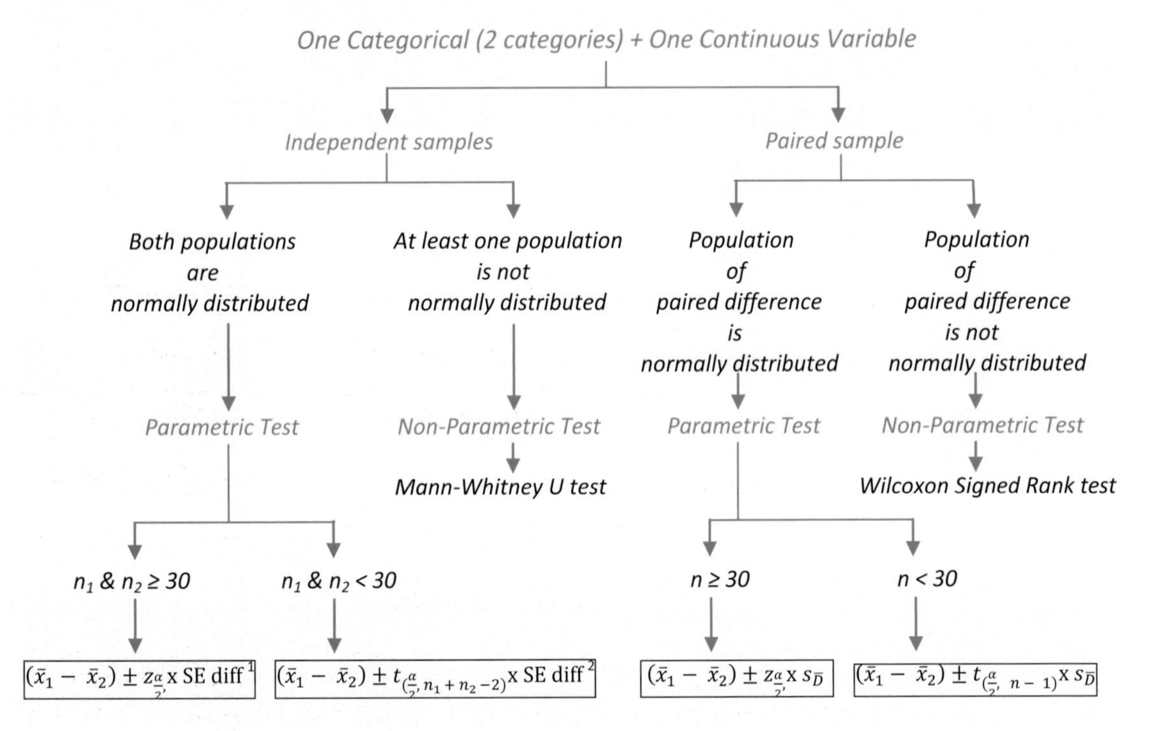

Notes:

1. *Standard error of the difference = SE diff =* $\sqrt{\left[\left(\frac{s_1^2}{n_1}\right) + \left(\frac{s_2^2}{n_2}\right)\right]}$
2. *Standard error of the difference = SE diff =* $\sqrt{s_p^2\left(\frac{1}{n_1} + \frac{1}{n_2}\right)}$ *and* $s_p^2 = \frac{(n_1-1).s_1^2 + (n_2-1).s_2^2}{(n_1 + n_2 - 2)}$
3. *This small sample confidence interval* $((\bar{x}_1 - \bar{x}_2) \pm t_{(\frac{\alpha}{2}, n_1 + n_2 - 2)}\ x\ SE\ diff)$ *is valid when we have good reason to believe that the populations from which the samples were drawn have equal variances* $\sigma_1^2 = \sigma_2^2$
4. *This small sample confidence interval* $((\bar{x}_1 - \bar{x}_2) \pm t_{(\frac{\alpha}{2}, n_1 + n_2 - 2)}\ x\ SE\ diff)$ *is valid when we have good reason to believe that the populations from which the samples were drawn have unequal variances as long as the samples selected are of equal size* $\sigma_1^2 = \sigma_2^2$
5. $S_{\bar{D}} = \frac{S_D}{\sqrt{n}}$ *where* $S_D = \sqrt{\frac{\sum(D-\bar{D})^2}{n-1}}$

7.3 Schematic Chart 3 – *Non-Parametric Tests on two population central locations*

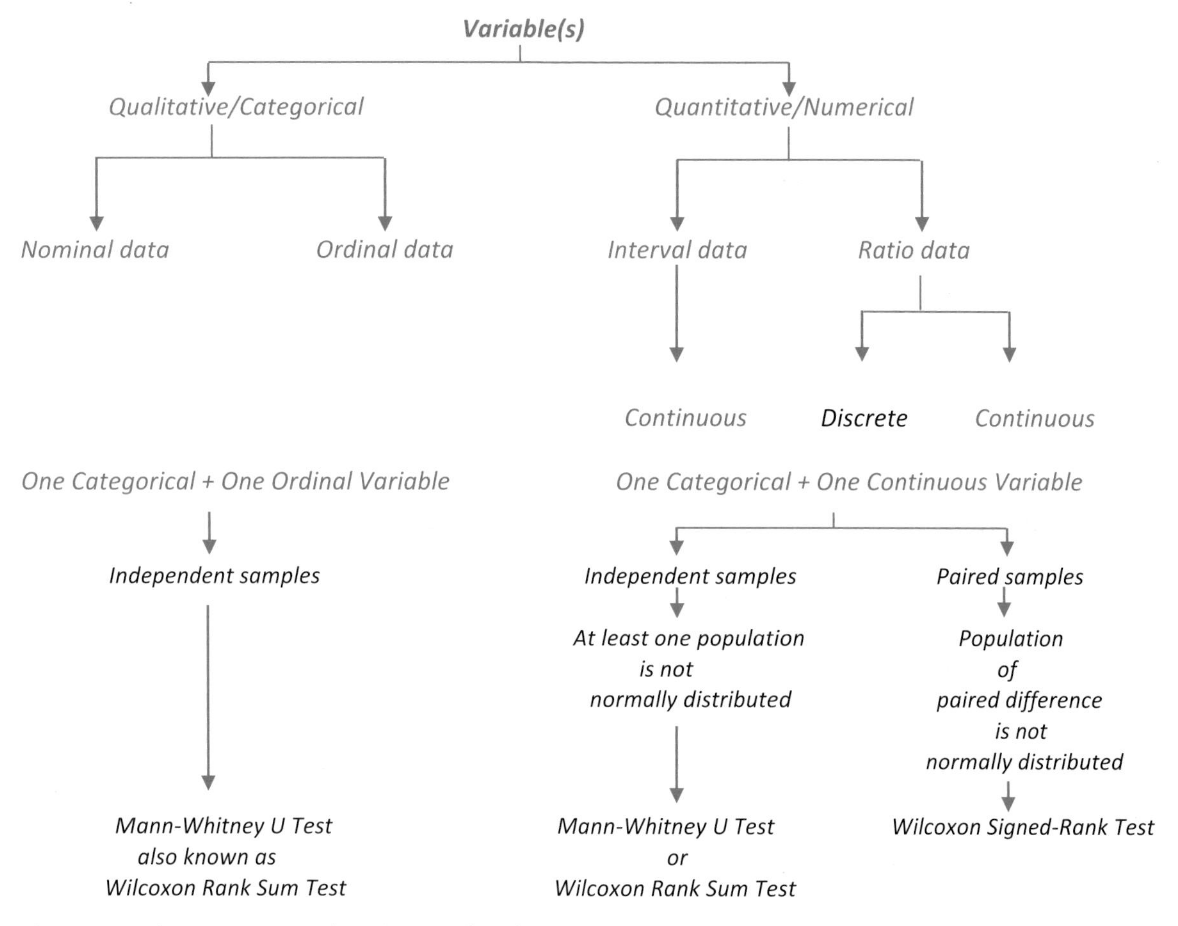

The Mann-Whitney U Test is based on ranks. The researcher either starts out with ranked data or the actual continuous sample data is converted to ranks. When the assumptions of the corresponding parametric tests are met, the non-parametric tests based on ranks are often about 95% as efficient as the parametric tests Aczel (2002). When the assumptions needed for the parametric tests (usually, a normal distribution) are not met, the tests based on ranks are powerful alternatives. The only assumptions required for this test is that the samples are randomly selected and that they be drawn independently of each other. The null and alternative hypothesis for this test can take a variety of formats:

H_0: *The distributions of the two populations are identical*
H_1: *The distributions of the two populations are not identical*

Other formats would have the H_0 *and* H_1 *written in terms of equality versus non-equality of two population means or of two population medians. These alternative formats relate specifically to tests of location and not about the similarity or dissimilarity of distributions.*

Wilcoxon Signed-Rank Test – The data must be a random sample of paired or matched values. Each matched pair must be chosen randomly and independent.

H_0: *The median difference between populations 1 and 2 is zero*
H_1: *The median difference between populations 1 and 2 is not zero*

7.4 Introductory Comments

In this chapter we will explore test procedures which are appropriate for comparing the means of two populations.

The following is a summary of what is covered in this chapter:

1. Two population means - Two independent samples

Two independent random samples are selected to test whether there is a difference between two population means.

I wish to investigate whether the mean weight (kg) of one week old babies is different between male and females. The following table summarises my findings:

Male	$n_1 = 48$	$\bar{x}_1 = 4.7$	$s_1 = 0.52$
Female	$n_2 = 52$	$\bar{x}_2 = 4.41$	$s_2 = 0.60$

Is there a difference between the mean weights (kg) of males versus the mean weight (kg) of females at the 0.05 level of significance?

We set up the null and alternative hypothesis in accordance with the options table introduced in Chapter 5. The alternative hypothesis will be written to reflect what is being tested i.e. *Is there a difference between* ...and the null hypothesis will be written as the only other possible outcome i.e. *no difference*.

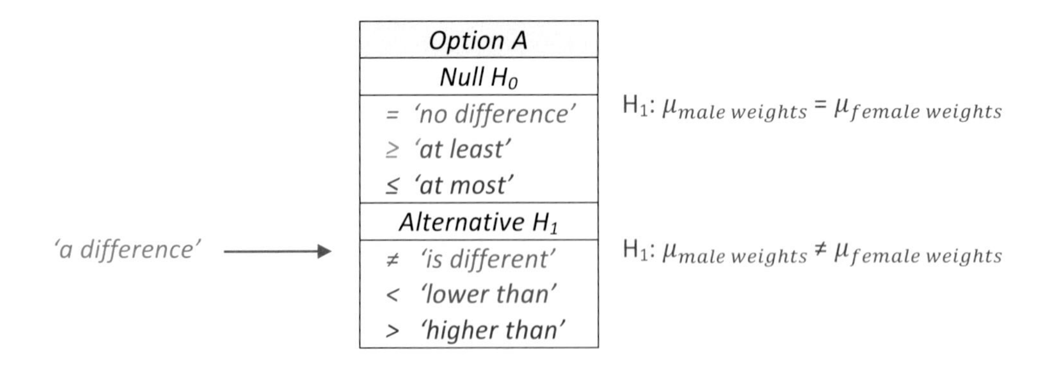

2. Two population means - Matched/Paired/Repeated samples

Two matched/paired/repeated samples are derived from one sample group. The task is to test whether there is a difference between two population means.

I wish to investigate whether a course, intended to improve performance, actually works! An IQ test was given to a random sample of 40 students (n = 40) before a course and after the course was completed.

Before	$n_B = 40$	$\bar{x}_B = 95$	$S_B = 12$	$\bar{x}_B - \bar{x}_A$	S_d = standard deviation of paired differences
After	$n_A = 40$	$\bar{x}_A = 99$	$S_A = 13$	- 4	10

Is there a difference between the mean IQ before versus the mean IQ after the course at the 0.05 level of significance?

We set up the null and alternative hypothesis in accordance with the options table introduced in Chapter 5. The alternative hypothesis will be written to reflect what is being tested i.e. *Is there a difference between* ...and the null hypothesis will be written as the only other possible outcome i.e. *no difference*.

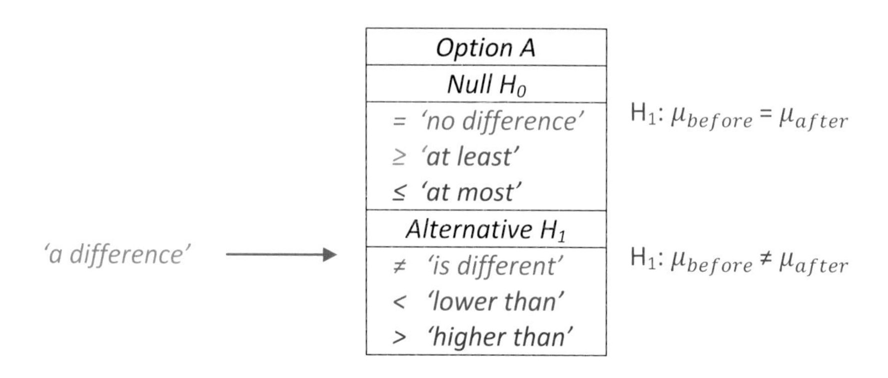

7.5 **Template** – *Statistical inference procedure for comparing two means*

The following inference procedures should be following during the course of your statistical analysis:

1. *Statistical Test Procedure*
2. *Confidence Interval Procedure*
3. *Effect Size Procedure*

Statistical Test Procedure

1. State the necessary conditions required to validate the test
2. State the null hypothesis and alternative hypothesis
3. State the statistical decision rule given your selected level of significance
4. Select and calculate the appropriate test statistic
5. Compare the calculated test statistic with the critical value
6. Derive an approximate p value

Confidence Interval Procedure

1. Select a confidence interval and confidence level
2. Construct the selected confidence interval
3. State your inferences

Effect Size Procedure

1. Identify the difference between the means
2. Calculate the 'measure of effect'
3. State your inferences

Two-Sample t Test – Appropriate or required sample size (Total) for selected input parameters

Independent Samples t test

Sample Size Required			Effect Size		
α= 0.05			0.2	0.5	0.8
Power	0.75	1 - tail	540	88	36
		2 - tail	696	114	46
	0.80	1 - tail	620	102	42
		2 - tail	788	128	52
	0.85	1 - tail	722	118	48
		2 - tail	900	146	60

Matched/Paired Samples t test

Sample Size Required			Effect Size		
α= 0.05			0.2	0.5	0.8
Power	0.75	1 - tail	136	23	10
		2 - tail	176	30	13
	0.80	1 - tail	156	27	12
		2 - tail	199	34	15
	0.85	1 - tail	182	31	13
		2 - tail	227	38	17

7.6 Statistical Inference: *Comparing two large independent samples-Two tailed z test*

Example 1

I wish to investigate whether the mean weight (kg) of one week old babies is different between male and females. The following table summarises my findings:

Male	$n_1 = 48$	$\bar{x}_1 = 4.7$	$s_1 = 0.52$
Female	$n_2 = 52$	$\bar{x}_2 = 4.41$	$s_2 = 0.60$

*Is there a difference between the mean weights (kg) of males versus the mean weight (kg) of females at the 0.05 level of significance? Use G*power 3 to calculate the post hoc power of the statistical test.*

Statistical Test Procedure

1. *State the assumptions required to validate this test*

   a. Two independent random samples were taken at the outset.
   b. One variable is categorical and one variable is continuous.
   c. The population of measurements *(continuous variable)* for each group is normally distributed. If both sample sizes ≥ 30, then the statistical test procedure is robust even when this assumption is violated.
   d. The variance of measurements *(continuous variable)* for each group is equal. $\sigma_1^2 = \sigma_2^2$.
   e. The measurements recorded in one group has no influence on the measurements recorded in the other group i.e. Independence of values in each group.

2. *State the null hypothesis and alternative hypothesis*

   H_0: $\mu_{male\ weights} = \mu_{female\ weights}$
   H_1: $\mu_{male\ weights} \neq \mu_{female\ weights}$ *Two-tailed test (determined by the operator ≠ in H_1)*

3. *State the statistical decision rule for a selected level of significance*

   a. Appropriate test statistic is the z test since n_1 & $n_2 \geq 30$ and assumption 3 in part *(1)*.
   b. The level of significance for this test: $\alpha = 0.05$
   c. Identify the critical values in the diagram below *(A segment of the z tables is included here)*

   Identifying ± 1.96 *in the diagram below requires 0.05 to be divided between both tails. Each tail has, therefore, an area equal to 0.025 each. Use the z tables to derive the critical values (z values) for an area equal to 0.025. Since the bell curve is symmetrical, the critical values are* ± 1.96

   d. Reject the null hypothesis *(H_0)* when the calculated test statistic *(z test)* from part 4 below > Critical value ± 1.96

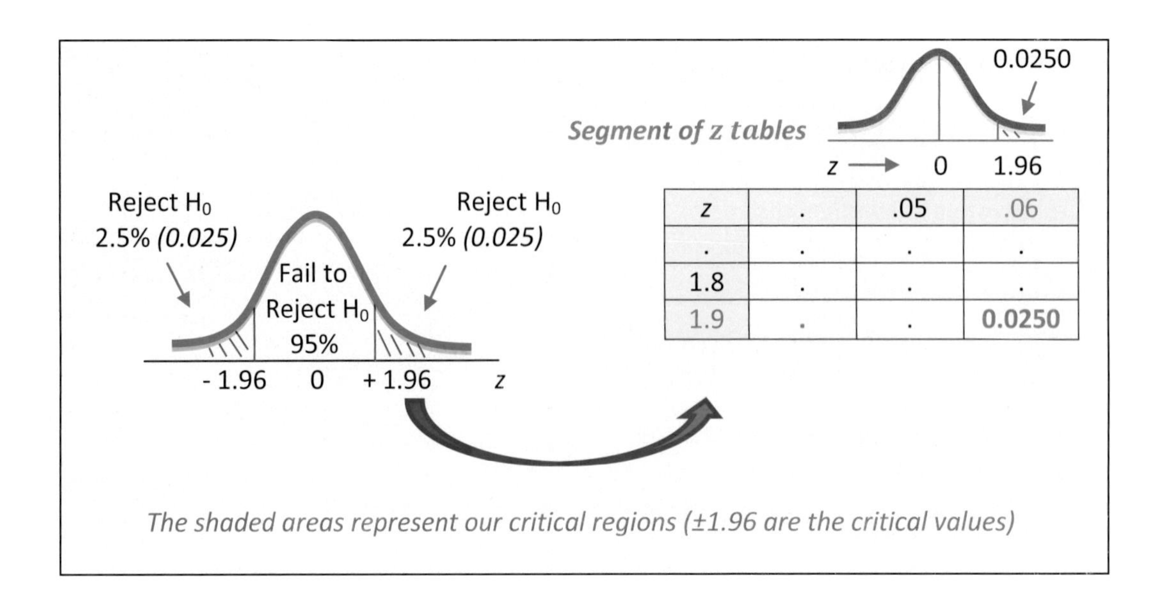

4. *Select and calculate the appropriate test statistic*

(if σ_1^2 & σ_2^2 are unknown we can use s_1^2 and s_2^2 since n_1 & $n_2 \geq 30$)

$$z \text{ test } = \frac{\bar{x}_1 - \bar{x}_2 - 0}{\sqrt{\frac{\sigma_1^2}{n_1} + \frac{\sigma_2^2}{n_2}}} = \frac{4.7 - 4.41 - 0}{\sqrt{\frac{(0.52)^2}{48} + \frac{(0.60)^2}{52}}} = \frac{0.29}{\sqrt{\frac{0.27}{48} + \frac{0.36}{52}}} = \frac{0.29}{\sqrt{0.0056 + 0.0069}} = 2.59$$

5. *Compare the calculated test statistic with the critical value*

The calculated *z* test statistic *(2.59)* falls into the rightward critical region *(above 1.96)* where we reject H_0. In rejecting H_0, we are inferring that the difference between the mean weight of males versus the mean weight of females is *statistically significant* at the 0.05 level of significance.

6. *Derive or locate an approximate p value working with a segment of the z tables*

The *p* value is the sum of the areas under the curve defined by the calculated z test statistic.

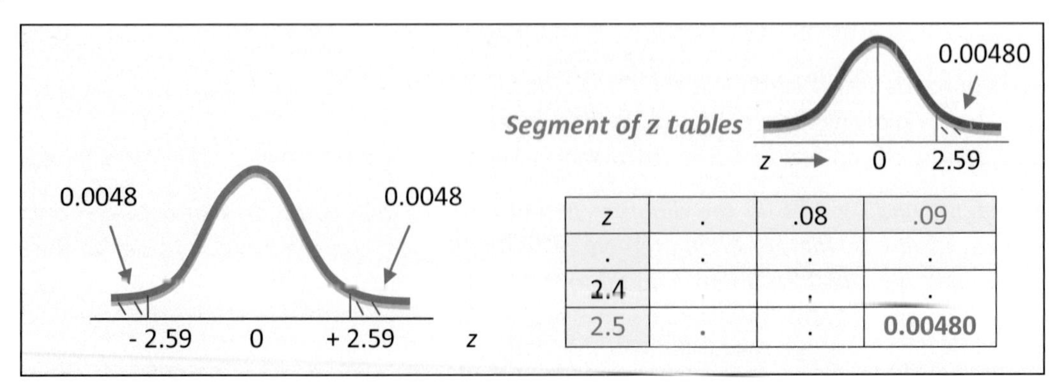

The sum of the shaded areas under the curve gives us a *p* value of 0.0096 *(2 x 0.00480 = 0.0096)*.

Interpreting the p value

a. Traditional approach – explicit reference to a selected cut-off point of say α = 0.05:

Since the p value of 0.0096 is below the 0.05 level of significance, we can reject H_0 at the 0.05 level of significance (Applying the p value decision rule: If the p value < 0.05 reject H_0). The observed mean difference is too large to be solely attributed to sampling error (chance).

b. Current approach – no explicit reference to a selected cut-off point of say α = 0.05. The cut-off point is implicitly assumed as a guide value. The current approach is to report an exact *p* value *(included in the output of all statistical software packages)*. Using tables will only give us approximations.

The p value reveals the likelihood of being wrong if we reject H_0 (the p value is 0.0096 i.e. less than 1 time in 100).

7. Additional Inferences

Male	**Female**	
48	52	
$\bar{x}_1 = 4.7$	$\bar{x}_2 = 4.41$	
Null Hypothesis	*p value*	
1. $\mu_{male\ weights} = \mu_{female\ weights}$	*0.0096*	*Reject H_o*
2. $\mu_{male\ weights} \leq \mu_{female\ weights}$	*0.0048*	*Reject H_o*
3. $\mu_{male\ weights} \geq \mu_{female\ weights}$	*0.9952*	

If we have no reason to believe that male babies are heavier than female babies or vice versa, then we can start out with the first null hypothesis. This hypothesis was rejected since the *p* value *(0.0096)* < 0.05 level of significance. If we wish to follow this conclusion with a directional null hypothesis *(prompted by the observed sample means which suggest that male babies are heavier than female babies)*, we also reject that male babies are lighter than female babies since the *p* value *(0.0049 = 0.0096/2)* < 0.05 level of significance.

Confidence Interval Procedure

Construct 95% confidence interval to estimate a range for the true difference between the means

1. *Identify the difference between the means*

Difference between the means: $(\bar{x}_1 - \bar{x}_2) = (4.7 - 4.41) = 0.29$

2. *Select a confidence interval and confidence level*

The appropriate confidence interval for n_1 & $n_2 \geq 30$ is:

$$(\bar{x}_1 - \bar{x}_2) \pm z_{\alpha/2} \text{ x SE diff.}$$

3. *Construct the 95% confidence interval the true difference between the two groups*

z	0.05	0.06
.	.	.
1.8	.	.
1.9	.	0.0250

$(\bar{x}_1 - \bar{x}_2) \pm z_{\alpha/2}$ x SE diff *where* $z_{\alpha/2} = z_{0.05/2} = z_{(0.025)} = 1.96$

$(\bar{x}_1 - \bar{x}_2) \pm 1.96$ x SE diff *where* SE diff = $\sqrt{\left[\left(\frac{s_1^2}{n_1}\right) + \left(\frac{s_2^2}{n_2}\right)\right]}$

$(4.7 - 4.41) \pm 1.96$ x 0.1118 *where* SE diff = $\sqrt{\left[\left(\frac{(0.52)^2}{48}\right) + \left(\frac{(0.60)^2}{52}\right)\right]} = 0.1118$

0.29 ± 1.96 x 0.1118

0.29 ± 0.22

The 95% confidence interval is 0.07 to 0.51

4. *State your inferences*

   a. *The evidence (data gathered for both groups) available is compatible with a decision to reject the null hypothesis since the confidence interval (0.07 to 0.51) does not include zero*

   b. *The probability that the calculated interval (0.07 to 0.51) contains the true population mean difference (μ_1 - μ_2) is 95%. This is an intuitive but not strictly a correct interpretation of a confidence interval.*

Effect Size Procedure

How large is the difference between the groups?

1. *Identify the difference between the means*

Difference between the means: $(\bar{x}_1 - \bar{x}_2)$ = $(4.7 - 4.41)$ = 0.29

2. *Calculate the 'measure of effect'*

$$\text{Effect Size} = \frac{(\bar{x}_1 - \bar{x}_2)}{s_p} = \frac{(4.7-4.41)}{0.57} = \frac{0.29}{0.57} = 0.51$$

Where $s_p = \sqrt{\frac{(n_1-1).s_1^2 + (n_2-1).s_2^2}{(n_1 + n_2 - 2)}} = \sqrt{0.32} = 0.57$ *When sample sizes are unequal*

Where $s_p = \sqrt{\frac{s_1^2 + s_2^2}{2}}$ *When sample sizes are equal*

3. *State your inferences*

To interpret this value, we refer to guidelines proposed by Cohen, 1988.

Effect Size *(d)*	Interpretation	% of overlap	
If d = 0	No effect	100%	
If d = 0.2	Small	85%	
If d = 0.5	Medium	67%	
If d = 0.8	Large	53%	

Reported results using the current approach (implicit cut-off guide point of α = 0.05):

The difference between the mean weight (kg) of one week old male babies ($\bar{x}_1 = 4.7$; $s_1 = 0.52$) compared to the mean weight (kg) of one week old female babies is statistically significant ($\bar{x}_1 = 4.41$; $s_1 = 0.60$); p = 0.0096 (two-tailed). The mean difference of 0.29 is a medium effect size (d = 0.51).The 95% confidence interval for the true population mean difference ($\mu_1 - \mu_2$) is 0.07 and 0.51.

Power of the statistical test procedure using *G*power 3* software = 72.41%

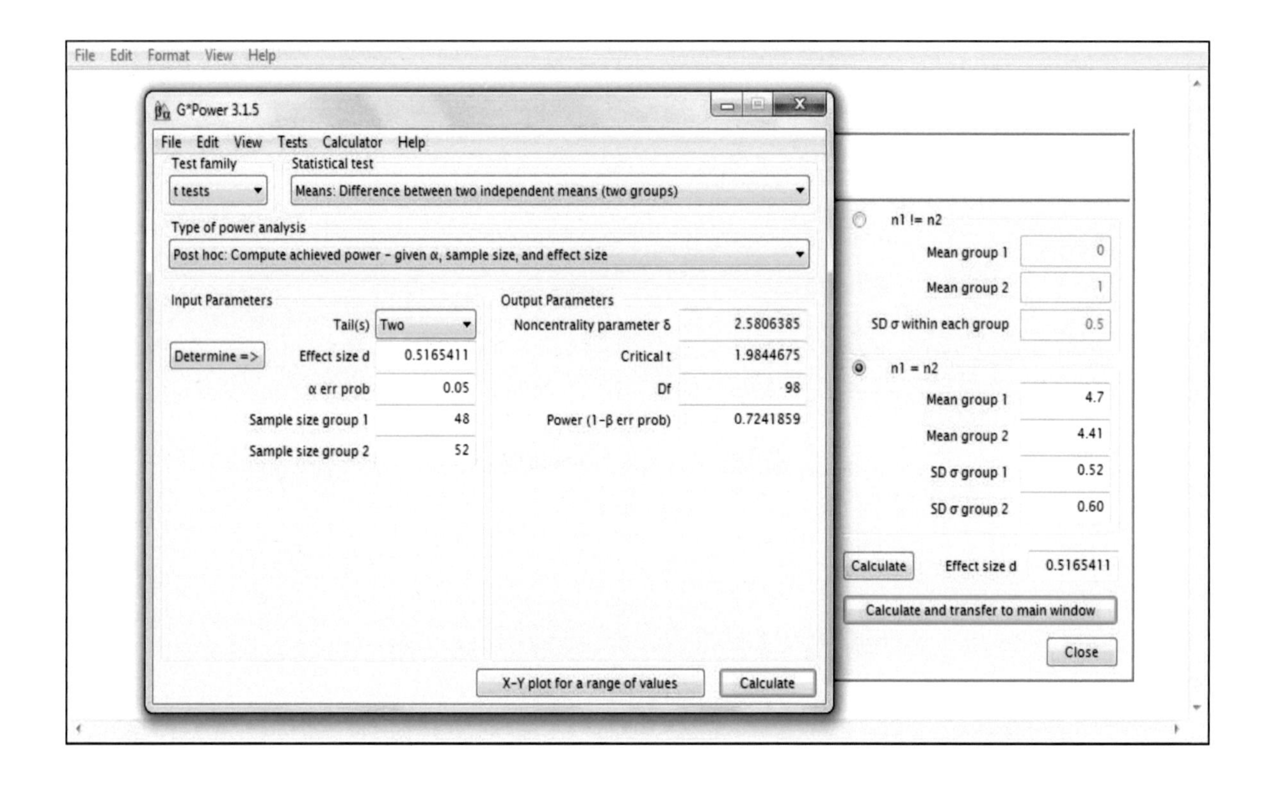

7.7 Statistical Inference: *Comparing two small independent samples – Two tailed test*

Example 2

I wish to investigate whether the mean wages per week (€) is different between seaside lifeguards and poolside lifeguards. The following table summarises my findings:

Seaside Lifeguards	$n_1 = 8$	$\bar{x}_1 = 835.75$	$s_1 = 34.40$
Poolside Lifeguards	$n_2 = 12$	$\bar{x}_2 = 826.75$	$s_2 = 22.84$

*Is there a difference between the mean wages per week (€) of seaside lifeguards versus the mean wages of poolside lifeguards at the 0.05 level of significance? The researcher gave no consideration to what would constitute an appropriate sample size. Use G*power 3 to calculate the post hoc power of the statistical test. If the statistical test procedure fails to detect statistical significance, use G*power 3 to calculated the appropriate sample size.*

Statistical Test Procedure

1. *State the assumptions required to validate this test*

   As per example 1

2. *State the null hypothesis and alternative hypothesis*

   H_0: $\mu_{seaside\ wages} = \mu_{poolside\ wages}$
   H_1: $\mu_{seaside\ wages} \neq \mu_{poolside\ wages}$

3. *State the statistical decision rule for a selected level of significance*

   a. Appropriate test statistic is the *t* test since n_1 & $n_2 < 30$ and assumption 3 in part *(1)*
   b. The level of significance for this test: $\alpha = 0.05$
   c. Identify the critical values in the diagram below *(A segment of the t tables is included here)*

      Identifying ± 2.101 *in the diagram below requires 0.05 to be divided between both tails. Each tail has, therefore, an area equal to 0.025 each. Use the t tables to derive the critical values (t values) for an area equal to 0.025 @* $n_1 + n_2 - 2$ *degrees of freedom. Since the bell curve is symmetrical, the critical values are* ± 2.101.

   d. Reject the null hypothesis *(H_0)* when the calculated test statistic *(t test)* from part 4 below > Critical value ± 2.101

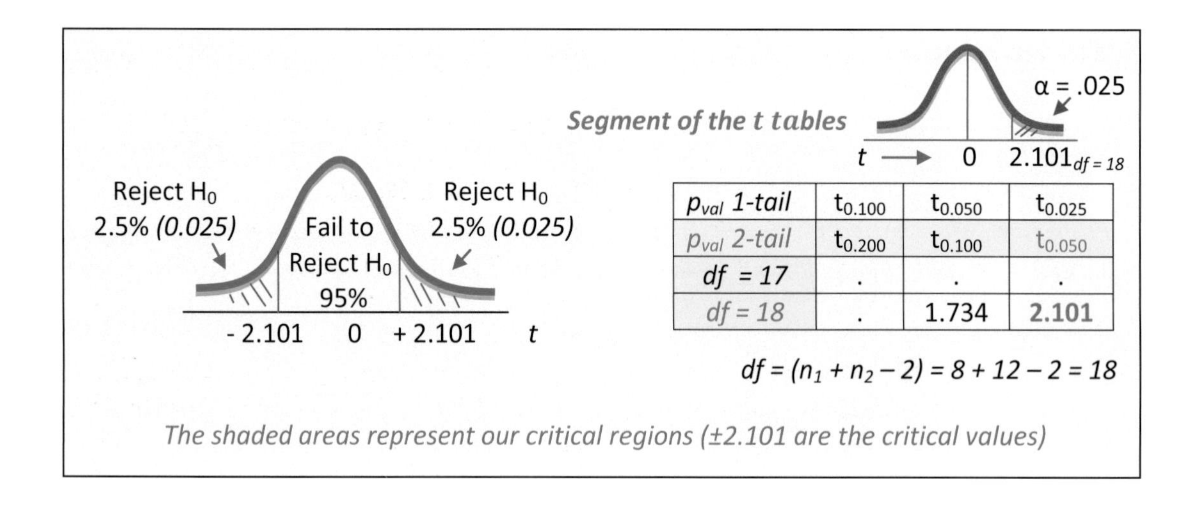

p_{val} 1-tail	$t_{0.100}$	$t_{0.050}$	$t_{0.025}$
p_{val} 2-tail	$t_{0.200}$	$t_{0.100}$	$t_{0.050}$
df = 17	.	.	.
df = 18	.	1.734	**2.101**

The shaded areas represent our critical regions (±2.101 are the critical values)

4. *Select and calculate the appropriate test statistic*

$$t\ test = \frac{\bar{x}_1 - \bar{x}_2 - 0}{\sqrt{s_p^2\left(\frac{1}{n_1}+\frac{1}{n_2}\right)}} = \frac{835.75 - 826.75 - 0}{\sqrt{779\left(\frac{1}{8}+\frac{1}{12}\right)}} = \frac{9}{\sqrt{162.29}} = \frac{9}{12.74} = 0.71$$

$$where \quad s_p^2 = \frac{(n_1-1)s_1^2 + (n_2-1)s_2^2}{n_1 + n_2 - 2} = \frac{(8-1)(34.4)^2 + (12-1)(22.84)^2}{8 + 12 - 2} = 779$$

5. *Compare the calculated test statistic with the critical value*

The calculated t test statistic *(0.71)* falls between the critical values $(\pm\ 2.101)$ where we fail to reject H_0. In failing to reject H_0, we are inferring that the difference between the mean wages of seaside lifeguards versus the mean wages of poolside lifeguards is *not statistically significant* at the 0.05 level of significance.

6. *Derive or locate an approximate p value – Working with a segment of the t tables*

Segment of t tables

p_{val} 1-tail	$t_{0.100}$	$t_{0.050}$	$t_{0.025}$
p_{val} 2-tail	$t_{0.200}$	$t_{0.100}$	$t_{0.050}$
Above 0.05 ⟵			
df = 17	.	.	.
df = 18	1.330	1.734	2.101

We search the t table for a value which comes nearest to our calculated t test statistics *(0.71, sign ignored)* at 18 degrees of freedom for a two tailed test *(1.330 comes closest in this particular table)*. This value *(1.330)* corresponds to a p value of 0.20 *($t_{0.200}$)*.

Interpreting the p value

a. Traditional approach – explicit reference to a selected cut-off point of say α = 0.05:

The p value which corresponds to the calculated t value (0.71) at 18 df (two-tailed) is above 0.05. Since this p value is above 0.05, we fail to reject H_0 at the 0.05 level of significance (applying the p value decision rule: If p value > 0.05 we fail to reject H_0). The observed difference is most likely to be solely attributed to sampling error (chance).

b. Current approach – no explicit reference to a selected cut-off point of say α = 0.05. The cut-off point is implicitly assumed as a guide value. The current approach is to report an exact *p* value *(included in the output of all statistical software packages)*. Using tables will only give us approximations.

The p value reveals the likelihood of being wrong if we reject H_0 (the p value is well above 0.20 i.e. 20 times in 100).

7. Additional Inferences

Seaside Lifeguards		**Poolside Lifeguards**	
8		12	
$\bar{x}_1 = 835.75$		$\bar{x}_2 = 826.75$	
Null Hypothesis		*Approximate p value (range)*	
1. $\mu_{seaside\ wages} = \mu_{poolside\ wages}$	→	> 0.2000	*Fail to reject H_o*
2. $\mu_{seaside\ wages} \leq \mu_{poolside\ wages}$	→	> 0.1000	*Fail to reject H_o*
3. $\mu_{seaside\ wages} \geq \mu_{poolside\ wages}$	→	< 0.9000	

If we have no reason to believe that seaside lifeguards are paid more than poolside lifeguards or vice versa, then we can start out with the first null hypothesis. We failed to reject this null hypothesis since the *p* value *(> 0.2000)* > 0.05 level of significance. If we wish to follow this conclusion with a directional null hypothesis *(prompted by the observed sample means which suggest that seaside lifeguards are paid more than poolside lifeguards)*, we also reject that seaside lifeguards are paid less than poolside lifeguards since the *p* value *(> 0.1000 = 0.2000/2)* > 0.05 level of significance.

Confidence Interval Procedure

Construct 95% confidence interval to estimate a range for the true difference between the means

1. *Identify the difference between the means*

Difference between the means: $(\bar{x}_1 - \bar{x}_2) = (835.75 - 826.75) = 9$

2. *Select a confidence interval and confidence level*

The appropriate confidence interval for n_1 & $n_2 < 30$ is:

$$(\bar{x}_1 - \bar{x}_2) \pm t_{(\alpha/2, n_1 + n_2 - 2)} \text{ x SE diff.}$$

3. *Construct the 95% confidence interval of the true difference between the two groups*

$(\bar{x}_1 - \bar{x}_2) \pm t_{(\alpha/2, n_1 + n_2 - 2)}$ x SE diff *where* SE diff = $\sqrt{s_p^2\left(\frac{1}{n_1} + \frac{1}{n_2}\right)}$ and $s_p^2 = \frac{(n_1-1).s_1^2 + (n_2-1).s_2^2}{(n_1 + n_{2-2})}$

$t_{(\alpha/2, n_1 + n_2 - 2)} = t_{(0.05/2,\ 8 + 12 - 2 = 18)} = t_{(0.025,\ 18)} = 2.101$

p_{val} 1-tail	$t_{0.050}$	$t_{0.025}$
p_{val} 2-tail	$t_{0.100}$	$t_{0.050}$
df = 17	.	.
df = 18	.	**2.101**

$(835.75 - 826.75) \pm 2.101 \text{ x } \sqrt{779\left(\frac{1}{8} + \frac{1}{12}\right)}$

$(9) \pm 2.101 \text{ x } 12.74$

$(9) \pm 26.77$

The 95% confidence interval is -17.77 to 35.77

4. *State your inferences*

Since this confidence interval includes zero then:

a. *The evidence (data gathered for both groups) available is compatible with a failure to reject the null hypothesis since the confidence interval (-17.77 to 35.77) does include zero.*
b. *The probability that the calculated interval (-17.77 to 35.77) contains the true population mean difference (μ_1 - μ_2) is 95%. This is an intuitive but not strictly a correct interpretation of a confidence interval.*

Effect Size Procedure

How large is the difference between the groups?

This procedure is often regarded as unnecessary when we fail to reject the null hypothesis. However, this policy may be unwise in every instance. If we are using the traditional approach to declaring or not declaring significance based on whether the p value is < 0.05 or > 0.05, then there is the danger of painting all p values above and below 0.05 with the same brush. As Howell (2007) observes, is it reasonable to treat 0.051 and 0.75 as being equally non-significant by reporting them both as $p > 0.05$? Moreover, should 0.049 and 0.00001 be thought of as being equally significant by reporting them both as $p < 0.05$? Whilst this is a strong argument in favour of reporting exact p values, there is also real value in employing the effect size procedure when the p value is within reasonable distance of a traditional selected significance value such as 0.05. In this example, the effect size procedure is not employed since the p value ($p < 0.20$) is quite a distance from the 0.05 level of significance.

Reported results using the current approach (implicit cut-off guide point of $\alpha = 0.05$):

The difference between the mean wage of seaside lifeguards ($\bar{x}_1 = 835.75$; $s_1 = 34.40$) compared to the mean wage of poolside lifeguards is not statistically significant ($\bar{x}_1 = 826.75$; $s_1 = 22.84$); $p < 0.20$ (two-tailed). The 95% confidence interval for the true population mean difference (μ_1 - μ_2) is between – 17.77 and 35.77.

Power of the statistical test procedure using *G*power 3* software = 9.80%

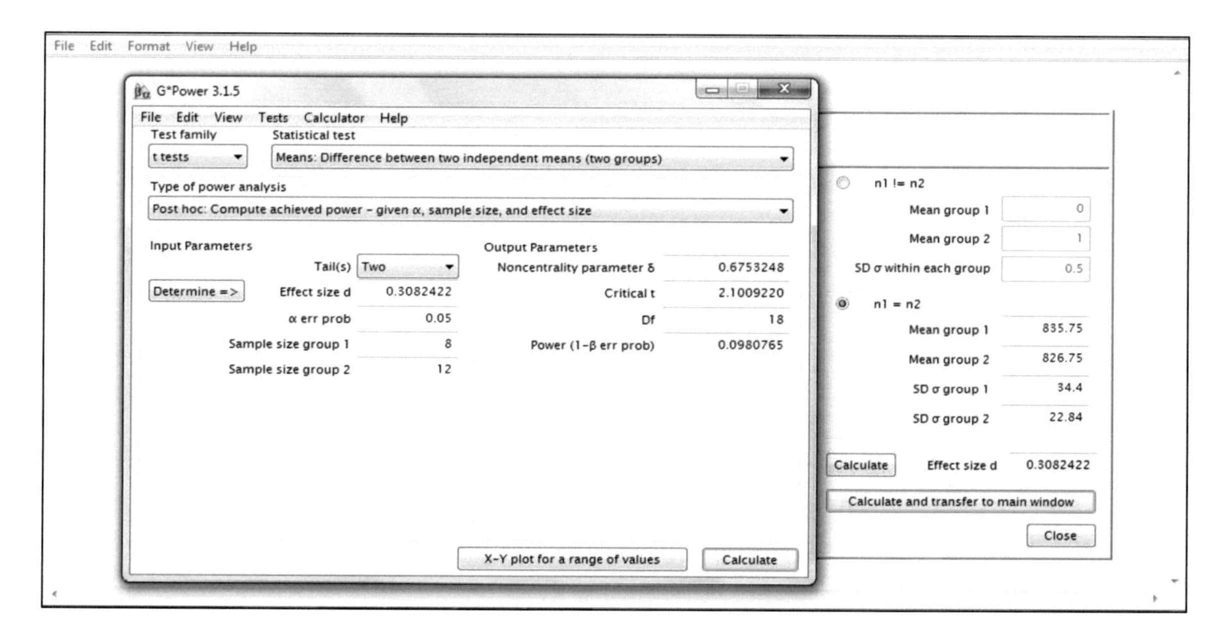

Appropriate sample size using *G*power 3* software

The appropriate sample size for the following input parameters is 114:

a. *α = 0.05*
b. *Desire effect size i.e. d = 0.50 (d = 0.50 assumed in the absence of context specific guidelines)*
c. *Power level for the test = 0.75*
d. *Two-sided test*

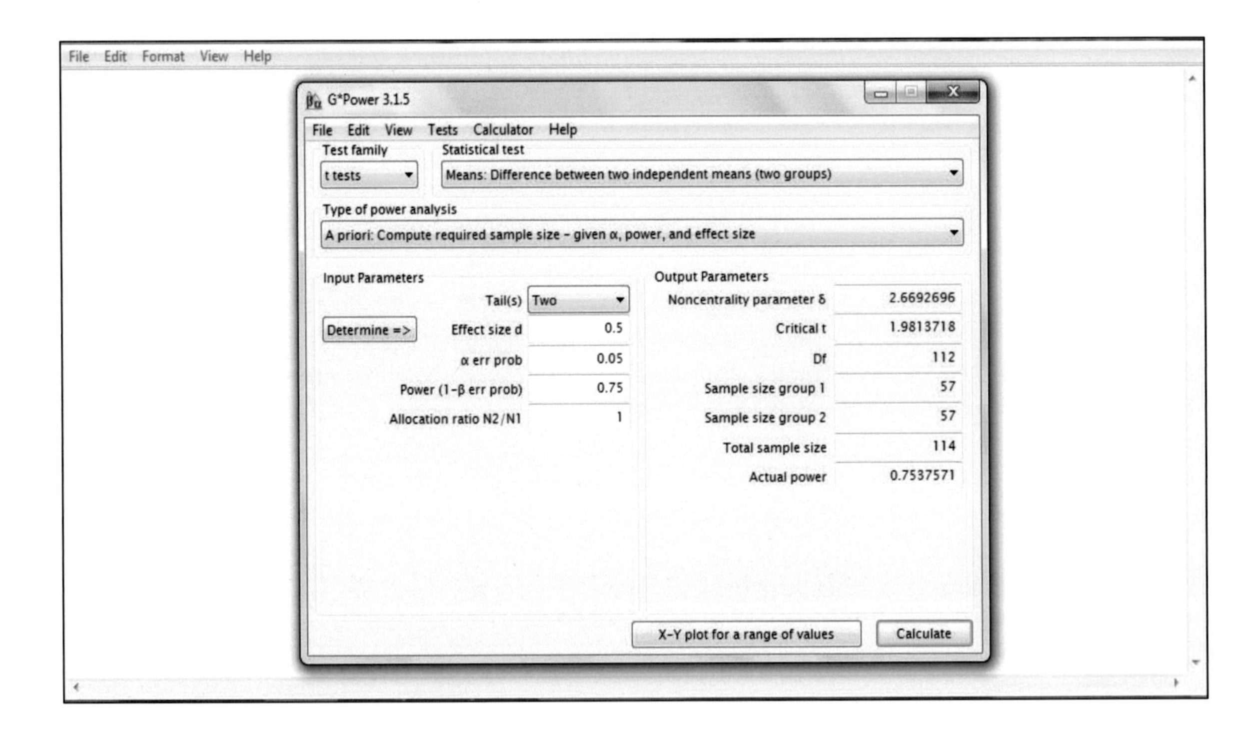

7.8 Statistical Inference: *Comparing two large independent samples – One tailed test*

Example 3

I wish to investigate whether the pulse rates (beats per minute) of smokers are higher than the pulse rates (bpm) of non-smokers. A sample of 100 of both groups was selected and the results are as follows:

Smokers	$n_S = 100$	$\bar{x}_S = 90$	$S_S = 5$
Non-Smokers	$n_{NS} = 100$	$\bar{x}_{NS} = 88$	$S_{NS} = 6$

*Can I conclude that smokers have higher pulse rates (bpm) than non-smokers? Use G*power 3 to calculate the post hoc power of the statistical test.*

Statistical Test Procedure

1. *State the assumptions required to validate this test*

   As per example 1

2. *State the null hypothesis and alternative hypothesis*

   H_0: $\mu_S \leq \mu_{NS}$
   H_1: $\mu_S > \mu_{NS}$ *One-tailed test (left tail as determined by the operator > in H_1)*

3. *State the statistical decision rule for a selected level of significance*

   a. Appropriate test statistic is the *z* test since n_1 & $n_2 \geq 30$ and assumption 3 in part *(1)*
   b. The level of significance for this test: $\alpha = 0.05$
   c. Identify the critical value in the diagram below *(A segment of the z tables is included here)*

      Identifying 1.65 *in the diagram below requires 0.05 to be allocated to the right tail. Use the z tables to derive the critical value (z value) for an area equal to 0.05.*

   d. Reject the null hypothesis *(H_0)* when the calculated test statistic *(z test)* from part 4 below > Critical value 1.65.

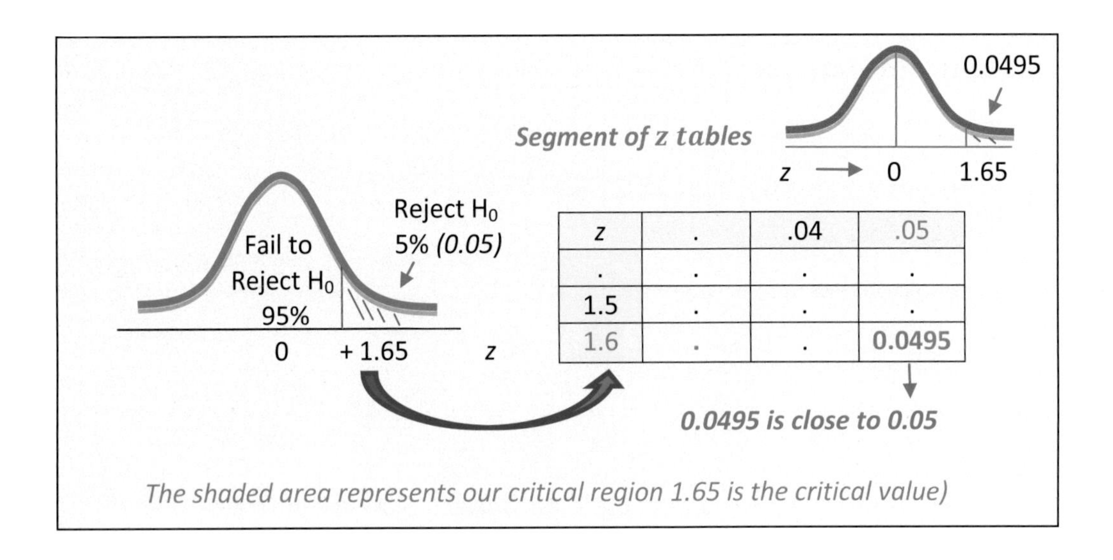

The shaded area represents our critical region 1.65 is the critical value)

4. *Select and calculate the appropriate test statistic*

(if σ_1^2 & σ_2^2 are unknown we can use s_1^2 and s_2^2 since n_1 & $n_2 \geq 30$)

$$z\ test = \frac{\bar{x}_1 - \bar{x}_2 - 0}{\sqrt{\frac{\sigma_1^2}{n_1} + \frac{\sigma_2^2}{n_2}}} = \frac{90-88-0}{\sqrt{\frac{(5)^2}{100} + \frac{(6)^2}{100}}} = \frac{2}{\sqrt{0.61}} = 2.56$$

5. *Compare the calculated test statistic with the critical value*

The calculated *z* test statistic *(2.56)* falls into the critical region where we reject H_0. In rejecting H_0, we are inferring that the pulse rates of smokers are higher than the pulse rates of non-smokers at the 0.05 level of significance *(statistical significance is declared).*

6. *Derive or locate an approximate p value working with a segment of the z tables*

The *p* value is the area under the curve defined by the calculated z value derived from the *z test* in step 4.

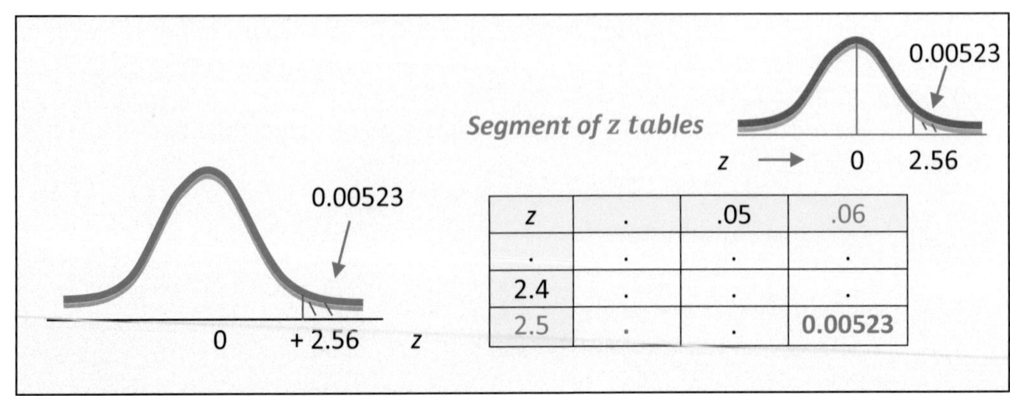

Interpreting the p value

a. Traditional approach – explicit reference to a selected cut-off point of say α = 0.05:

Since the p value of 0.00523 is below the 0.05 level of significance, we can reject H_0 at the 0.05 level of significance (Applying the p value decision rule: If p value < 0.05 reject H_0). The observed difference is too large to be solely attributed to sampling error (chance).

b. Current approach – no explicit reference to a selected cut-off point of say α = 0.05. The cut-off point is implicitly assumed as a guide value. The current approach is to report an exact *p* value *(included in the output of all statistical software packages)*. Using tables will only give us approximations.

The p value reveals the likelihood of being wrong if we reject H_0 (the p value 0.00523 i.e. < 1 time in 100).

Confidence Interval Procedure

Construct 95% confidence interval to estimate a range for the true difference between the means

1. *Identify the difference between the means*

Difference between the means: $(\bar{x}_1 - \bar{x}_2) = (90 - 88) = 2$

2. *Select a confidence interval and confidence level*

The appropriate confidence interval for n_1 & $n_2 \geq 30$ is:

$$(\bar{x}_1 - \bar{x}_2) \pm z_{\alpha/2} \text{ x SE diff.}$$

3. *Construct the 95% confidence interval of the true difference between the two groups*

$(\bar{x}_1 - \bar{x}_2) \pm z_{\alpha/2}$ x SE diff *where* $z_{\alpha/2} = z_{0.05/2} = z_{(0.025)} = 1.96$

z	0.05	0.06
.	.	.
1.8	.	.
1.9	.	0.0250

$(\bar{x}_1 - \bar{x}_2) \pm 1.96$ x SE diff where SE diff = $\sqrt{\left[\left(\frac{s_1^2}{n_1}\right) + \left(\frac{s_2^2}{n_2}\right)\right]}$

$(90 - 88) \pm 1.96 \text{ x } 0.1118$ where SE diff = $\sqrt{\left[\frac{(5)^2}{100} + \frac{(6)^2}{100}\right]}$ =

0.781

$2 \pm 1.96 \text{ x } 0.781$

2 ± 1.53

The 95% confidence interval is 0.47 to 3.53

4. State your inferences

Since this interval does not include zero then:

a. *The evidence (data gathered for both groups) available is compatible with a decision to reject the null hypothesis.*
b. *The probability that the calculated interval (0.47 to 3.53) contains the true population mean difference (μ_1 - μ_2) is 95%. This is an intuitive but not strictly a correct interpretation of a confidence interval.*

Effect Size Procedure

How large is the difference between the groups?

1. Identify the difference between the means

Difference between the means: $(\bar{x}_1 - \bar{x}_2) = \big((90 - 88)\big) = 2$

2. Calculate the 'measure of effect'

$$\text{Effect Size} = \frac{(\bar{x}_1 - \bar{x}_2)}{s_p} = \frac{(90-88)}{3.9} = \frac{2}{5.52} = 0.36$$

Where $s_p = \sqrt{\frac{(n_1-1).s_1^2 + (n_2-1).s_2^2}{(n_1 + n_2 - 2)}} = \sqrt{779} = 27.91$ *When sample sizes are unequal*

Where $s_p = \sqrt{\frac{s_1^2 + s_2^2}{2}} = 5.52$ *When sample sizes are equal*

3. State your inferences

To interpret this value, we refer to guidelines proposed by Cohen, 1988.

Effect Size *(d)*	Interpretation	% of overlap	
If d = 0	No effect	100%	
If d = 0.2	Small	85%	
If d = 0.5	Medium	67%	
If d = 0.8	Large	53%	

Reported results using the current approach (implicit cut-off guide point of α = 0.05):

The mean pulse rate (bpm) of smokers ($\bar{x}_1$ = 90; s_1 = 5) is higher than the mean pulse rate (bpm) of non-smokers ($\bar{x}_1$ = 88; s_1 = 6); p = 0.00523 (one-tailed). The mean difference of 2 is a small to medium effect size (d = 0.36). The 95% confidence interval for the true population mean difference (μ_1 - μ_2) is between 0.47 and 3.53.

Power of the statistical test procedure using *G*power 3* software = 81.78%

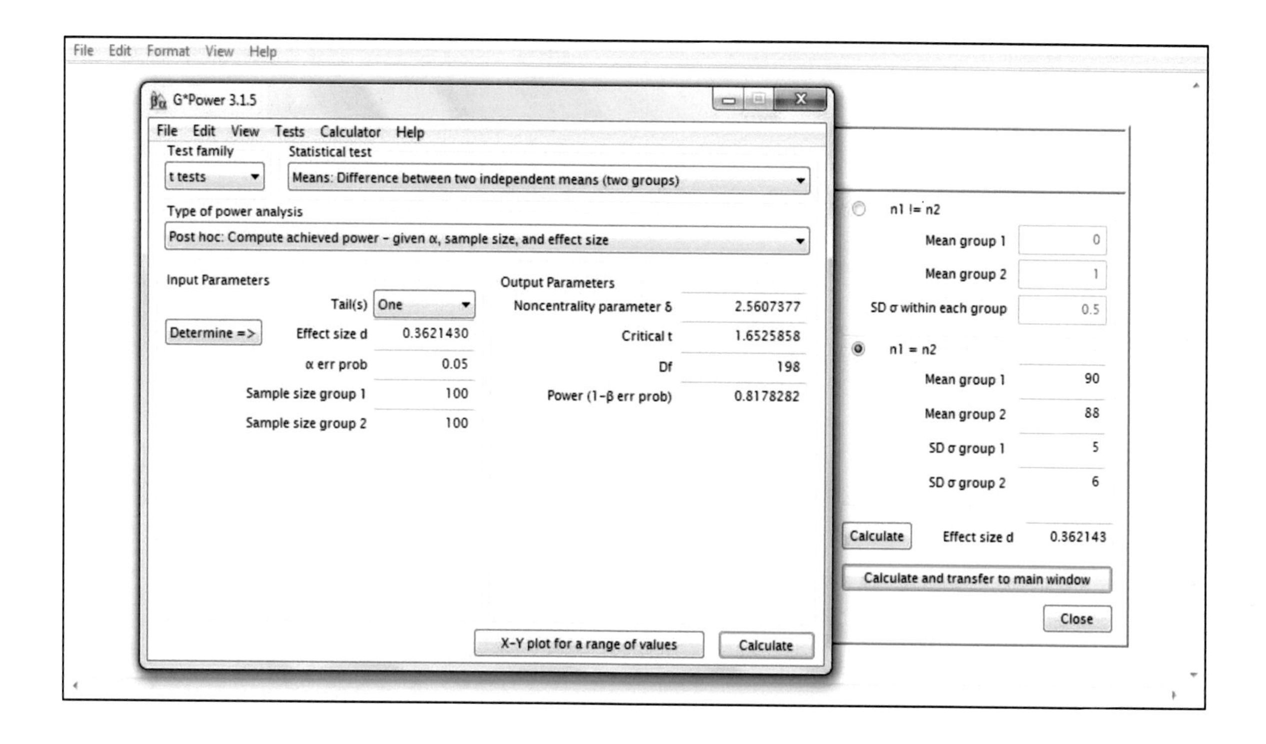

Example 4

I wish to investigate whether female students scored a better mean grade (%) than male students in a statistics exam. The following results were compiled:

Female Students	$n_1 = 7$	$\bar{x}_1 = 79$	$s_1 = 6.88$
Male Students	$n_2 = 9$	$\bar{x}_2 = 78$	$s_2 = 9.49$

*Is the mean grade for female students higher than the mean grade (%) scored by male students? Test at the 0.05 level of significance. The researcher gave no consideration to what would constitute an appropriate sample size. Use G*power 3 to calculate the post hoc power of the statistical test. If the statistical test procedure fails to detect statistical significance, use G*power 3 to calculated the appropriate sample size.*

Statistical Test Procedure

1. *State the assumptions required to validate this test*

   As per example 1

2. *State the null hypothesis and alternative hypothesis*

   $H_0: \mu_{Female} \leq \mu_{Male}$
   $H_1: \mu_{Female} > \mu_{Male}$ *One-tailed test (right tail as determined by the operator > in H_1)*

3. *State the statistical decision rule for a selected level of significance*

   a. Appropriate test statistic is the *t* test since n_1 & $n_2 < 30$ and assumption 3 in part *(1)*
   b. The level of significance for this test: $\alpha = 0.05$
   c. Identify the critical value in the diagram below. *(A segment of the t tables is included here.)*

      Identifying 1.761 *in the diagram below requires 0.05 to be allocated to the right tail. Use the t tables to derive the critical value (t value) for an area equal to 0.05 @ 14 degrees of freedom.*

   d. Reject the null hypothesis *(H_0)* when the calculated test statistic *(t test)* from part 4 below > Critical value 1.761.

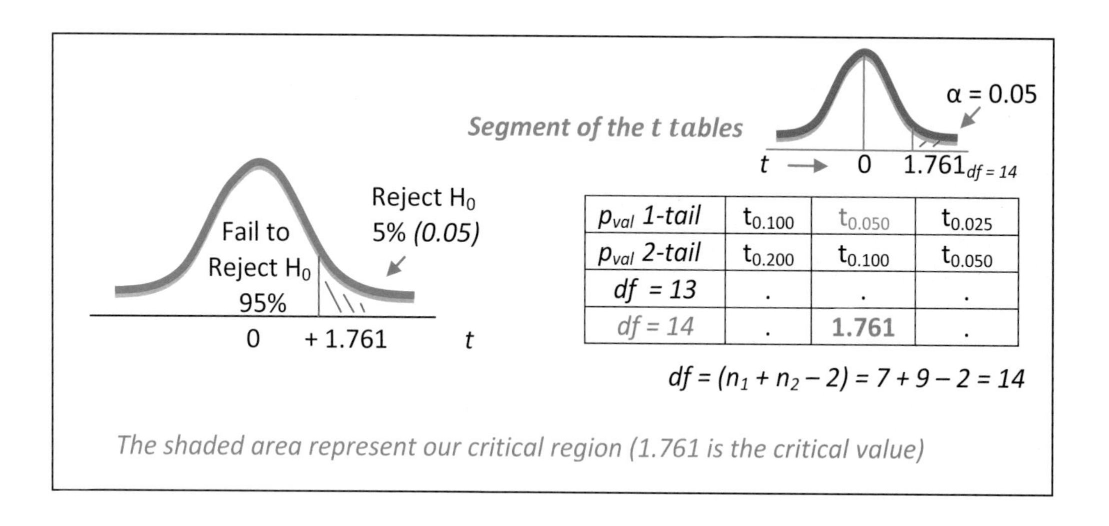

p_{val} *1-tail*	$t_{0.100}$	$t_{0.050}$	$t_{0.025}$
p_{val} *2-tail*	$t_{0.200}$	$t_{0.100}$	$t_{0.050}$
df = 13	.	.	.
df = 14	.	**1.761**	.

4. *Select and calculate the appropriate test statistic*

$$t\ test = \frac{79-78-0}{\sqrt{71.75\left(\frac{1}{7}+\frac{1}{9}\right)}} = \frac{1}{\sqrt{9.11}} = 0.33$$

$$where\ s_p^2 = \frac{(n_1-1)s_1^2+(n_2-1)s_2^2}{n_1+n_2-2} = \frac{(7-1)(6.88)^2+(9-1)(9.49)^2}{7+9-2} = 71.75$$

5. *Compare the calculated test statistic with the critical value*

The calculated *t* test statistic *(0.33)* falls into the region where we fail to reject H_0. In failing to reject H_0, we are inferring that the mean grade of female students is not higher than the mean grade of male students, at the 0.05 level of significance *(Non-statistical significance is declared)*.

6. *Derive or locate an approximate p value working with a segment of the t tables*

Segment of t tables

p_{val} *1-tail*	$t_{0.100}$	$t_{0.050}$	$t_{0.025}$
p_{val} *2-tail*	$t_{0.200}$	$t_{0.100}$	$t_{0.050}$
Above 0.05 ⟵			
df = 13	.	.	.
df = 14	**1.345**	1.761	2.145

We search the *t* table for a value which comes nearest to our calculated *t* test statistic *(0.33, sign ignored)* at 14 degrees of freedom for a one tailed test *(1.345 comes closest in this particular table)*. This value *(1.345)* corresponds to a *p* value of 0.10.

Interpreting the p value

a. Traditional approach – explicit reference to a selected cut-off point of say $\alpha = 0.05$:

Since this p value is above 0.05, we fail to reject H_0 at the 0.05 level of significance (Applying the p value decision rule: If p value > 0.05 we fail to reject H_0). The observed difference is most likely to be solely attributed to sampling error (chance).

b. Current approach – no explicit reference to a selected cut-off point of say $\alpha = 0.05$. The cut-off point is implicitly assumed as a guide value. The current approach is to report an exact *p* value *(included in the output of all statistical software packages)*. Using tables will only give us approximations.

The p value reveals the likelihood of being wrong if we reject H_0 (the p value is well above 0.10 i.e. 10 times in 100).

Confidence Interval Procedure

Construct 95% confidence interval to estimate a range for the true difference between the means

1. *Identify the difference between the means*

Difference between the means: $(\bar{x}_1 - \bar{x}_2) = (79 - 78) = 1$

2. *Select a confidence interval and confidence level*

The appropriate confidence interval for n_1 & $n_2 < 30$ is:

$$(\bar{x}_1 - \bar{x}_2) \pm t_{(\alpha/2, n_1 + n_2 - 2)} \text{ x SE diff.}$$

3. *Construct the 95% confidence interval of the true difference between the two groups*

$(\bar{x}_1 - \bar{x}_2) \pm t_{(\alpha/2, n_1 + n_2 - 2)}$ x SE diff *where* SE diff = $\sqrt{s_p^2\left(\frac{1}{n_1} + \frac{1}{n_2}\right)}$ and $s_p^2 = \frac{(n_1 - 1).s_1^2 + (n_2 - 1).s_2^2}{(n_1 + n_{2-2})}$

$t_{(\alpha/2, n_1 + n_2 - 2)} = t_{(0.05/2,\ 7+9-2=14)} = t_{(0.025,\ 14)} = 2.145$

p_{val} 1-tail	$t_{0.050}$	$t_{0.025}$
p_{val} 2-tail	$t_{0.100}$	$t_{0.050}$
df = 13	.	.
df = 14	.	**2.145**

$(79 - 78) \pm 2.145 \text{ x } \sqrt{71.75\left(\frac{1}{7} + \frac{1}{9}\right)}$

$(1) \pm 2.145 \text{ x } 3.02$

$(1) \pm 6.48$

The 95% confidence interval is -5.48 to 7.48

4. State your inferences

Since this interval does include zero then:

a. *The evidence (data gathered for both groups) available is compatible with a failure to reject the null hypothesis.*
b. *The probability that the calculated interval (-5.48 to 7.48) contains the true population mean difference (μ_1 - μ_2) is 95%. This is an intuitive but not strictly a correct interpretation of a confidence interval.*

Effect Size Procedure

How large is the difference between the groups?

This procedure is often regarded as unnecessary when we fail to reject the null hypothesis. However, this policy may be unwise in every instance. See example 2 above. In this example, the effect size procedure is not employed since the p value ($p > 0.10$) is quite a distance from the 0.05 level of significance.

Reported results using the current approach (implicit cut-off guide point of $\alpha = 0.05$):

The mean grade of female students ($\bar{x}_1 = 79$; $s_1 = 6.88$) is not higher the mean grade of male students ($\bar{x}_1 = 79$; $s_1 = 9.49$); $p > 0.10$ (one-tailed). The 95% confidence interval for the true population mean difference (μ_1 - μ_2) is between -5.84 and 7.48.

Power of the statistical test procedure using *G*power 3* software = 7.82%

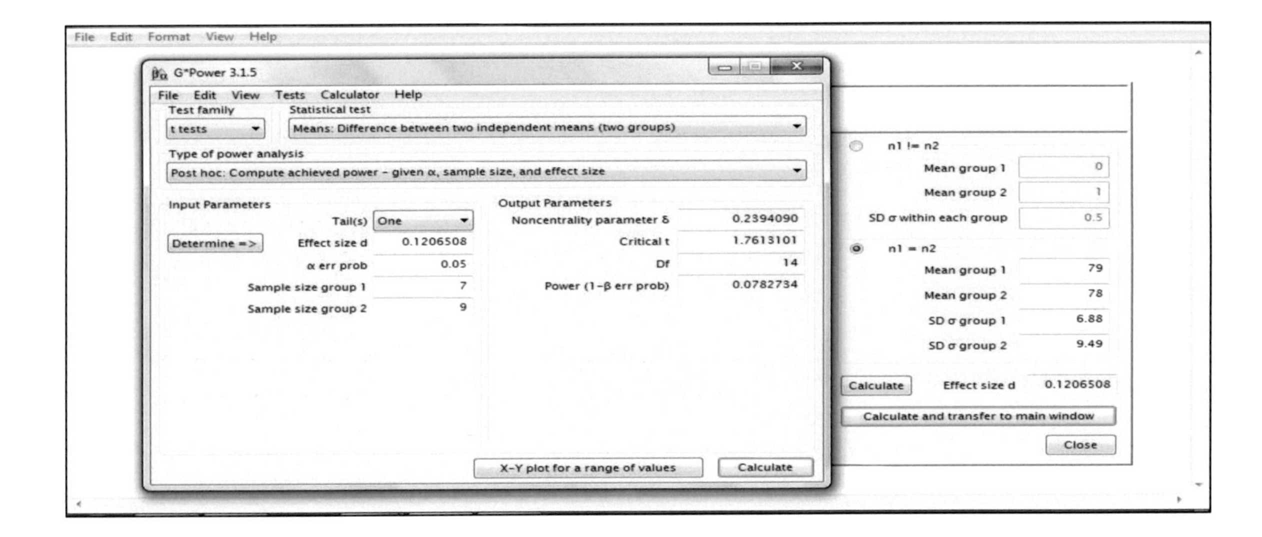

Appropriate sample size using *G*power 3* software

The appropriate sample size for the following input parameters is 88:

a. *α = 0.05*
b. *Desire effect size i.e. d = 0.50 (d = 0.50 in the absence of context specific guidelines)*
c. *Power level for the test = 0.75*
d. *One-sided test*

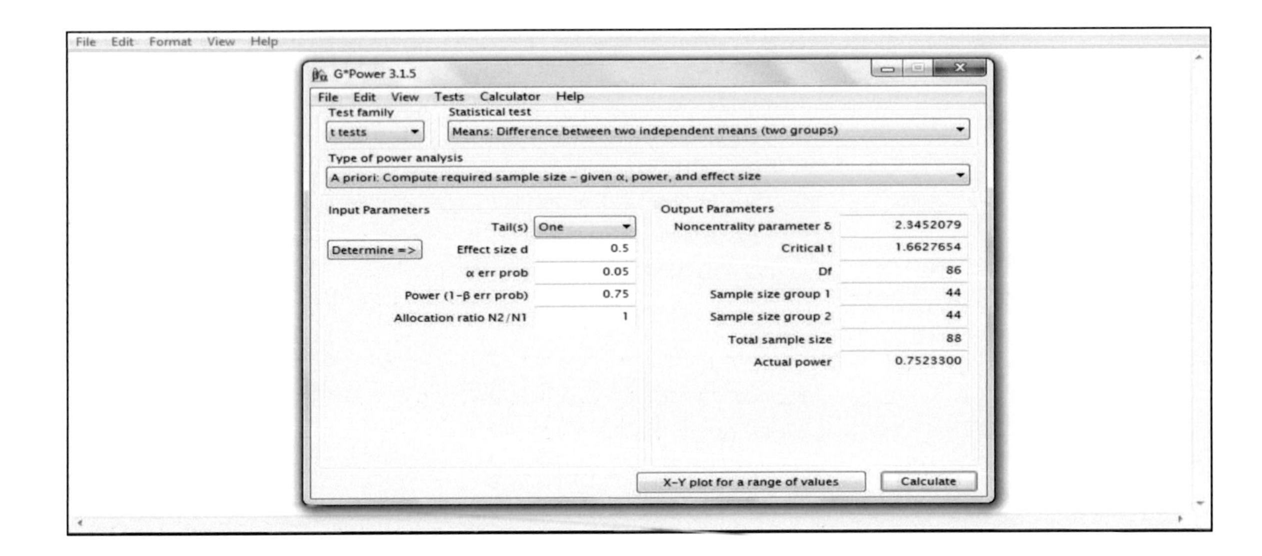

7.10 Statistical Inference: *Comparing two large matched samples – Two tailed test*

Example 5

I wish to investigate whether a course, intended to improve performance, actually works! An IQ test was given to a random sample of 40 students (n = 40) before a course and after the course was completed.

Before	$n_B = 40$	$\bar{x}_B = 95$	$S_B = 12$	$\bar{x}_B - \bar{x}_A$	S_d = standard deviation of paired differences
After	$n_A = 40$	$\bar{x}_A = 99$	$S_A = 13$	- 4	10

*Is there a difference between the mean IQ before versus the mean IQ after the course at the 0.05 level of significance? Was the course effective? Use G*power 3 to calculate the post hoc power of the statistical test.*

Statistical Test Procedure

1. *State the assumptions required to validate this test*

   a. That the measurement variable is continuous
   b. I will assume that the population of IQ for both groups are normally distributed
   c. I will assume that the population of paired differences is normally distributed
   d. I will assume that the variance of the population of IQ for both groups is equal. $\sigma_1^2 = \sigma_2^2$

2. *State the null hypothesis and alternative hypothesis*

   H_0: $\mu_d = 0$ where $\mu_d \rightarrow \mu_1 - \mu_2$
   H_1: $\mu_d \neq 0$ *Two-tailed test (determined by the operator ≠ in H_1)*

3. *State the statistical decision rule for a selected level of significance*

   a. Appropriate test statistic is the *z* test since n > 30 and assumption 3 in part *(1)*
   b. The level of significance for this test: $\alpha = 0.05$
   c. Identify the critical value in the diagram below *(A segment of the z tables is included here)*

   Identifying ± 1.96 in the diagram below requires 0.05 to be divided between both tails. Each tail has, therefore, an area equal to 0.025 each. Use the z tables to derive the critical values (z values) for an area equal to 0.025. Since the bell curve is symmetrical, the critical values are ± 1.96.

   d. Reject the null hypothesis *(H_0)* when the calculated test statistic *(t test)* from part 4 below > Critical value ± 1.96

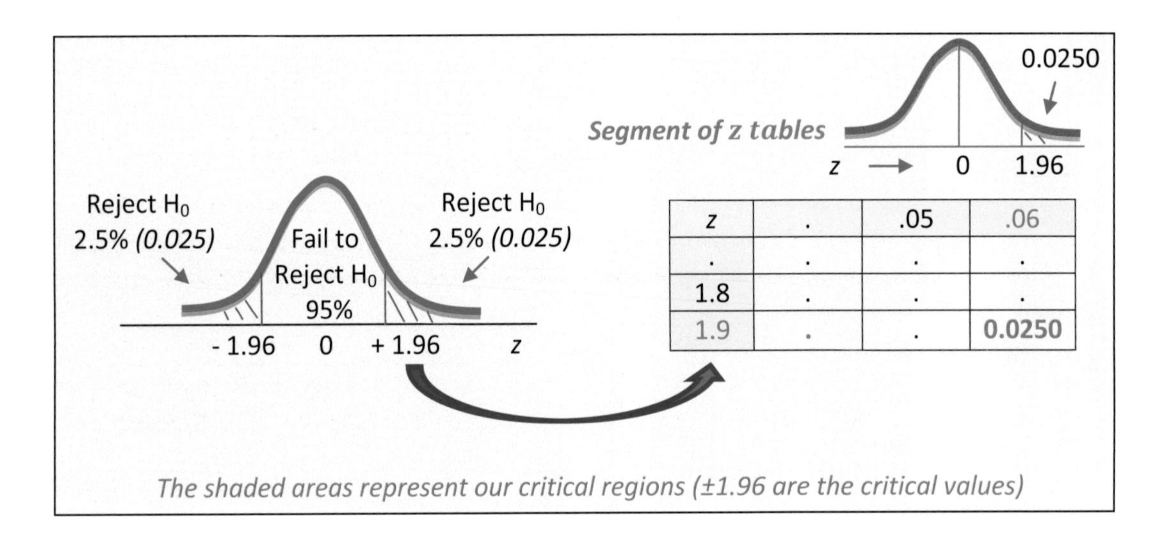

The shaded areas represent our critical regions (±1.96 are the critical values)

4. *Select and calculate the appropriate test statistic*

$$z = \frac{\bar{D} - \mu_d}{s_{\bar{D}}} \quad \textit{where } s_{\bar{D}} = \frac{\sigma_d}{\sqrt{n}} \quad \textit{where } s_{\bar{D}} = \frac{10}{\sqrt{40}} = 1.58 \ (s_d = \sigma_d \text{ when } n \geq 30)$$

$$z = \frac{-4 - 0}{1.58} = -2.53$$

5. *Compare the calculated test statistic with the critical value*

The calculated *z test* statistic of -2.53 falls into the leftward critical region where we reject H_0. In rejecting H_0, we are inferring that the difference between the mean IQ before versus the mean IQ after is *statistically significant* at the 0.05 level of significance.

6. *Derive or locate an approximate p value working with a segment of the z tables*

The *p* value is the sum of the areas under the curve defined by the calculated z value derived from the *z test* in step 4.

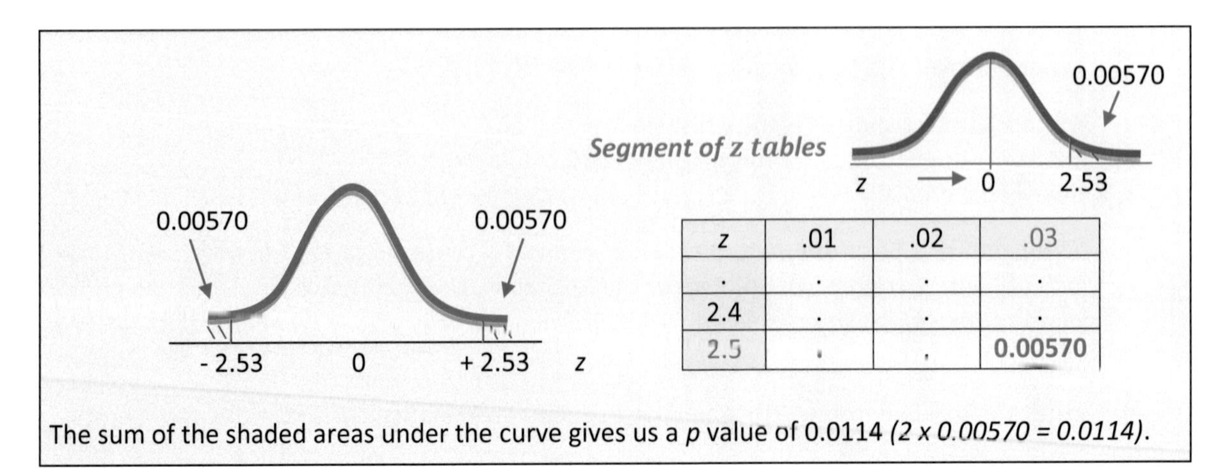

The sum of the shaded areas under the curve gives us a *p* value of 0.0114 *(2 x 0.00570 = 0.0114)*.

Interpreting the p value

a. Traditional approach – explicit reference to a selected cut-off point of say $\alpha = 0.05$:

Since the p value of 0.0114 is below the 0.05 level of significance, we can reject H_0 at the 0.05 level of significance (Applying the p value decision rule: If p value < 0.05 reject H_0). The observed difference is too large to be solely attributed to sampling error (chance).

b. Current approach – no explicit reference to a selected cut-off point of say $\alpha = 0.05$. The cut-off point is implicitly assumed as a guide value. The current approach is to report an exact *p* value *(included in the output of all statistical software packages)*. Using tables will only give us approximations.

The p value reveals the likelihood of being wrong if we reject H_0 (the p value is 0.0114 i.e. just over 1 time in 1000).

Confidence Interval Procedure

Construct 95% confidence interval to estimate a range for the true difference between the means

1. *Identify the difference between the means*

Difference between the means: $(\bar{x}_1 - \bar{x}_2) = (95 - 99) = -4$

2. *Select a confidence interval and confidence level*

The appropriate confidence interval for $n \geq 30$ is:

$$(\bar{x}_1 - \bar{x}_2) \pm z_{\alpha/2} . s_{\bar{D}}$$

3. *Construct the 95% confidence interval of the difference between the two groups*

$(\bar{x}_1 - \bar{x}_2) \pm z_{\alpha/2} . s_{\bar{D}}$ *where* $z_{\alpha/2} = z_{0.05/2} = z_{(0.025)}$

$(\bar{x}_1 - \bar{x}_2) \pm 1.96 \text{ x } s_{\bar{D}}$ where $s_{\bar{D}} = \frac{10}{\sqrt{40}} = 1.58$

$(95 - 109) \pm 1.96 \text{ x } 1.58$

$-4 \pm 1.96 \text{ x } 1.58$

-4 ± 3.10

z	0.05	0.06
.	.	.
1.8	.	.
1.9	.	**0.0250**

The 95% confidence interval is – 0.9 to – 7.10

4. State your inferences

Since this interval does not include zero then:

a. *The evidence available is compatible with a decision to reject the null hypothesis.*
b. *The probability that the calculated interval (-17.1 to -10.9) contains the true population mean difference (μ_1 - μ_2) is 95%. This is an intuitive but not strictly a correct interpretation of a confidence interval.*

Effect Size Procedure

How large is the difference between the measurements before and the measurements after?

1. Identify the difference between the means

Difference between the means: $(\bar{x}_1 - \bar{x}_2) = (95 - 109)$ = - 4

2. Calculate the 'measure of effect'

Effect Size = $\frac{(\bar{x}_1 - \bar{x}_2)}{s_p} = \frac{(95-99)}{10} = \frac{-4}{10}$ = - 0.4 *where s_p = standard deviation of paired differences*

3. State your inferences

To interpret this value, we refer to guidelines proposed by Cohen, 1988.

Effect Size *(d)*	Interpretation	% of overlap	
If d = 0	No effect	100%	
If d = 0.2	Small	85%	
If d = 0.5	Medium	67%	
If d = 0.8	Large	53%	

Reported results using the current approach (implicit cut-off guide point of α = 0.05):

The difference between the mean score before the course ($\bar{x}_B$ = 95; s_B = 12) compared to the mean score after the course is statistically significant ($\bar{x}_A$ = 99; s_A = 13); p = 0.0114 (two-tailed).The mean difference of -4 has a medium effect size (d = - 0.4). The 95% confidence interval for the true population mean difference (μ_1 - μ_2) is between -0.9 and -7.10.

Power of the statistical test procedure using *G*power 3* software = 69.39%

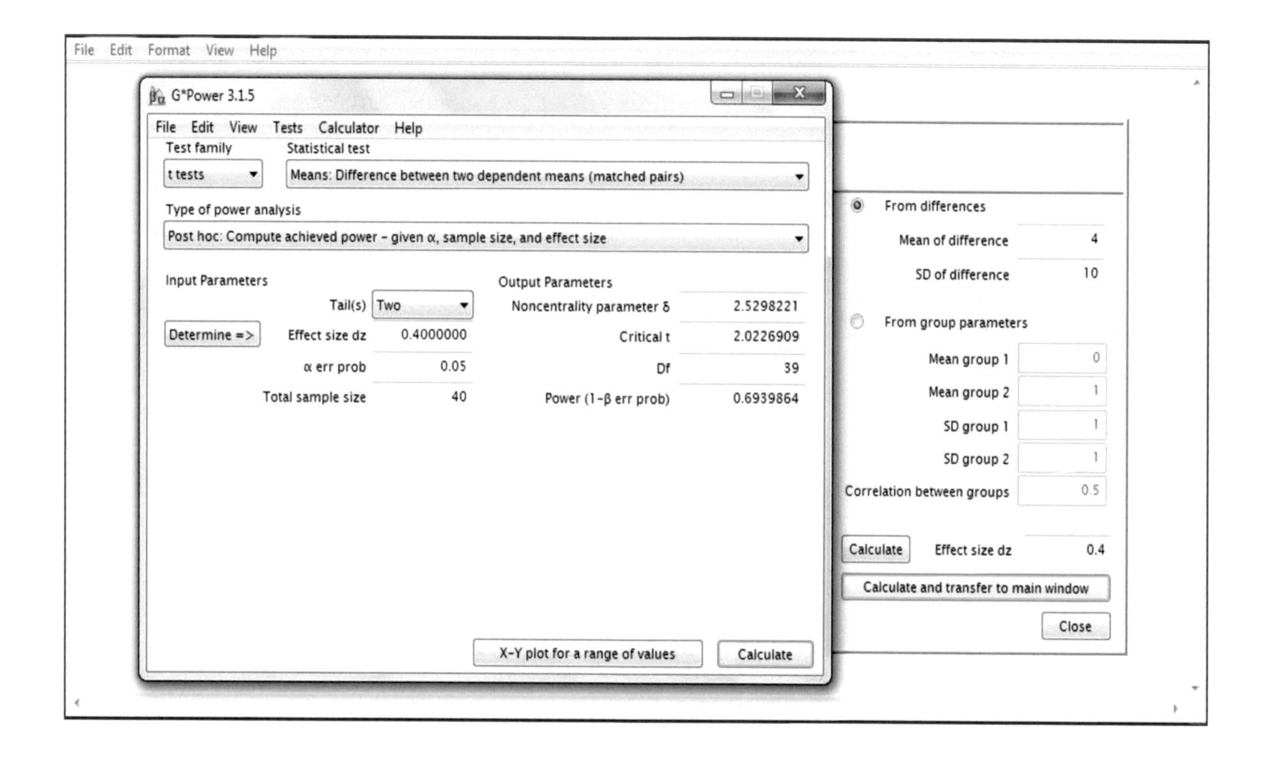

7.11 Statistical Inference: *Comparing two small matched samples – Two tailed test*

Example 6

*I wish to investigate whether a personal training programme (PTP) had an effect on a sample of 12 staff. In week 1 the 12 members of staff were timed after they completed a 24 km walk. After a 10 week programme the same members of staff undertook the 15 km walk and their new times were recorded. Use G*power 3 to calculate the post hoc power of the statistical test.*

Times in Week 1 X_1	Times in Week 10 X_2	$D = X_1 - X_2$	D^2
140	115	25	625
84	68	16	256
79	63	16	256
130	89	41	1681
105	76	29	841
204	170	34	1156
132	92	40	1600
170	151	19	361
106	77	29	841
160	125	35	1225
90	72	18	324
160	150	10	100
1,560	1,248	$\sum D = 312$	$\sum D^2 = 9266$
$\bar{X}_1 = \frac{1,560}{12} = 130$ $s_1 = \sqrt{\frac{\sum(X - \bar{X}_1)^2}{n-1}} = 38.72$	$\bar{X}_2 = \frac{1,248}{12} = 104$ $s_2 = \sqrt{\frac{\sum(X - \bar{X}_2)^2}{n-1}} = 37.08$	$\bar{D} = \frac{312}{12} = 26$ *(mean of paired differences)*	

$$S_p = \sqrt{\frac{\sum D^2 - \frac{(\sum D)^2}{n}}{n-1}} = S_p = \sqrt{\frac{9266 - \frac{(312)^2}{12}}{12-1}} = 10.24 \text{ (standard deviation of paired differences)}$$

Statistical Test Procedure

1. *State the assumptions required to validate this test*

   a. That the measurement variable is continuous
   b. I will assume that the population of IQ for both groups are normally distributed
   c. I will assume that the population of paired differences is normally distributed
   d. I will assume that the variance of the population of IQ for both groups is equal. $\sigma_1^2 = \sigma_2^2$

2. *State the null hypothesis and alternative hypothesis*

H_0: $\mu_d = 0$ where $\mu_d \rightarrow \mu_1 - \mu_2$
H_1: $\mu_d \neq 0$ *Two-tailed test (determined by the operator ≠ in H_1)*

3. *State the statistical decision rule for a selected level of significance*

a. Appropriate test statistic is the *t* test since n < 30 and assumption 3 in part *(1)*
b. The level of significance for this test: $\alpha = 0.05$
c. Identify the critical value in the diagram below *(A segment of the t tables is included here)*

Identifying ± 2.201 *in the diagram below requires 0.05 to be divided between both tails. Each tail has, therefore, an area equal to 0.025 each. Use the t tables to derive the critical values (t values) for an area equal to 0.025 @ n – 1 degrees of freedom. Since the bell curve is symmetrical, the critical values are* ± 2.201.

d. Reject the null hypothesis *(H_0)* when the calculated test statistic *(t test)* from part 4 below > Critical value ± 2.201

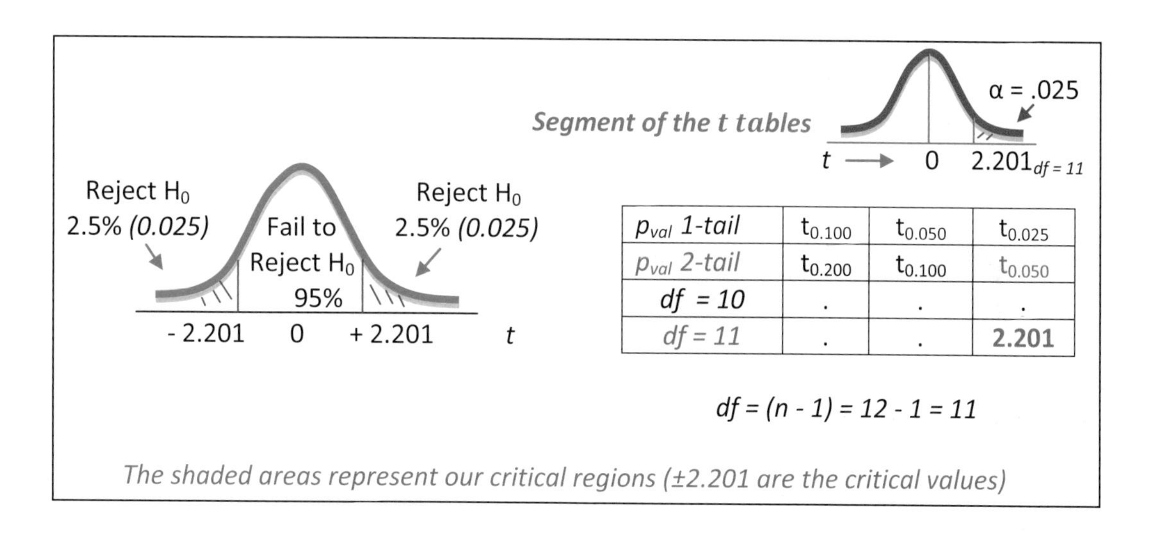

p_{val} 1-tail	$t_{0.100}$	$t_{0.050}$	$t_{0.025}$
p_{val} 2-tail	$t_{0.200}$	$t_{0.100}$	$t_{0.050}$
df = 10	.	.	.
df = 11	.	.	**2.201**

The shaded areas represent our critical regions (±2.201 are the critical values)

4. *Select and calculate the appropriate test statistic*

$$t = \frac{\bar{D} - \mu_d}{s_{\bar{D}}} \quad \text{where } s_{\bar{D}} = \frac{s_d}{\sqrt{n}}$$

$$t = \frac{26 - 0}{2.96} = 8.78 \qquad \text{where } s_{\bar{D}} = \frac{10.24}{\sqrt{12}} = 2.96$$

5. *Compare the calculated test statistic with the critical value*

The calculated *t* test statistic of 8.78 falls into the rightward critical region where we reject H_0. In rejecting H_0, we are inferring that difference between the mean times before versus the mean times after is *statistically significant* at the 0.05 level of significance.

6. *Derive or locate an approximate p value working with a segment of the t tables*

Segment of t tables

p_{val} *1-tail*	$t_{0.100}$	$t_{0.050}$	$t_{0.025}$	$t_{0.010}$	$t_{0.005}$	$t_{0.0005}$
p_{val} *2-tail*	$t_{0.200}$	$t_{0.100}$	$t_{0.050}$	$t_{0.02}$	$t_{0.01}$	$t_{0.001}$
			→		*Below 0.05*	
df = 10	.	.	.	.	.	.
df = 11	1.363	1.796	2.201	2.718	3.106	4.437

We search the *t* table for a value which comes nearest to our calculated *t* test statistic *(8.78, sign ignored)* at 11 degrees of freedom for a two tailed test *(4.437 comes closest in this particular table)*. This value *(4.437)* corresponds to a *p* value of 0.001. Since this *p* value is well below 0.05, we reject H_0 *(Applying the p value decision rule: If p value < 0.05 we reject H_0)*.

Interpreting the p value

a. Traditional approach – explicit reference to a selected cut-off point of say α = 0.05:

   Since this p value of 0.001 is well below 0.05, we reject H_0 at the 0.05 level of significance (Applying the p value decision rule: If p value < 0.05 we reject H_0). The observed difference is too large to be solely attributed to sampling error (chance).

b. Current approach – no explicit reference to a selected cut-off point of say α = 0.05. The cut-off point is implicitly assumed as a guide value. The current approach is to report an exact *p* value *(included in the output of all statistical software packages)*. Using tables will only give us approximations.

   The p value reveals the likelihood of being wrong if we reject H_0 (the p value is well below 0.001 i.e. 1 time in 1000).

Confidence Interval Procedure

Construct 95% confidence interval to estimate a range for the true difference between the means

1. *Identify the difference between the means*

Difference between the means: $(\bar{x}_1 - \bar{x}_2) = (130 - 104) = 26$

2. Select a confidence interval and confidence level

The appropriate confidence interval for n < 30 is:

$(\bar{x}_1 - \bar{x}_2) \pm t_{(\alpha/2,\ n-1)} \cdot s_{\bar{D}}$. The confidence level = 95%.

3. Construct the 95% confidence interval of the difference between the two group

$(\bar{x}_1 - \bar{x}_2) \pm t_{(\alpha/2,\ n-1)} \cdot s_{\bar{D}}$ *where* $t_{(\alpha/2, n_1 - 1)} = t_{(0.05/2,\ 12-1=11)} = t_{(0.025,\ 11)}$ = 2.201

p_{val} *1-tail*	$t_{0.050}$	$t_{0.025}$
p_{val} *2-tail*	$t_{0.100}$	$t_{0.050}$
df = 10	.	.
df = 11	.	**2.201**

$(130 - 104) \pm t_{(\alpha/2,\ n-1)} \cdot s_{\bar{D}}$ where $s_{\bar{D}} = \frac{10.24}{\sqrt{12}} = 2.96$

$(130 - 104) \pm 2.201 \times 2.96$

$26 \pm 2.201 \times 2.96$

26 ± 6.51

The 95% confidence interval is 19.49 to 32.51

4. State your inferences

Since this interval does not include zero then:

a. *The evidence (data gathered for both groups) available is not compatible with the null hypothesis being correct i.e. reject* H_0
b. *The probability that the calculated interval (19.49 to 32.51) contains the true population mean difference* ($\mu_1 - \mu_2$) *is 95%. This is an intuitive but not strictly a correct interpretation of a confidence interval.*

Effect Size Procedure

How large is the difference between the measurements before and the measurements after?

1. Identify the difference between the means

Difference between the means: $(\bar{x}_1 - \bar{x}_2) = (130 - 104) = 26$

2. Calculate the 'measure of effect'

Effect Size = $\frac{(\bar{x}_1 - \bar{x}_2)}{s_p} = \frac{(130-104)}{10.24} = 2.54$ *where* s_p *= standard deviation of paired differences*

3. State your inferences

To interpret this value, we refer to guidelines proposed by Cohen, 1988.

Effect Size *(d)*	Interpretation	% of overlap	
If d = 0	No effect	100%	
If d = 0.2	Small	85%	
If d = 0.5	Medium	67%	
If d = 0.8	Large	53%	

Reported results using the current approach (implicit cut-off guide point of $\alpha = 0.05$):

The difference between the mean score before the PTP ($\bar{x}_B = 130$; $s_B = 38.72$) compared to the mean score after the PTP is statistically significant ($\bar{x}_A = 104$; $s_A = 37.08$); $p < 0.001$ (two-tailed).The mean difference of 26 has a large effect size ($d = 2.54$). The 95% confidence interval for the true population mean difference ($\mu_1 - \mu_2$) is between 19.49 and 32.51.

Power of the statistical test procedure using *G*power 3* software = 100%

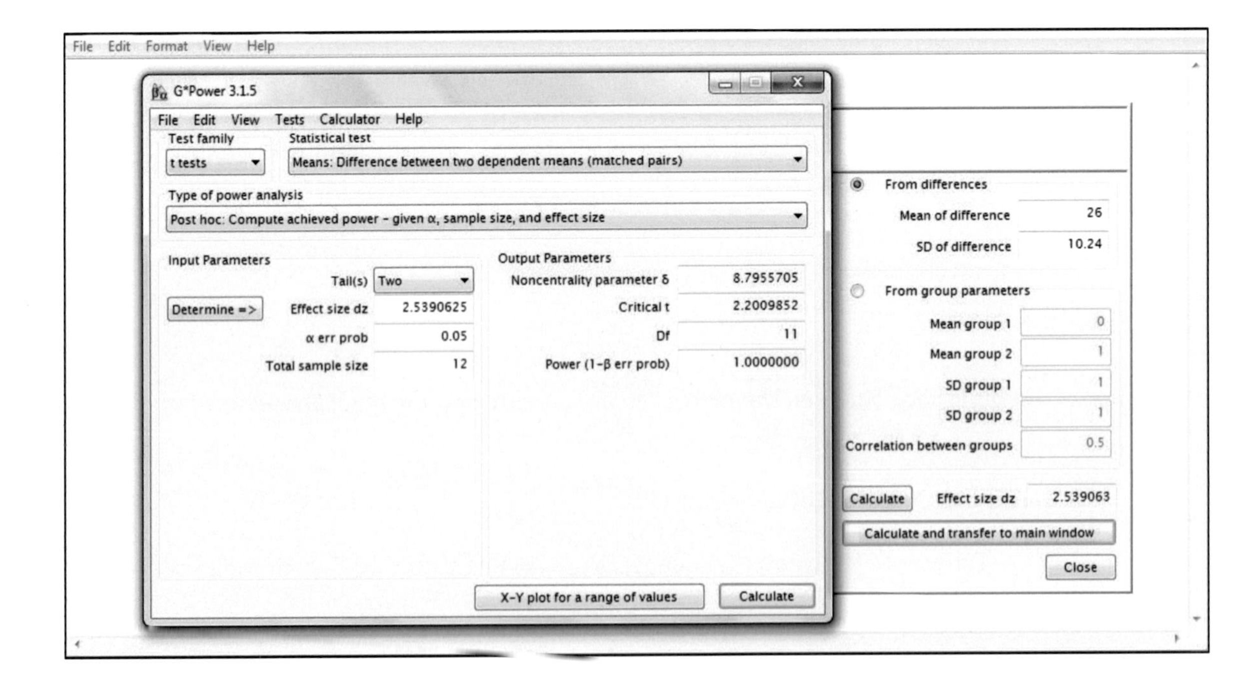

7.12 Statistical Inference: *MCQs and solutions*

Questions 1 to 3 relate to the following example:

I wish to investigate whether the mean exam grade is different between male and females. The following results were compiled:

Male	$n_1 = 48$	$\bar{x}_1 = 75$	$s_1 = 3.8$
Female	$n_2 = 52$	$\bar{x}_2 = 73$	$s_2 = 1.5$

1. A statistical test procedure tells us:

   (a) How large is the difference between two means
   (b) The range of values that contains the true difference between two means
   (c) If the observed difference between two means is statistically significant
   (d) None of the above

2. A confidence interval procedure tells us:

   (a) How large is the difference between two means
   (b) The range of values that contains the true mean difference
   (c) The range of values that excludes the true mean difference
   (d) None of the above

3. An effect size procedure tells us:

   (a) How large is the difference between two means
   (b) The range of values that contains the true mean difference
   (c) If the observed difference between two means is statistically significant
   (d) None of the above

4. An independent samples t-test is used when:

   (a) When we are undertaking a test on a single mean
   (b) When we are undertaking a test on paired/matched samples
   (c) When we undertaking a test on two unpaired/unmatched samples
   (d) None of the above

5. Consider the following distribution:

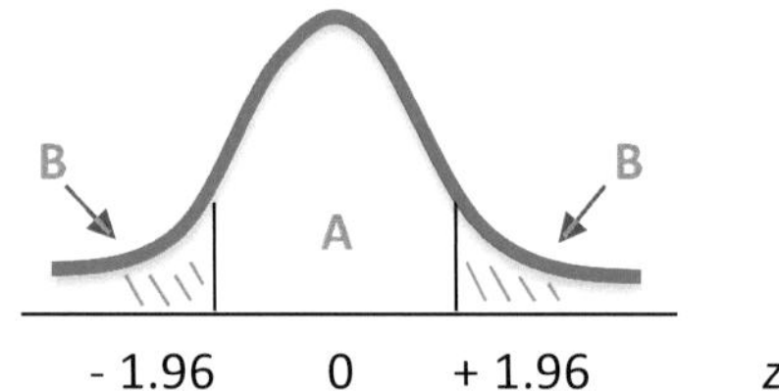

Which of the following is correct?

(a) If the calculated test statistic falls in A then reject H_0
(b) If the calculated test statistic falls in B then we fail to reject H_0
(c) If the calculated test statistic falls in A then we fail to reject H_0
(d) None of the above

6. A *p* value < 0.05 implies that we:

(a) Must redo the test
(b) Fail to reject H_0
(c) Reject H_0
(d) None of the above

7. Which of the following is an example of a two tailed test:

(a) H_0: $\mu_1 = \mu_2$ & H_1: $\mu_1 \neq \mu_2$
(b) H_0: $\mu_1 \leq \mu_2$ & H_1: $\mu_1 > \mu_2$
(c) H_0: $\mu_1 \geq \mu_2$ & H_1: $\mu_1 < \mu_2$
(d) None of the above

8. Which of the following is an example of a one tailed test *(right tail):*

(a) H_0: $\mu_1 = \mu_2$ & H_1: $\mu_1 \neq \mu_2$
(b) H_0: $\mu_1 \leq \mu_2$ & H_1: $\mu_1 > \mu_2$
(c) H_0: $\mu_1 \geq \mu_2$ & H_1: $\mu_1 < \mu_2$
(d) None of the above

9. Which of the following is an example of a one tailed test *(Left tail)*:

(a) H_0: $\mu_1 = \mu_2$ & H_1: $\mu_1 \neq \mu_2$
(b) H_0: $\mu_1 \leq \mu_2$ & H_1: $\mu_1 > \mu_2$
(c) H_0: $\mu_1 \geq \mu_2$ & H_1: $\mu_1 < \mu_2$
(d) None of the above

10. When the 95% confidence interval around the difference between two mean values includes a zero value, this indicates that:

(a) The difference is *not statistically* significant
(b) The difference *is statistically* significant
(c) The difference is quite small
(d) None of the above

11. An independent samples is used when:

(a) The people in one group are not included in the other group
(b) The sample group are involved in a before and after experiment concerning a new diet.
(c) The data collected from each independently sampled group is measured at the ordinal level
(d) The distribution of scores for each independently sampled group is non-normal

12. For a paired/matched samples t test, the degrees of freedom with 16 participants is:

(a) 30
(b) 15
(c) 14
(d) 16

13. For an independent samples t test, the degrees of freedom with 16 participants in each group is:

(a) 30
(b) 15
(c) 14
(d) 16

14. Twenty students were weighed in week one and again in week eight, after they underwent a special weight adjustment programme. The distribution of paired difference is assumed to be normally distributed. Which of the following is the most appropriate statistical test:

(a) Independent sample t test
(b) Paired/Matched samples t test
(c) Wilcoxon Signed Rank test
(d) None of the above

15. A 95% confidence interval can be interpreted as:

(a) If we repeat our study a large number of times and construct a confidence interval each time, then 95% of those intervals will contain the true population parameter
(b) If we repeat our study a large number of times and construct a confidence interval each time, then 5% of those intervals will contain the true population parameter
(c) The confidence interval which always contains the null hypothesis
(d) The confidence interval that always contains the alternative hypothesis

16. In an analysis using an independent samples t test, interpret the following statistical output:

Levene's Test Results: F = 0.6, p = 0.25

(a) The variance of both groups can be assumed unequal
(b) The variance of both groups can be assumed equal
(c) The variance of both groups can be assumed to be normally distributed
(d) None of the above

Questions 17 to 19 relate to the following statistical output:

Independent Samples Test summarised from SPSS

Gender	n	Mean	SD	*Levene's Test*		*t- test*		95% Confidence interval Of the difference
				F	*p* value	t	*p* value	
Male	48	75	3.5	0.87	0.38	0.35	0.25	- 0.3 to 0.5
Female	52	76	3.3					

17. The variances of the two groups are assumed to be:

(a) Unequal
(b) Equal
(c) Indeterminate
(d) None of the above

18. Interpret the p value from the t test:

(a) Since $p < 0.05$ we fail to reject H_0
(b) Since $p > 0.05$ we reject H_0
(c) Since $p < 0.05$ we reject H_0
(d) Since $p > 0.05$ we fail to reject H_0

19. Interpret the 95% confidence interval for the mean difference of two populations:

(a) Since the interval contains zero we fail to reject H_0
(b) Since the interval contains zero we reject H_0
(c) If we repeat this exercise a large number of times 95% of the constructed confidence intervals will not contain the true population mean difference
(d) If we repeat this exercise a large number of times 5% of the constructed confidence intervals will contain the true population mean difference

20. Effect size procedure give us an indication of:

(a) Magnitude of the difference between two distributions i.e. the percentage overlap between the two distributions
(b) The range of values that contain the true population mean difference
(c) Whether the variances of both groups can be assumed equal
(d) None of the above

MCQ Solutions

1. (c)	6. (c)	11. (a)	16. (b)
2. (b)	7. (a)	12. (b)	17. (b)
3. (a)	8. (b)	13. (a)	18. (d)
4. (c)	9. (c)	14. (b)	19. (a)
5. (c)	10. (a)	15. (a)	20. (a)

7.13 IBM SPSS Statistics 20 - *Input and Output*

Individuals	*Gender* Male = 1 Female = 2	*Intelligence Quotient*	*Weight (kgs)*
1	1	100	82
2	1	105	91
3	1	95	86
4	1	100	95
5	1	105	98
6	1	100	91
7	1	95	82
8	1	100	79
9	1	95	91
10	1	105	95
11	1	110	86
12	1	110	84
13	1	105	91
14	1	100	89
15	1	95	91
16	2	110	68
17	2	115	70
18	2	115	73
19	2	105	75
20	2	115	77
21	2	120	79
22	2	110	82
23	2	110	64
24	2	120	66
25	2	115	64
26	2	110	68
27	2	115	70
28	2	105	73
29	2	105	64
30	2	105	66

A random sample of 30 first year students was selected from the population of 600 first year students. No consideration was given to appropriate sample size.

The researcher's task is to test the following:

1. Is there a difference between the mean IQ of males versus the mean IQ of females at the 0.05 level of significance? Use IBM SPSS Statistics 20 to address this question.

2. Is there a difference between the mean weights of males versus the mean weight of females at the 0.05 level of significance? Use IBM SPSS Statistics 20 to address this question.

*3. Use G*Power to calculate the 'post hoc' power for the independent samples t test procedure, using the following information:*

a. $\alpha = 0.05$
b. *Actual effect size d*
c. *Two sided test*
d. $n_1 = 15$ and $n_2 = 15$

4. Generate error bar charts for each variable. Use IBM SPSS Statistics 20 to address this question.

IBM SPSS Statistics 20 Instructions

Step 1 – Open *IBM SPSS Statistics 20* select *Type in data* and click *OK*. Click *Variable View* at the bottom left corner and enter the variables as shown.

Variable View Editor

File Edit View Data Transform Analyze Graphs Utilities Add-ons Window Help

	Name	Type	Width	Decimals	Label	Values	Missing	Columns	Align	Measure	Role
1	Gender	Numeric	8	0	Gender	{1, Male Stu...	None	8	Right	Nominal	Input
2	Score	Numeric	8	0	IQ Score	None	None	8	Right	Scale	Input
3	Weight	Numeric	8	0	Weight	None	None	8	Right	Scale	Input

Data View | Variable View

IBM SPSS Statistics Processor is ready

Step 2 – Click *Data View* at the bottom left corner and enter the data.

Data View Editor

File Edit View Data Transform Analyze Graphs Utilities Add-ons Window Help

Visible: 3 of 3 Variables

	Gender	Score	Weight
1	1	100	82
2	1	105	91
3	1	95	86
4	1	100	95
5	1	105	98
6	1	100	91
7	1	95	82
8	1	100	79
9	1	95	91
10	1	105	95
11	1	110	86
12	1	110	84
13	1	105	91
14	1	100	89
15	1	95	91

Data View | Variable View

IBM SPSS Statistics Processor is ready

Step 3 – Click *Analyse* and select *Compare Means* and then select *Independent-Samples T Test.*

Data View Editor

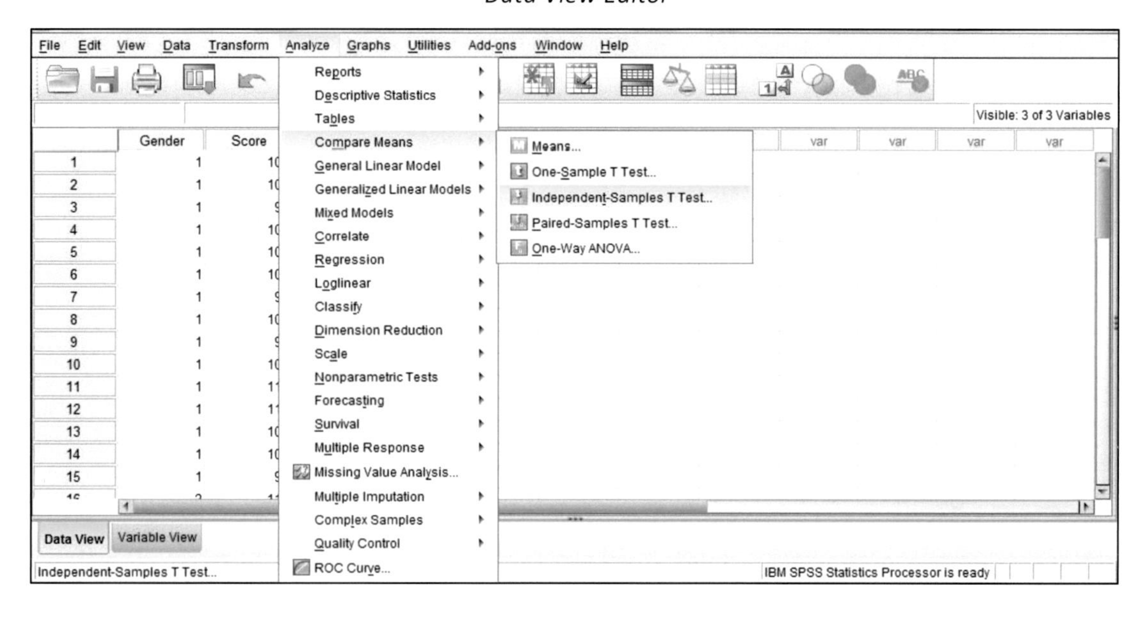

Step 4 – Move *IQ Score* into *Test Variable(s)* and move *Gender* into *Grouping Variable*. Click *Define Groups* and place 1 *(the code for male)* into the *Group 1* box and place 2 *(the code for female)* into the Group 2 box. Then click *Continue* and *OK*

Data View Editor

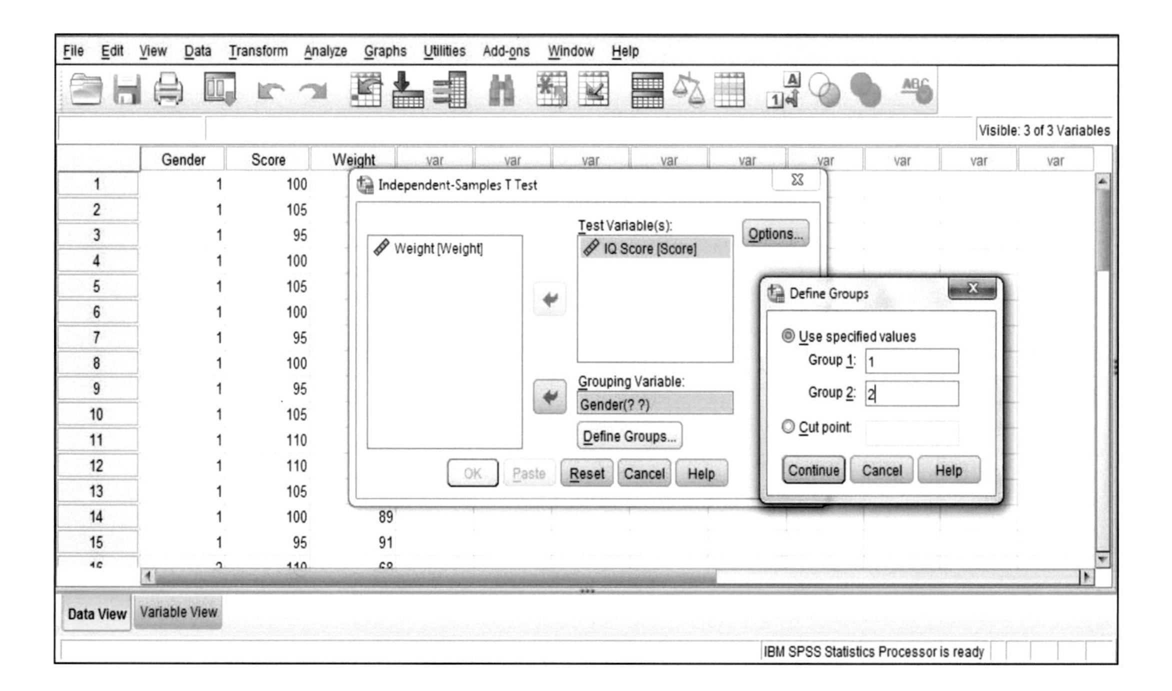

IBM SPSS Statistics 20 Output

Group Statistics

	Gender	n	Mean	Standard Deviation	Std. Error Mean
IQ Score	Male Student	15	101.33	5.164	1.333
	Female student	15	111.67	5.233	1.351

Independent Samples Test

		Levene's Test For Equality of variances		t-test for Equality of Means						
		F	Sig.	t	df	Sig. (2 tailed)	Mean Diff.	Std. Error Difference	95% Confidence Interval Of the difference	
									Lower	Upper
IQ Score	Equal Variances Assumed	0.035	0.852	-5.44	28	0.000	-10.333	1.898	-14.22	-6.44
	Equal Variances not Assumed			-5.44	27.99	0.000	-10.333	1.898	-14.22	-6.44

Since Sig > 0.05 we use Equal Variances Assumed row

Always report this value (0.000) as p < 0.001

Use *G*Power 3* to address part 3 above

Power of the independent samples t test = 99.95%

*G*Power 3*

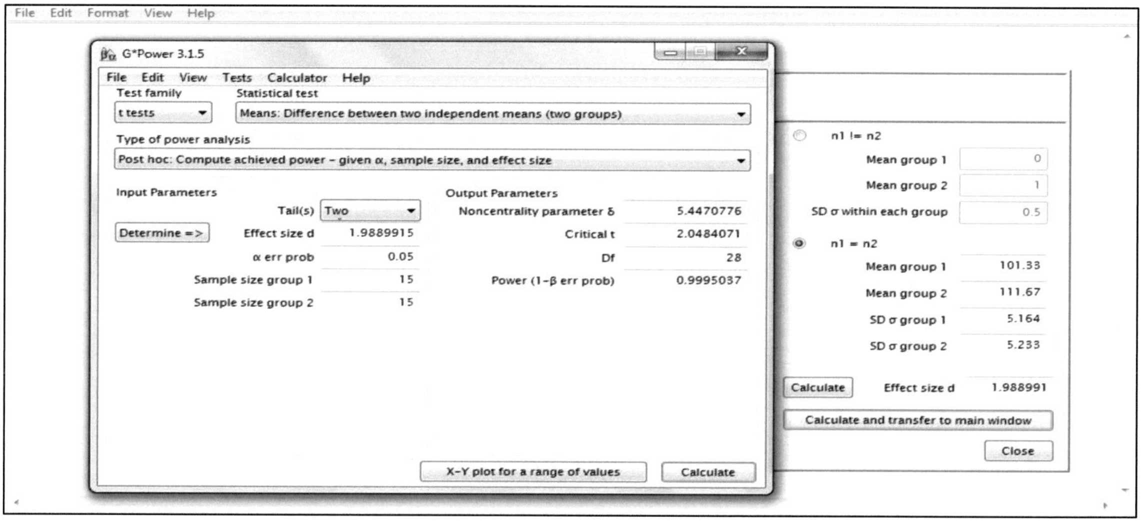

File Edit Format View Help

G*Power 3.1.5

File Edit View Tests Calculator Help

Test family: t tests

Statistical test: Means: Difference between two independent means (two groups)

Type of power analysis: Post hoc: Compute achieved power – given α, sample size, and effect size

Input Parameters		Output Parameters	
Tail(s)	Two	Noncentrality parameter δ	5.4470776
Determine => Effect size d	1.9889915	Critical t	2.0484071
α err prob	0.05	Df	28
Sample size group 1	15	Power (1-β err prob)	0.9995037
Sample size group 2	15		

X-Y plot for a range of values | Calculate

n1 != n2	
Mean group 1	0
Mean group 2	1
SD σ within each group	0.5
n1 = n2	
Mean group 1	101.33
Mean group 2	111.67
SD σ group 1	5.164
SD σ group 2	5.233
Calculate Effect size d	1.988991

Calculate and transfer to main window

Close

Use *IBM SPSS Statistics 20* to address part 4 above

Step 1 – Click *Graphs* and select *Legacy Dialogs* and then select *Error Bar.*

Data View Editor

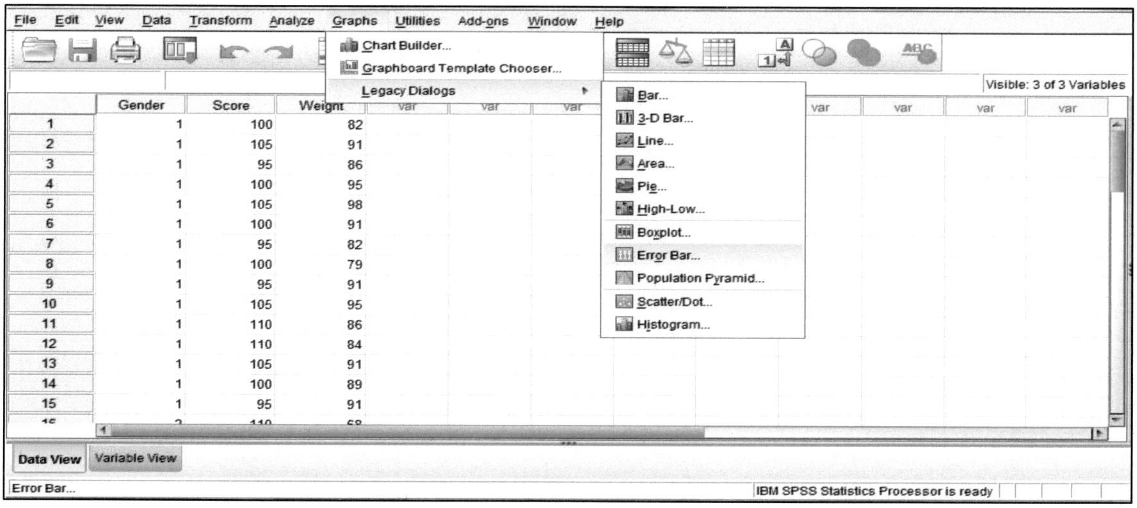

File Edit View Data Transform Analyze Graphs Utilities Add-ons Window Help

Graphs menu: Chart Builder... | Graphboard Template Chooser... | Legacy Dialogs ▸

Legacy Dialogs: Bar... | 3-D Bar... | Line... | Area... | Pie... | High-Low... | Boxplot... | Error Bar... | Population Pyramid... | Scatter/Dot... | Histogram...

Visible: 3 of 3 Variables

	Gender	Score	Weight
1	1	100	82
2	1	105	91
3	1	95	86
4	1	100	95
5	1	105	98
6	1	100	91
7	1	95	82
8	1	100	79
9	1	95	91
10	1	105	95
11	1	110	86
12	1	110	84
13	1	105	91
14	1	100	89
15	1	95	91

Data View | Variable View

Error Bar... | IBM SPSS Statistics Processor is ready

Step 2 – Select *Simple* and select *Summaries for groups of cases* and then *click Define.* For Paired or Matched samples, one would select *Simple* and *Summaries of separate variables*.

Data View Editor

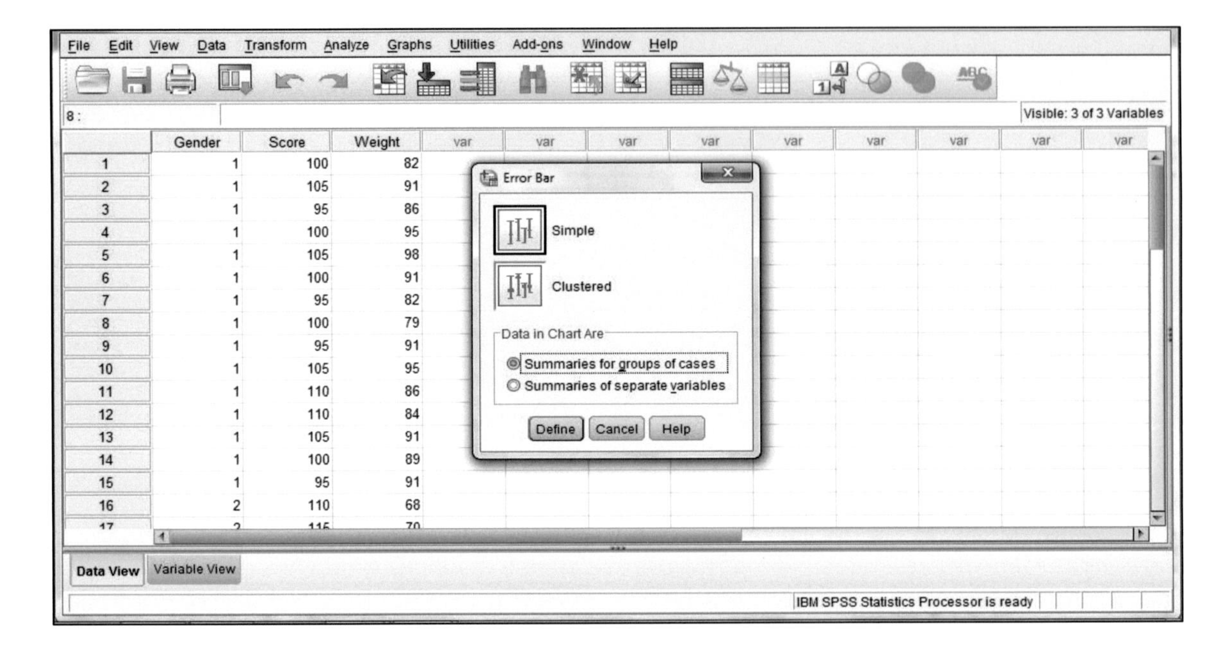

Step 3 – Place the quantitative variable *Score* into *Variable* and place the qualitative variable *Gender* into *Category Axis* and click *OK.*

Data View Editor

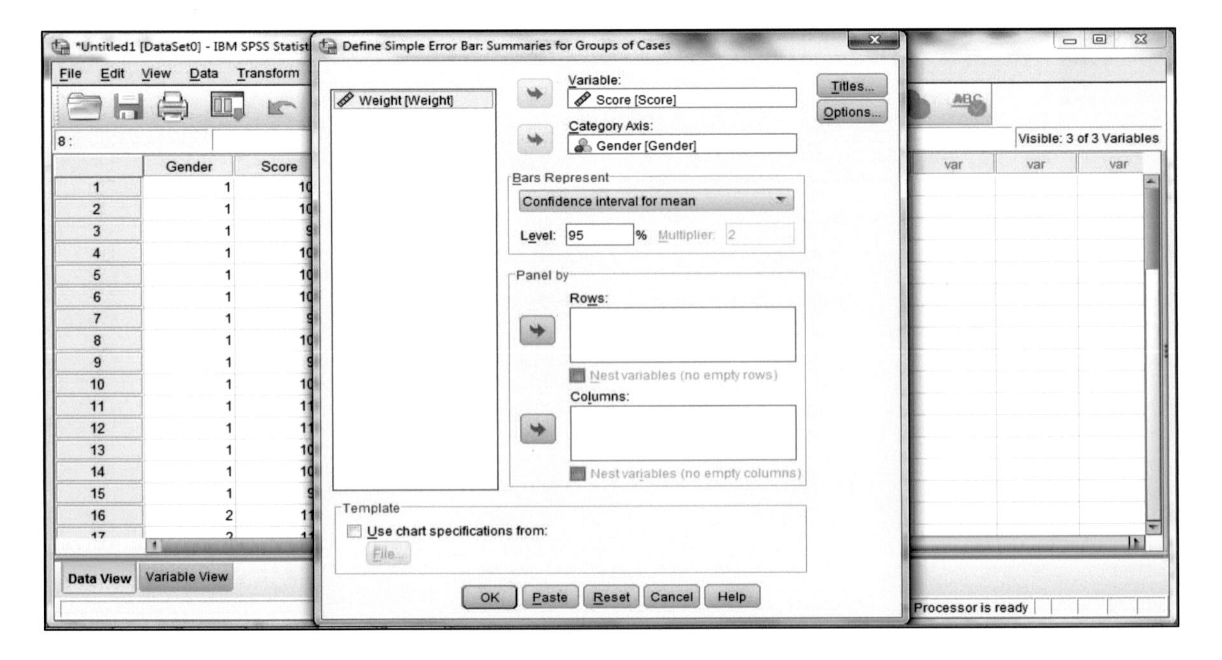

Step 4 – Repeat step 1 to step 3 for the second quantitative variable *Weight*

IBM SPSS Statistics 20 Output

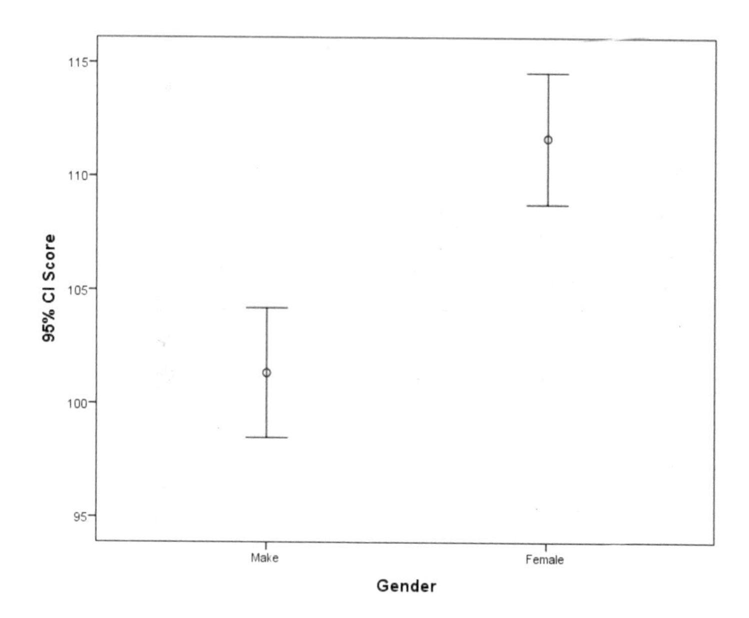

Chapter 8 Inferential Procedures for Comparing Proportions

OVERVIEW

APPLICATIONS

'It is better to be roughly right than precisely wrong.'

John Maynard Keynes (1883 – 1946)

8.1 Schematic Chart – *Goodness of Fit Test and Tests for Association*

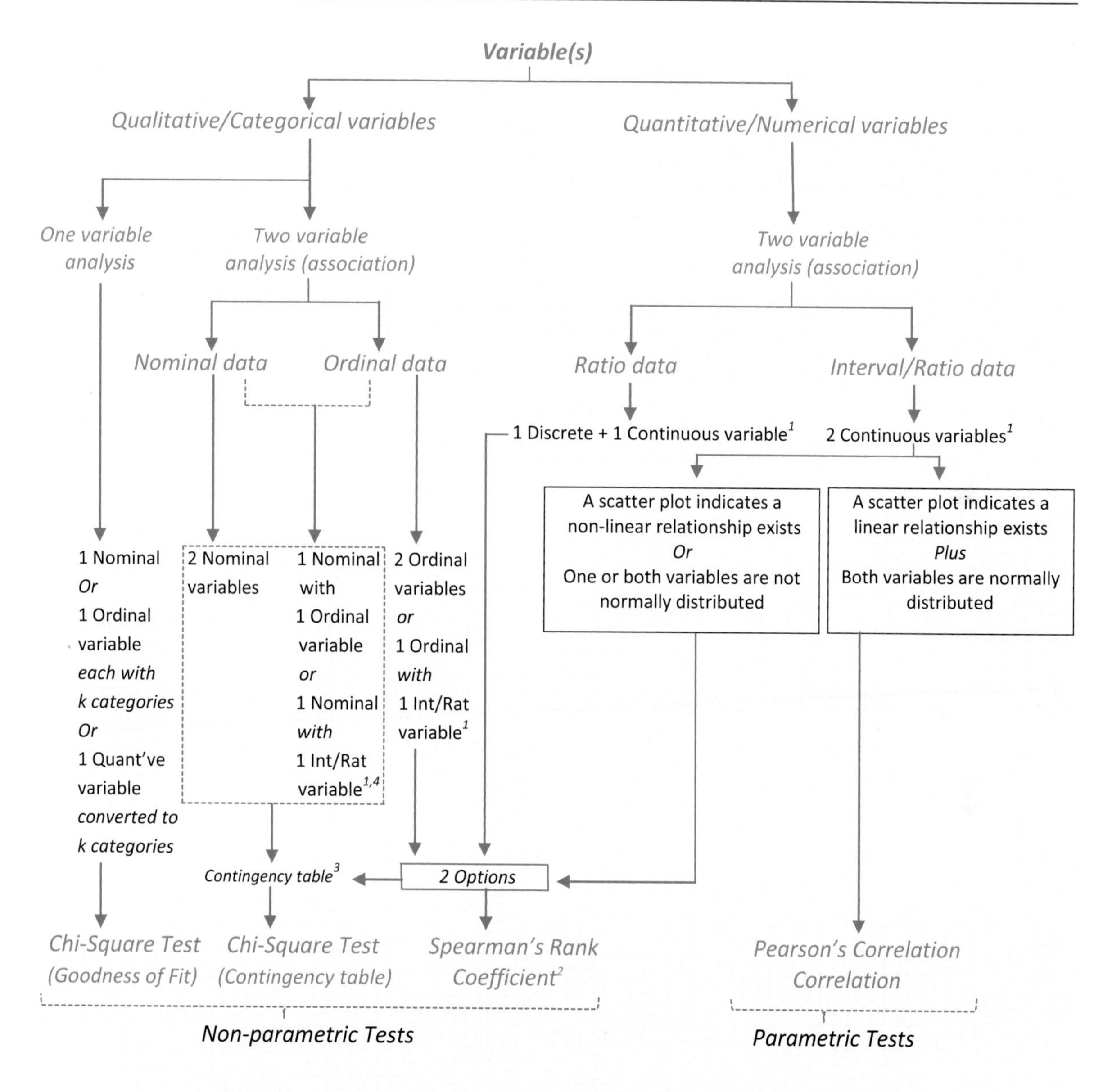

Notes:

1. *Quantitative variables (continuous or discrete) can be converted into qualitative variables (categorical) but at the risk of diminishing the power of your statistical test, Streiner (2002)*
2. *Prior to conducting the Spearman's Rank Correlation, both variables must be expressed as ranks*
3. *This option is valid even when both variables are discrete quantitative variables. One does not need to convert the two discrete quantitative variables into qualitative variables.*
4. *One nominal/ ordinal variable with either one discrete quantitative variable or one dummy variable.*

8.2 Introductory Comments

The schematic chart will guide the researcher in his quest to select the most appropriate test procedure. In this chapter we will explore test procedures which cater for both one and two variable situations. The following is a summary of what is covered in this chapter: *(1a, 1b, 2a, 2b, 3).*

1. **One variable analysis** – *Chi-square test (goodness of fit test)*

The Chi-square test allows us to discover if a pattern of observed frequencies 'fits' a pattern of expected frequencies *(a claimed pattern which is assumed to be true)*. The pattern of expected frequencies can assume one of the following:

a. Equal expected frequencies pattern - *derived theoretically or assumed at the outset.*

	Variable = colour preference for a lollipop				*Frequencies*
k = 4 categories	Purple	Orange	Yellow	Red	*OF = Observed freq* *EF = Expected freq*
n = 80	12	40	8	20	*Pattern of OF*
Equal expected frequencies in null hypothesis = 1/k	¼ = 0.25	¼ = 0.25	¼ = 0.25	¼ = 0.25	*Assumed (outset)*
(1/k) x n = 0.25 x 80	20	20	20	20	*Pattern of EF*

One group of contestants on 'Celebrity Apprentice' must launch a new lollipop and they need to discover if their target market has a colour preference, or if all colours under consideration are equally preferred. A random sample of 80 potential target buyers is selected and questioned about their colour preference.

b. Unequal expected frequencies pattern - *derived empirically.*

An examination, by the national federation of insurers, of road deaths over the past 20 years, revealed the following historical proportions (i.e. likelihood that a fatality would take place on a particular day).

	Variable = road fatalities							
k = 7 Categories	Mon	Tue	Wed	Thurs.	Fri	Sat	Sun	
n = 383	65	55	40	45	50	68	60	*Pattern of OF*
Unequal expected frequencies in null hypothesis	0.16	0.15	0.10	0.14	0.14	0.16	0.15	*Derived empirically*
Empirical probability X 383	61.28	57.45	38.3	53.62	53.62	61.28	57.45	*Pattern of EF*

c. Some distributional pattern - *Normal distribution or Poisson distribution etc.*

The Chi-square test *(goodness of fit test)* can be used to discover, for example, if a pattern of observed frequencies 'fits' a pattern of expected frequencies that conforms to a normal distribution. This chi-square test *(goodness of fit test)* may be undertaken under the following two scenarios:

3. *When one is investigating whether the observed distribution (i.e. the sample data) comes from a normal population where the mean and standard deviation is known (specified).*
4. *When one is investigating whether the observed distribution (i.e. the sample data) is normal. In this test type, the mean and standard deviation is unknown (unspecified) and must be estimated.*

2. **Two variable analysis** – *Chi-square test – (2 rows x 2 columns contingency table)*

a. Sampling from one population – *A Chi-square test for independence*

Suppose we are investigating the relationship between gender and preferences for soft drinks. 100 consumers are selected at random *(one population)* at the beginning of the study, and dichotomised *(divided into two Groups/Classes)* with respect to 'gender' and 'preference'. The *Chi-square test for independence* allows us to determine whether a preference for soft drinks depends on gender. Our table may look as follows (in this example each categorical variable has two levels):

		Preference		
		Brand A	*Brand B*	*Total*
Gender	*Male*	50	10	60
	Female	15	25	40
	Total	65	35	100

We set up the null and alternative hypothesis in the following manner:

H_0: Gender and Preference are independent
H_1: Gender and Preference are dependent

b. Sampling from two populations – *A Chi-square test for equality of proportions (Homogeneity)*

If we are investigating whether males and females differ in terms of their preference for a brand of soft drink, 50 male and 50 female soft drink consumers might be sampled *(two independent populations identified and sampled at the beginning of the study)*. The *Chi-square test for equality of proportions* allows us to determine whether males and females share the same distribution of the categorical variable 'brand preference'. Our table may look as follows *(in this example each categorical variable has two levels):*

		Preference		
		Brand A	*Brand B*	*Total*
Gender	*Male*	40	10	50
	Female	35	15	50
	Total	75	25	100

We set up the null and alternative hypothesis in the following manner:

H_0: The distribution (proportions) of preference is the same for both populations
H_1: The distribution (proportions) of preference is not the same for both populations

Whether we are sampling from one or two populations, our Chi-square test will follow the same procedure. Our interpretation of the results of each test must be made with the knowledge that we are making inferences about either one or two populations.

c. **Two variable analysis** – *Chi-Square Test – (r x c contingency table where one or both categorical variables has more than two levels)*

Chi-Square Test *(2 x 2 table)*

Sample Size Required			Effect Size		
α= 0.05			0.1	0.3	0.5
Power	0.75	*df =1*	695	78	28
		df =2	860	96	35
		df =3	977	109	40
		df =4	1073	120	43
	0.80	*df =1*	785	88	32
		df =2	964	108	39
		df =3	1091	122	44
		df =4	1194	133	48
	0.85	*df =1*	898	100	36
		df =2	1093	122	44
		df =3	1231	137	50
		df =4	1343	150	54

8.3 Statistical Inference: *Chi-Square Test (Goodness of fit)*

Example 1 - Consider the following example with equal expected frequencies in the null hypothesis.

One group of contestants on 'Celebrity Apprentice' must launch a new lollipop and they need to discover if their target market has a colour preference, or if all colours under consideration are equally preferred. A random sample of 80 potential target buyers is selected and questioned about their colour preference.

Number of people preferring different colours for a lollipop

K = 4 Categories	Purple	Orange	Yellow	Red	
80 target buyers	12	40	8	20	➡ Observed frequencies

*Test the hypothesis that all four colours are not equally preferred at the 0.05 level of significance. Use G*power 3 to calculate the post hoc power of the statistical test procedure.*

Statistical Test Procedure (Chi-Square 'Goodness of Fit' Test)

1. *State necessary conditions required to validate the test*

   a. A random sample has been employed at the outset.
   b. A conservative rule of thumb which insists that all expected frequencies > 5 is, debatably, too stringent, *(Cochran, 1954, cited in Everitt, 1980)*. A more relaxed assumption used in practice requires that at least 80% of expected frequencies be ≥ 5 *(assuming that there are more than 2 cells)*. If this requirement is breached, we may be able to pool *(collapse)* some of the rows and/or columns *(cells can be added together as long as they have something in common)*. However, this practice of pooling categories should be avoided if possible as the randomness of the sample may be affected. Increasing the sample size should be considered.
   c. Each participant's response appears just once thereby ensuring that the number of participants in each cell is independent.

2. *State the null hypothesis and alternative hypothesis*

   H_0: Pattern of observed frequencies does fit the pattern of expected frequencies.
   H_1: Pattern of observed frequencies does not fit the pattern of expected frequencies.
   or
   H_0: $p_p = p_o = p_Y = p_R = 0.25$ or All colours are equally preferred.
   H_1: At least one of p_p, p_o, p_Y, $p_R \neq 0.25$ or all colours are not equally preferred.

3. *Determine the presence or absence of statistical significance*

   a. Appropriate test statistic is the Chi-square 'Goodness of fit' test
   b. The level of significance for this test: $\alpha = 0.05$ *(right tail area in the diagram below)*
   c. Identify the critical value *(A segment of the χ^2 tables is included here)*

      Identifying 7.814 in the diagram below requires 0.05 to be allocated to the right tail @ (Categories – 1) degrees of freedom

   d. Reject the null hypothesis *(H_o)* when the calculated test statistic *(χ^2)* from part 4 below > Critical value *(7.814)*

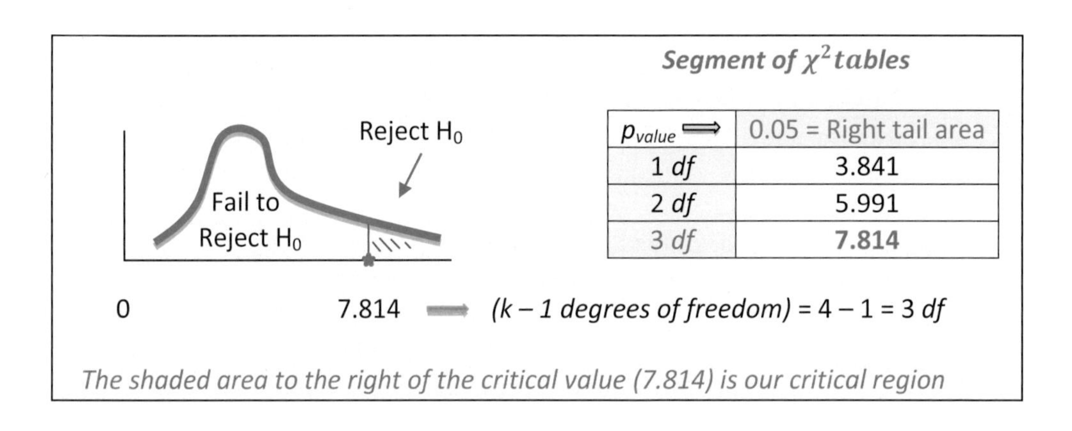

p_{value} ⟹	0.05 = Right tail area
1 df	3.841
2 df	5.991
3 df	**7.814**

The shaded area to the right of the critical value (7.814) is our critical region

4. *Select and calculate the appropriate test statistic*

   How to calculate expected frequencies:

   If there is no preference then each colour will have an equal chance of selection. Therefore, we would expect an equal number in each category approximately. There are 80 people and four categories. If there is no particular preference, we would expect $\frac{80}{4}$ = 20 to be in each category.

K = 4 Categories	Purple	Orange	Yellow	Red
Observed Frequencies *(O)*	12	40	8	20
Expected Frequencies *(E)*	20	20	20	20

Appropriate test statistic: One – variable χ^2 Goodness of fit test

$$\chi^2 = \sum \frac{(O_i - E_i)^2}{E_i} = \frac{(O_1 - E_1)^2}{E_1} + \frac{(O_2 - E_2)^2}{E_2} + \frac{(O_3 - E_3)^2}{E_3} + \frac{(O_4 - E_4)^2}{E_4} \quad \textit{(k – 1 degrees of freedom)}$$

$$\chi^2 = \sum \frac{(O_i - E_i)^2}{E_i} = \frac{(12-20)^2}{20} + \frac{(40-20)^2}{20} + \frac{(8-20)^2}{20} + \frac{(20-20)^2}{20} = 30.4 \quad (4 - 1 = 3\ df)$$

5. *Compare the calculated test statistic with the critical value*

The calculated χ^2 value of 30.4 falls into the critical region *(above 7.814)* or the shaded area in the diagram. In rejecting H_0, we are inferring that sufficient evidence is presented to allow us to conclude that all colours are not equally preferred at the 0.05 level of significance. The difference between the observed frequencies *(our collected data)* and the expected frequencies *(what we assume if H_0 were true)* has not occurred due to some error.

6. *Derive an approximate p value – Working with a segment of the χ^2 tables*

	→ 0.05 and below →				
p values ⇨	0.05	0.025	0.01	0.005 →	*p* value
1 *df*	3.841	5.023	6.634	7.879	
2 *df*	5.991	7.377	9.210	10.596	
3 *df*	7.814	9.348	11.344	12.838 →	30.4

Interpreting the p value

a. Traditional approach – explicit reference to a selected cut-off point of say $\alpha = 0.05$:

   The p value which corresponds to the calculated χ^2 value (30.4) at 3 degrees of freedom lies below 0.05. Since the p value is below 0.05, we can reject H_0 at the 0.05 level of significance (Applying the p value decision rule: If p value < 0.05 reject H_0).

b. Current approach – no explicit reference to a selected cut-off point of say $\alpha = 0.05$. The cut-off point is implicitly assumed as a guide value. The current approach is to report an exact *p* value *(included in the output of all statistical software packages)*. Using tables will only give us approximations.

   The p value reveals the likelihood of being wrong if we reject H_0 (the p value appears to be well below 0.005 i.e. 5 times in 1000).

Effect Size Procedure

How large is the variation of preference for the four colours or how large is the magnitude of difference between what was observed in the study with what might be expected under a true null hypothesis?

1. *Calculate the 'measure of effect'*

$$Effect\ Size\ w = \sqrt{\frac{\chi^2}{n}} = \sqrt{\frac{30.4}{80}} = 0.62\ Approx.$$

2. *State your inferences - To interpret this value, we refer to guidelines proposed by Cohen (1988).*

Effect size w	*Interpretation*
If w < .1	Negligible Effect
If w ≥.1 but <.3	Small Effect
If w ≥.3 but <.5	Medium / Moderate Effect
If w ≥.5	Large Effect

This measure indicates that the variation in preference between the four colours is large. The magnitude of difference between what was observed in the study and what might be expected under a true null hypothesis is large.

Reported results using the current approach (implicit cut-off guide point of α = 0.05):

The χ^2 value of 30 (df = 3) has an associated probability value of < 0.005 which reveals that the likelihood of being wrong if we reject H_0 is less than 5 times in 1000 (which suggests that a decision to reject H_0 is highly unlikely to be wrong) and the variation in preference between the colours is large (effect size w = 0.62). This evidence is sufficient to enable us to infer that all colours are not equally preferred and that the variation in preference is large.

Power of the statistical test procedure using *G*power 3* software = 99.85%.

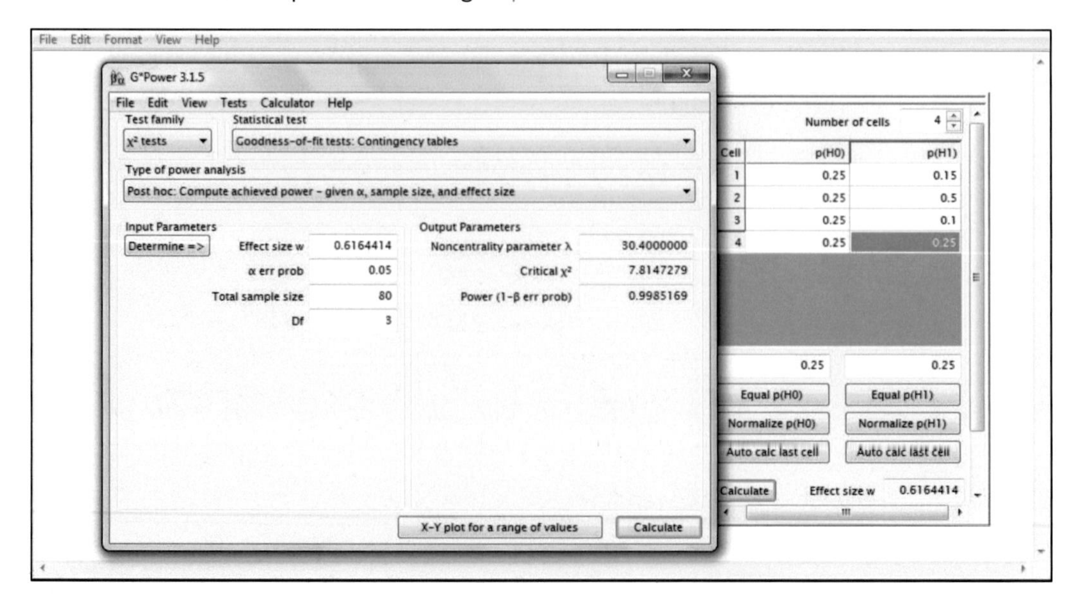

Example 2

You have reason to believe that there is a relationship or association between exposure to parental smoke and the presence of Asthma (in children ages 8 – 11 years). The following contingency table summarises the results of a survey of 550 children.

	Asthma present	No Asthma Present	Total
Parent – Smoker	30	170	200
Parent – Non Smoker	35	315	350
Total	65	485	550

Adapted from: Peat, Barton, Elliot (2008)

*Test the hypothesis that the incidence of asthma is dependent (is associated with) on exposure to smoking at the 0.05 level of significance. The researcher gave no consideration to what would constitute an appropriate sample size. Use G*power 3 to calculate (a) the post hoc power of the statistical test procedure and (b) an appropriate sample size.*

Statistical Test Procedure *(Chi-Square 'Contingency table' test/Yates's Continuity Correction)*

1. *State necessary conditions required to validate the test*

   a. A random sample is employed on one population at the outset.
   b. A conservative rule of thumb which insists that all expected frequencies > 5 is, debatably, too stringent, *(Cochran, 1954, cited in Everitt, 1980)*. A more relaxed assumption used in practice is acceptable:
      - ✓ For a 2 x 2 contingency table *(as in this example)*, the Chi-square should not be used if more than 25% of the expected frequencies is less than 5. If such a situation arises, we may employ Fisher's exact test *(available in most statistical packages)* as an alternative to the chi-square test.
      - ✓ For larger tables, the Chi-square should not be used if any of the expected frequencies is less than 1 or more than 20% of the expected frequencies are less than 5. If such a situation arises, one may consider increasing the sample size or pooling some of the rows and/or columns *(although, pooling categories after the data are seen may affect the random nature of the sample).* A preferred alternative is to employ an *exact test* for tables larger than 2 x 2 *(available in most statistical packages).*
   c. Each participant's response appears just once thereby ensuring that the number of participants in each cell is independent.

2. *State the null hypothesis and alternative hypothesis*

H_0: There is no association between exposure to smoking and incidence of Asthma.
H_1: There is an association between exposure to smoking and incidence of Asthma.
or
H_0: Exposure to smoking and incidence of Asthma are independent of each other.
H_1: Exposure to smoking and incidence of Asthma are dependent of each other.

3. *State the statistical decision rule for a selected level of significance*

a. Appropriate test statistic is the Chi-square *contingency table* test
b. The level of significance for this test: $\alpha = 0.05$ *(right tail area in the diagram below)*
c. Identify the critical value *(A segment of the χ^2 tables is included here)*

Identifying 3.814 in the diagram below requires 0.05 to be allocated to the right tail @ (rows – 1) x (columns – 1) degrees of freedom

d. Reject the null hypothesis *(H_o)* when the calculated test statistic *(χ^2)* from part 4 below > Critical value *(3.841)*

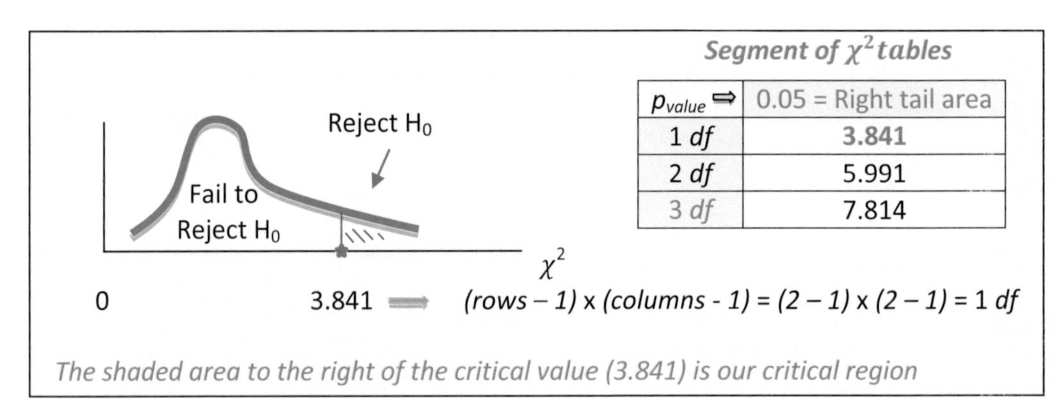

Segment of χ^2 tables

p_{value} ⇨	0.05 = Right tail area
1 *df*	**3.841**
2 *df*	5.991
3 *df*	7.814

4. *Select and calculate the appropriate test statistic*

How to calculate expected frequencies:

$$\mathbf{E_1} = \frac{Row\ total\ x\ column\ total}{overall\ total} = \frac{200\ x\ 65}{550} = 23.63 \text{ or } 24 \text{ approx.} \qquad \mathbf{E_3} = \frac{200\ x\ 485}{550} = 176.36 \text{ or } 176 \text{ approx.}$$

$$\mathbf{E_2} = \frac{Row\ total\ x\ column\ total}{overall\ total} = \frac{350\ x\ 65}{550} = 41.36 \text{ or } 41 \text{ approx.} \qquad \mathbf{E_4} = \frac{350\ x\ 485}{550} = 308.63 \text{ or } 309 \text{ approx.}$$

	Asthma present		No Asthma Present		Total
	Observed Frequency	Expected Frequency	Observed Frequency	Expected Frequency	
Parent – Smoker	30 (O_1)	24 (E_1)	170 (O_3)	176 (E_3)	**200**
Parent – Non Smoker	35 (O_2)	41 (E_2)	315 (O_4)	309 (E_4)	**350**
Total	**65**		**485**		**550**

Appropriate test statistic: *Chi-Square Test (χ^2): (For a 2 x 2 table Yates correction is preferred to χ^2 test – see below).*

$$\chi^2 = \sum \frac{(O_i - E_i)^2}{E_i} = \frac{(O_1 - E_1)^2}{E_1} + \frac{(O_2 - E_2)^2}{E_2} + \frac{(O_3 - E_3)^2}{E_3} + \frac{(O_4 - E_4)^2}{E_4} \qquad (r-1)(c-1) = df$$

$$\chi^2 = \sum \frac{(O_i - E_i)^2}{E_i} = \frac{(30-24)^2}{24} + \frac{(35-41)^2}{41} + \frac{(170-176)^2}{176} + \frac{(315-309)^2}{309} = 2.70 \qquad (2-1)(2-1) = 1\ df$$

5. *Compare the calculated test statistic with the critical value*

The calculated χ^2 value of 2.70 falls *(to the left of 3.841)* where we fail to reject H_0.
In failing to reject H_0, we are inferring that there is no association between exposure to smoking and incidence of Asthma at the 0.05 level of significance and that there is insufficient evidence to contradict this.

6. *Derive or locate an approximate p value – Working with a segment of the χ^2 tables*

Above 0.05 ⟵		
p values ⇨	0.10	0.05
1 df	2.705	3.841
.	....	......

The computed χ^2 = 2.70 approximately matches 2.705

Interpreting the p value

a. Traditional approach – explicit reference to a selected cut-off point of say $\alpha = 0.05$:

The p value which corresponds to the calculated χ^2 value (2.70) at 1 degrees of freedom lies at 0.10 approximately. Since the p value is above 0.05, we fail to reject H_0 at the 0.05 level of significance. (Applying the p value decision rule: If p value > 0.05 we fail to reject H_0).

b. Current approach – no explicit reference to a selected cut-off point of say $\alpha = 0.05$. The cut-off point is implicitly assumed as a guide value. The current approach is to report an exact *p* value *(included in the output of all statistical software packages)*. Using tables will only give us approximations.

   The p value reveals the likelihood of being wrong if we reject H_0 (the p value appears to fall on 0.10 approximately i.e. 10 times in 100).

Yates Correction with a 2 x 2 table *(A recommended alternative to the Chi-square test procedure, particularly when sample sizes are small)*

*You have reason to believe that there is a relationship or association between exposure to parental smoke and the presence of Asthma (in children ages 8 – 11 years). The following contingency table summarises the results of a survey of **550** children.*

	Asthma present	No Asthma Present	Total
Parent – Smoker	30	170	200
Parent – Non Smoker	35	315	350
Total	65	485	550

Adapted from: Peat, Barton, Elliot (2008)

Test the hypothesis that the incidence of asthma is dependent (is associated with) on exposure to smoking at the 0.05 level of significance.

It is often recommended that we 'correct' or 'adjust' the value of Chi-square (Yates, 1934). This involves subtracting the number 0.5 or ½ from the absolute value of the difference between the observed and expected frequencies before going on to square them as per the Chi-square. If the sample size is reasonably large Yates's correction will have little effect on the value of χ^2 (Everitt 1980).

Statistical Test Procedure *(Yates's Continuity for Correction)*

Appropriate test: (For a 2 x 2 table Yates Continuity correction)

$$\chi^2 = \sum \frac{(O_i - E_i)^2}{E_i} = \frac{(O_1 - E_1)^2}{E_1} + \frac{(O_2 - E_2)^2}{E_2} + \frac{(O_3 - E_3)^2}{E_3} + \frac{(O_4 - E_4)^2}{E_4} \qquad (r-1) \times (c-1) = df$$

$$\chi^2 = \sum \frac{(O_i - E_i)^2}{E_i} = \frac{(30-24)^2}{24} + \frac{(35-41)^2}{41} + \frac{(170-176)^2}{176} + \frac{(315-309)^2}{309} = 2.70 \qquad (2-1) \times (2-1) = 1\ df$$

$$\chi^2 = \sum \frac{(O_i - E_i)^2}{E_i} = \frac{(6)^2}{24} + \frac{(-6)^2}{41} + \frac{(-6)^2}{176} + \frac{(6)^2}{309} =$$

$$= \sum \frac{|O_i - E_i|^2}{E_i} = \frac{|6|^2}{24} + \frac{|6|^2}{41} + \frac{|6|^2}{176} + \frac{|6|^2}{309} =$$

$$\text{Adjusted } \chi^2 = \sum \frac{(|O_i - E_i| - 0.5)^2}{E_i} = \frac{(|6| - 0.5)^2}{24} + \frac{(|6| - 0.5)^2}{41} + \frac{(|6| - 0.5)^2}{176} + \frac{(|6| - 0.5)^2}{309} =$$

$$\text{Adjusted } \chi^2 = \sum \frac{(|O_i - E_i| - 0.5)^2}{E_i} = \frac{30.25}{24} + \frac{30.25}{41} + \frac{30.25}{176} + \frac{30.25}{309} = 2.27$$

The correction will yield a smaller computed value. However, this new value *(2.27)* still leads us to fail to reject H_0. In many instances, the Chi-square adjustment will not change the results of the Chi-square test.

Effect Size Procedure

This procedure is unnecessary when we fail to reject the null hypothesis. However, this policy may be unwise in every instance. If we are using the traditional approach to declaring or not declaring significance based on whether the p value is < 0.05 or > 0.05, then there is the danger of painting all p values above and below 0.05 with the same brush. As Howell (2007) observes, is it reasonable to treat 0.051 and 0.75 as being equally non-significant by reporting them both as p > 0.05? Moreover, should 0.049 and 0.00001 be thought of as being equally significant by reporting them both as p < 0.05? Whilst this is the strong argument in favour of reporting exact p values, there is also real value in employing the effect size procedure when the p value is within reasonable distance of a traditional selected significance value such as 0.05. Nevertheless, despite the distance of the p value (p = 0.10 approx.) from the 0.05 level of significance, the effect size procedure shall be undertaken to facilitate a comparison between example 2 and example 3.

How large or strong is the association between exposure to parental smoke and the presence of Asthma?

1. *Calculate Phi(ϕ) for a 2 x 2 contingency table*

Since we are working with a 2 x 2 contingency table, the recommended effect size measure will be Phi(ϕ) = $\sqrt{\frac{\chi^2}{n}}$. This will yield a value of Phi(ϕ) = $\sqrt{\frac{2.70}{550}}$ =0.07. In the case of a 2 x 2 table, 'effect size *w*' will equal the Phi(ϕ). We can therefore interpret the value for Phi(ϕ) by referring to the guidelines proposed by Cohen (1988).

2. *Calculate Cramer's V for contingency tables of all sizes*

A calculation for Cramer's *V* for a 2 x 2 contingency table will always lead us to the same conclusion as that derived from the calculation of Phi(ϕ).

Cramer's $V = \sqrt{\frac{\chi^2}{n\ x\ min(r-1,c-1)}}$ *Use r or c whichever is the smaller of the two*

Cramer's $V = \sqrt{\frac{2.70}{550(2-1)}} = 0.07$

3. *Convert Cramer's V to effect size w (Cowen, 1988)*

$w = V\sqrt{q-1}$ ⟶ $w = 0.07\sqrt{2-1}$ = 0.07

$w = V\sqrt{q-1}$ *(Adapted from Cohen, 1988)* where *w* = effect size *w*

V = Cramer's *V*, and *q* = the number of rows or columns *(whichever is the smaller of the two).*

4. *State your inferences - Guidelines proposed by Cohen (1988).*

Effect size w	*Interpretation*
If w < .1	Negligible Effect
If w ≥.1 but <.3	Small Effect
If w ≥.3 but <.5	Medium / Moderate Effect
If w ≥.5	Large Effect

This effect size value *(Phi(ϕ) = 0.07 or w = 0.07)* suggests a negligible effect. This suggests that the magnitude of association between exposure to parental smoke and the presence of Asthma is almost zero.

Reported results using the current approach (implicit cut-off guide point of α = 0.05):

The χ^2 value of 2.7 (df = 1) has an associated probability value of approximately 0.10 which reveals that the likelihood of being wrong if we reject H_0 is about 10 times in 100.

Summary comment

In this example, we failed to find significance. The following point is worth noting:

A larger sample size may detect significance even though effect size remains negligible

In example 3 we will increase the sample size and maintain the cell proportions used in example 2.

(a) Power of the statistical test procedure using *G*power 3* software = 42.05%

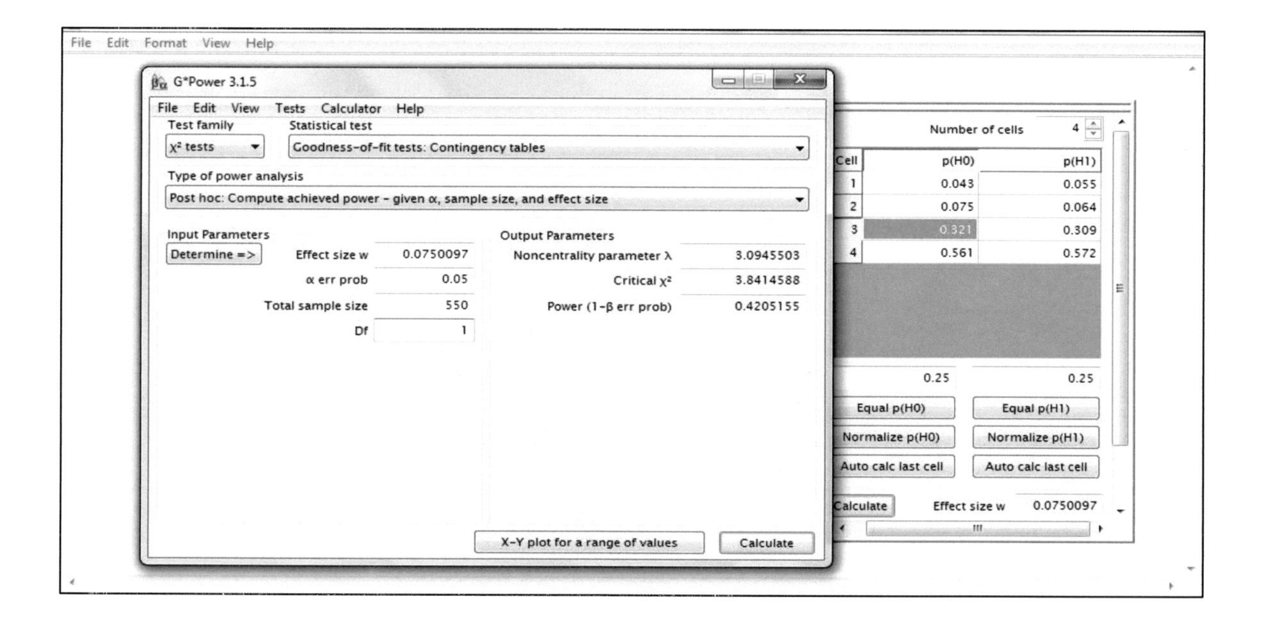

(b) Appropriate sample size using *G*power 3* software

The appropriate sample size for the following input parameters is 695:

a. *$\alpha = 0.05$*
b. *Desire effect size i.e. d = 0.1 (d = 0.1 is derived from experience or from past studies)*
c. *Power level for the test = 0.75*
d. *Degrees of freedom = 1*

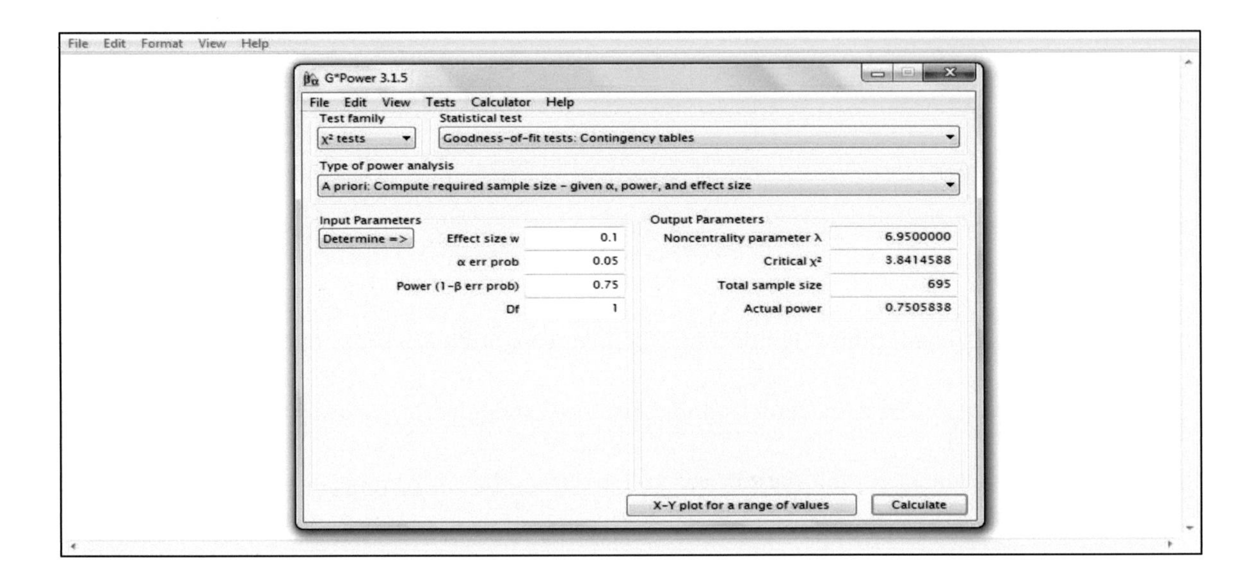

Example 3

You have reason to believe that there is a relationship or association between exposure to parental smoke and the presence of Asthma (in children ages 8 – 11 years). The following contingency table summarises the results of a survey of 1200 children. We will maintain the cell proportions from example 2 as follows:

	Asthma present	No Asthma Present	Total
Parent – Smoker	0.15	0.85	-
Parent – Non Smoker	0.10	0.90	-
Total	-	-	-

	Asthma present	No Asthma Present	Total
Parent – Smoker	45	255	300
Parent – Non Smoker	90	810	900
Total	135	1065	1200

Adapted from: Peat, Barton, Elliot (2008)

*Test the hypothesis that the incidence of asthma is dependent (is associated with) on exposure to smoking at the 0.05 level of significance. Use G*power 3 to calculate the post hoc power of the statistical test.*

Statistical Test Procedure *(Chi-Square 'Contingency table' Test /Yates's Continuity Correction)*

1. *State necessary conditions required to validate the test*

   As per Example 3

2. *State the null hypothesis and alternative hypothesis*

   H_0: There is no association between exposure to smoking and incidence of Asthma.
   H_1: There is an association between exposure to smoking and incidence of Asthma.
   or
   H_0: Exposure to smoking and incidence of Asthma are independent of each other.
   H_1: Exposure to smoking and incidence of Asthma are dependent of each other.

3. *State the statistical decision rule for a selected level of significance*

   a. Appropriate test statistic is the Chi-square *contingency table* test
   b. The level of significance for this test: $\alpha = 0.05$ *(right tail area in the diagram below)*
   c. Identify the critical value *(A segment of the χ^2tables is included here)*

   Identifying 3.814 in the diagram below requires 0.05 to be allocated to the right tail @ (rows – 1) x (columns – 1) degrees of freedom

   d. Reject the null hypothesis *(H_o)* when the calculated test statistic *(χ^2)* from part 4 below > Critical value *(3.841).*

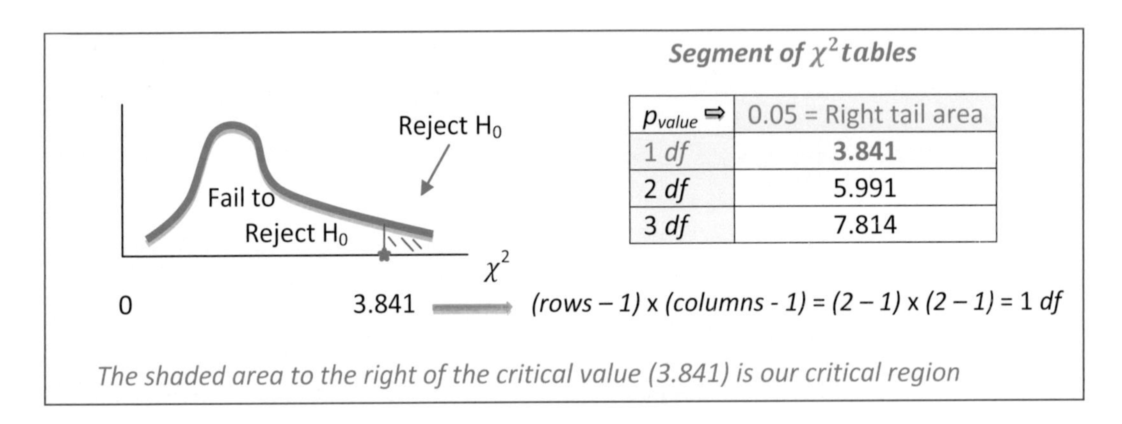

p_{value} ⇨	0.05 = Right tail area
1 df	**3.841**
2 df	5.991
3 df	7.814

4. *Select and calculate the appropriate test statistic*

How to calculate expected frequencies:

$$E_1 = \frac{Row\ total\ x\ column\ total}{overall\ total} = \frac{300\ x\ 135}{1200} = 34 \text{ approx.} \quad E_3 = \frac{300\ x\ 1065}{1200} = 266 \text{ approx.}$$

$$E_2 = \frac{Row\ total\ x\ column\ total}{overall\ total} = \frac{900\ x\ 135}{1200} = 101 \text{ approx.} \quad E_4 = \frac{900\ x\ 1065}{1200} = 799 \text{ approx.}$$

	Asthma present		No Asthma Present		Total
	Observed Frequency	Expected Frequency	Observed Frequency	Expected Frequency	
Parent – Smoker	45 (O_1)	34(E_1)	255 (O_3)	266(E_3)	**300**
Parent – Non Smoker	90 (O_2)	101(E_2)	810 (O_4)	799(E_4)	**900**
Total	**135**		**1065**		**1200**

Appropriate test statistic: *Chi-Square Test* (χ^2) *: (For a 2 x 2 table Yates correction is preferred to* χ^2 *test)*

$$\chi^2 = \sum\frac{(O_i-E_i)^2}{E_i} = \frac{(O_1-E_1)^2}{E_1} + \frac{(O_2-E_2)^2}{E_2} + \frac{(O_3-E_3)^2}{E_3} + \frac{(O_4-E_4)^2}{E_4} \qquad (r-1) \times (c-1) = df$$

$$\chi^2 = \sum\frac{(O_i-E_i)^2}{E_i} = \frac{(45-34)^2}{34} + \frac{(90-101)^2}{101} + \frac{(255-266)^2}{266} + \frac{(810-799)^2}{799} = 5.36 \qquad (2-1) \times (2-1) = 1\ df$$

5. *Compare the calculated test statistic with the critical value*

The calculated χ^2 value of 5.36 falls into the critical region *(above 3.84)* or the shaded area in the diagram. In rejecting H_0, we are inferring that sufficient evidence is presented to allow us to conclude that there is an association between exposure to smoking and incidence of Asthma at the 0.05 level of significance.

6. *Derive or locate an approximate p value – Working with a segment of the* χ^2 *tables*

			0.05 and below	
p values ⇨	0.10	0.05	0.025	0.01
1 df	2.705	3.841	5.023	6.634
.	……	……		

χ^2 = 5.36 lies between 5.023 and 6.634

Interpreting the p value

a. Traditional approach – explicit reference to a selected cut-off point of say α = 0.05:

   The *p* value which corresponds to the calculated χ^2 value *(5.36)* at 1 degrees of freedom lies between 0.025 and 0.01. Since the *p* value is below 0.05, we reject H_0 at the 0.05 level of significance. *(Applying the p value decision rule: If p value < 0.05 we reject* H_0*).*

b. Current approach – no explicit reference to a selected cut-off point of say α = 0.05. The cut-off point is implicitly assumed as a guide value. The current approach is to report an exact *p* value *(included in the output of all statistical software packages)*. Using tables will only give us approximations.

   The p value reveals the likelihood of being wrong if we reject H_0 *(the p value appears to fall between 0.025 and 0.01 i.e. between 2.5 times and 1 time in 100).*

Effect Size Procedure

How large or strong is the association between exposure to parental smoke and the presence of Asthma?

1. *Calculate Phi(ϕ) for a 2 x 2 contingency table*

$$\text{Phi}(\phi) = \sqrt{\frac{\chi^2}{n}} = \sqrt{\frac{5.36}{1200}} = 0.07 \textit{ (approx.)}$$

2. *Calculate Cramer's V for contingency tables of all sizes*

$$\text{Cramer's } V = \sqrt{\frac{\chi^2}{n \; x \; min(r-1, c-1)}}$$

Use r or c whichever is the smaller of the two

$$\text{Cramer's } V = \sqrt{\frac{5.36}{1200(2-1)}} = 0.07 \textit{ (approx.)}$$

3. *Convert Cramer's V to effect size w (Cowen, 1988)*

$$w = V\sqrt{q-1} \longrightarrow w = 0.07\sqrt{2-1} = 0.07$$

$w = V\sqrt{q-1}$ *(Adapted from Cohen, 1988)* where *w* = effect size *w*,

V = Cramer's *V*, and *q* = the number of rows or columns *(whichever is the smaller of the two).*

4. *State your inferences - Guidelines proposed by Cohen (1988).*

Effect size w	*Interpretation*
If w < .1	Negligible Effect
If w ≥.1 but <.3	Small Effect
If w ≥.3 but <.5	Medium / Moderate Effect
If w ≥.5	Large Effect

This effect size value *(Phi(ϕ) = 0.07 or w = 0.07)* suggests a negligible effect. This suggests that the association between exposure to parental smoke and the presence of Asthma is almost zero.

Reported results using the current approach (implicit cut-off guide point of α = 0.05):

The χ^2 value of 5.36 (df = 1) has an associated probability value between 0.025 and 0.01 which reveals that the likelihood of being wrong if we reject H_0 is between 1 and 2.5 times in 100. However, the strength of association between exposure to parental smoke and the presence of Asthma is almost zero *(Cramer's V = 0.07).*

Summary comments

In this example, we did find significance. Whether we achieve significance or not is very much related to sample size. If a study has a large number of respondents, a statistically significant finding might well be declared with a very small effect size *(whilst not quite a zero association in this example, it is certainly close to it)*. A statistically significant finding merely confirms that the declared *(observed)* association is unlikely to have occurred due to sampling error. Whether the tiny association *(small effect size in this example)* is considered large enough to be of practical importance is a matter of debate. This debate is not statistical and may require that the researcher has considerable experience in her area of study.

Statistical significance does not necessarily equal practical significance

Power of the statistical test procedure using *G*power 3* software = 69.7%

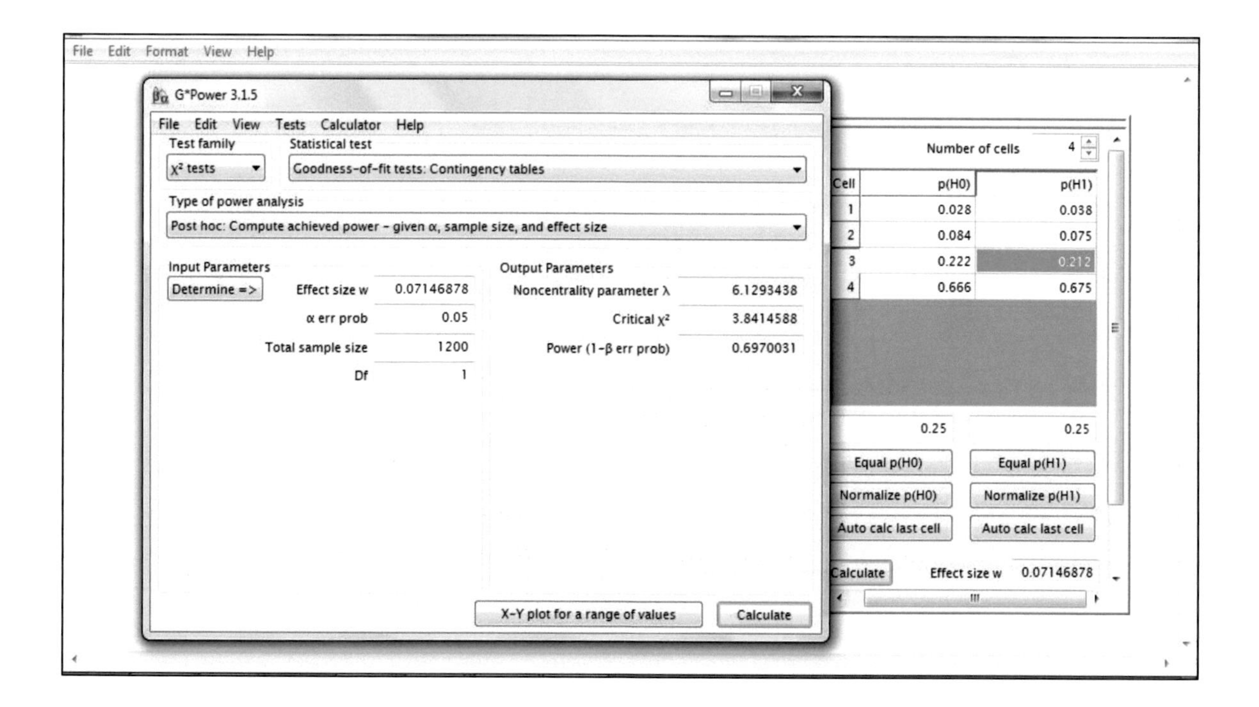

Example 4

A conscientious lecturer asked her students to evaluate her performance. In particular, she wished to know if the assessment of her performance was independent of gender. She selected a random sample of 155 students and compiled the following contingency table.

	'The lecture explains things very clearly'					
	Strongly disagree	Disagree	Neutral	Agree	Strongly agree	Total
Male students	8	12	8	30	17	75
Female students	6	8	8	40	18	80
Total	14	20	16	70	35	155

*Test the hypothesis that an assessment of her performance is dependent (is associated with) on gender at the 0.05 level of significance. The researcher gave no consideration to what would constitute an appropriate sample size. Use G*power 3 to calculate (a) the post hoc power of the statistical test and (b) an appropriate sample size.*

Statistical Test Procedure *(Chi-Square 'Contingency table' Test)*

1. *State necessary conditions required to validate the test*

   As per Example 3

2. *State the null hypothesis and alternative hypothesis*

   H_0: There is no association between gender and assessment of performance.
   H_1: There is an association between gender and assessment of performance.
   or
   H_0: assessment performance is independent of gender.
   H_1: assessment performance is dependent of gender.

3. *State the statistical decision rule for a selected level of significance*

   a. Appropriate test statistic is the Chi-square *contingency table* test
   b. The level of significance for this test: $\alpha = 0.05$ *(right tail area in the diagram below)*
   c. Identify the critical value *(A segment of the χ^2tables is included here).*

      Identifying 9.487 in the diagram below requires 0.05 to be allocated to the right tail @ (rows – 1) x (columns – 1) degrees of freedom

   d. Reject the null hypothesis *(H_o)* when the calculated test statistic *(χ^2)* from part 4 below > Critical value *(9.487)*

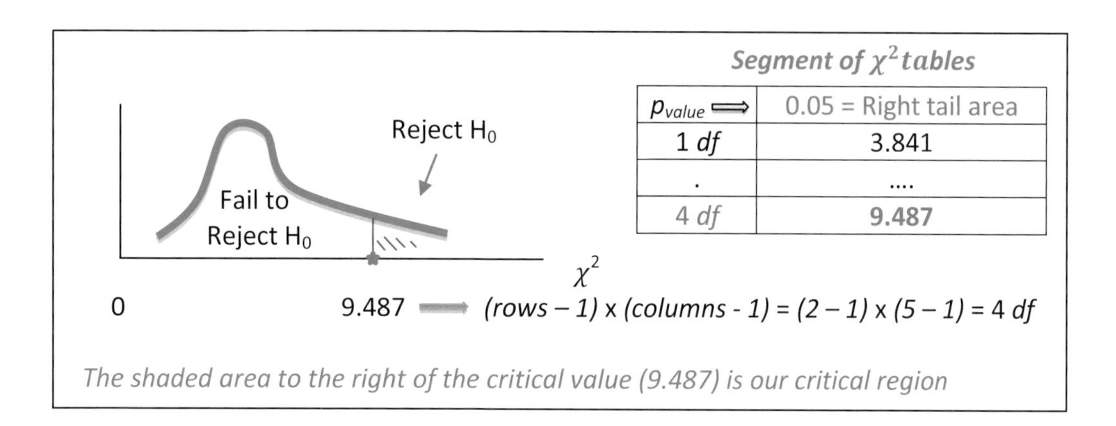

4. *Select and calculate the appropriate test statistic*

How to calculate expected frequencies:

$$E = \frac{Row\ total\ x\ column\ total}{overall\ total}$$

$\mathbf{E_1} = \frac{75\ x\ 14}{155} = 6.77$ $\mathbf{E_2} = \frac{75\ x\ 20}{155} = 9.68$ $\mathbf{E_3} = \frac{75\ x\ 16}{155} = 7.74$ $\mathbf{E_4} = \frac{75\ x\ 70}{155} = 33.9$ $\mathbf{E_5} = \frac{75\ x\ 35}{155} = 16.9$

$\mathbf{E_6} = \frac{80\ x\ 14}{155} = 7.22$ $\mathbf{E_7} = \frac{80\ x\ 20}{155} = 10.3$ $\mathbf{E_8} = \frac{80\ x\ 16}{155} = 8.26$ $\mathbf{E_9} = \frac{80\ x\ 70}{155} = 36.1$ $\mathbf{E_{10}} = \frac{80\ x\ 35}{155} = 18.1$

	'The lecture explains things very clearly'										
	Strongly Disagree		Disagree		Neutral		Agree		Strongly Agree		Total
	O	E	O	E	O	E	O	E	O	E	
Male	8	6.77 $\mathbf{E_1}$	12	9.68 $\mathbf{E_2}$	8	7.74 $\mathbf{E_3}$	30	33.9 $\mathbf{E_4}$	17	16.9 $\mathbf{E_5}$	**75**
Female	6	7.22 $\mathbf{E_6}$	8	10.3 $\mathbf{E_7}$	8	8.26 $\mathbf{E_8}$	40	36.1 $\mathbf{E_9}$	18	18.1 $\mathbf{E_{10}}$	**80**
Total	**14**		**20**		**16**		**70**		**35**		**155**

Appropriate test statistic: Chi-Square Test χ^2:

$$\chi^2 = \sum \frac{(O_i - E_i)^2}{E_i} = \frac{(O_1 - E_1)^2}{E_1} + \frac{(O_2 - E_2)^2}{E_2} + \cdots + \frac{(O_{10} - E_{10})^2}{E_{10}}$$

df = (r – 1) x (c – 1)

$$= \frac{(8-6.77)^2}{6.77} + \frac{(12-9.68)^2}{9.68} + \frac{(8-7.74)^2}{7.74} + \frac{(30-33.9)^2}{33.9} + \frac{(17-16.9)^2}{16.9}$$

$$= \frac{(6-7.22)^2}{7.22} + \frac{(8-10.3)^2}{10.3} + \frac{(8-8.26)^2}{8.26} + \frac{(40-36.1)^2}{36.1} + \frac{(18-18.1)^2}{18.1} = 2.47$$

df = (2 – 1) x (5 – 1) = 4 df

5. *Compare the calculated test statistic with the critical value*

The calculated χ^2 value of 2.47 falls *(to the left of 9.487)* where we fail to reject H_0. In failing to reject H_0, we are inferring that there is no association between gender and assessment of performance at the 0.05 level of significance and that there is insufficient evidence to contradict this.

6. *Derive or locate an approximate p value – Working with a Segment of the χ^2 tables*

		Above 0.05 ⟵		
p values ⇒	0.90	*p* value ⟵	0.10	0.05
1 *df*	0.015	......	2.705	3.841
.	......	......	......	......
4 *df*	0.063	**2.47** ⟵	7.77	9.48

Interpreting the p value

a. Traditional approach – explicit reference to a selected cut-off point of say $\alpha = 0.05$:

The *p* value which corresponds to the calculated χ^2 value *(2.47)* at 4 degrees of freedom lies above 0.05. Since the *p* value is above 0.05, we fail to reject H_0 at the 0.05 level of significance. *(Applying the p value decision rule: If p value > 0.05 we fail to reject H_0).*

b. Current approach – no explicit reference to a selected cut-off point of say $\alpha = 0.05$. The cut-off point is implicitly assumed as a guide value. The current approach is to report an exact *p* value *(included in the output of all statistical software packages)*. Using tables will only give us approximations.

The p value reveals the likelihood of being wrong if we reject H_0 (the p value appears to fall well above 0.10 i.e. more than 10 times in 100).

Effect Size Procedure

This procedure was deemed unnecessary since we failed to reject the null hypothesis (well above 0.10).

Reported results using the current approach (implicit cut-off guide point of $\alpha = 0.05$):

The χ^2 value of 2.47 (df = 4) has an associated probability value which is well above 0.10 which reveals that the likelihood of being wrong if we reject H_0 is well above 10 times in 100.

Summary comments

Whilst we still have two categorical variables, we can have more rows and columns. In addition to the *(2 x 2) and (2 x 4)* contingency tables used in this chapter, we can have *(3 x 3) or (3 x 4) or (4 x 4) or (4 X 5)* tables should we so desire. However, interpretation of tables with many cells becomes complicated. Ideally, we would prefer to extend our analysis of contingency tables beyond establishing *statistical significance* or otherwise. In addition to declaring an association which is *statistical significant*, we should be able to shed some light on the direction of the association *(positive or negative)*. This task may become impossible with very large contingency tables.

(a) Power of the statistical test procedure using *G*power 3* software = 23.57%

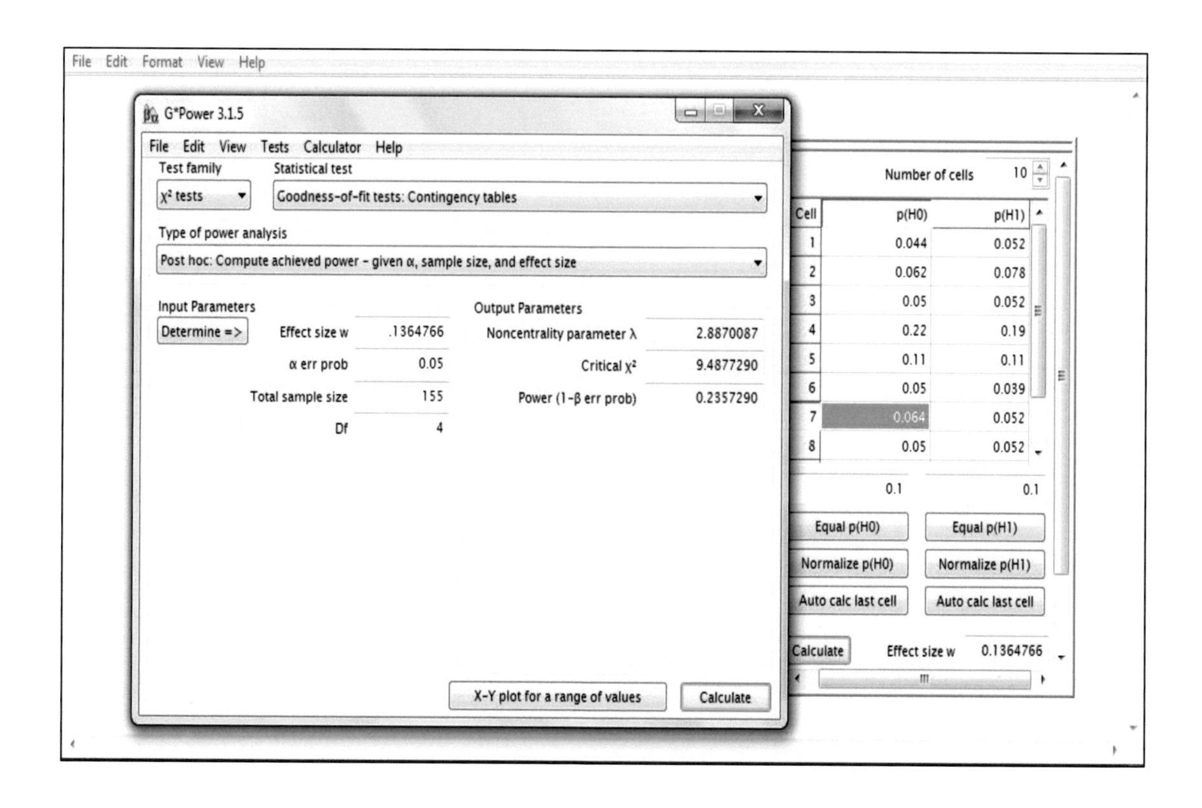

(b) Appropriate sample size using *G*power 3* software

The appropriate sample size for the following input parameters is 172:

a. *$\alpha = 0.05$*
b. *Desire effect size i.e. d = 0.25 (this value is derived from experience or from past studies)*
c. *Power level for the test = 0.75*
d. *Degrees of freedom = 4*

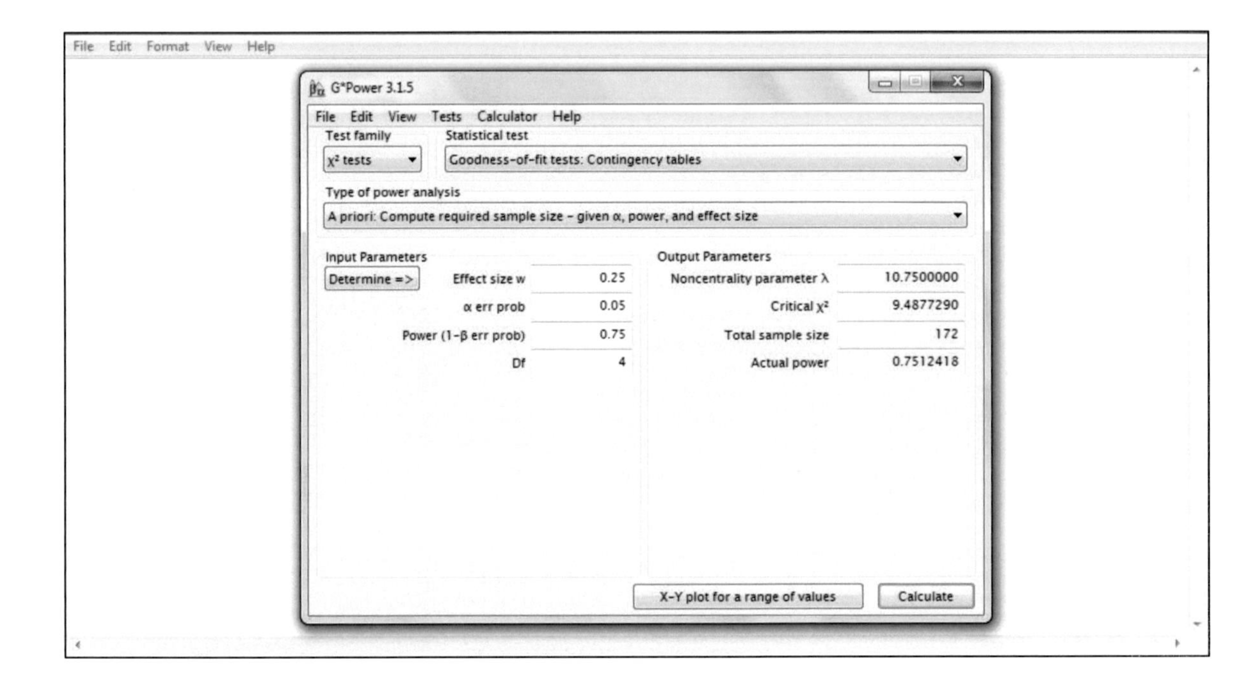

Example 5

Consider the following outcomes of 409 penalty kicks taken during the period 1976 – 2004 at three major tournaments. These penalty kicks were taken after additional time produced no winner.

	Penalty		
	Success (Code = 1)	*Failure (Code = 0)*	Total
World Cup	**109**	**44**	153
Copa America	**110**	**23**	133
European Championships	**104**	**19**	123
Total	323	86	409

*Test the hypothesis that proportion of successes is different at each tournament at the 0.05 level of significance. Use G*power 3 to calculate the post hoc power of the statistical test.*

Statistical Test Procedure *(Chi-Square 'Contingency table' Test)*

1. *State necessary conditions required to validate the test*

   a. A random sample is employed on each population at the outset. In this example, we can identify three populations at the outset. In effect, our three samples equates to three entire populations as we are looking at *all* the penalties.

   b. A conservative rule of thumb which insists that all expected frequencies > 5 is, debatably, too stringent, *(Cochran, 1954, cited in Everitt, 1980)*. A more relaxed assumption used in practice is acceptable:
      - ✓ For a 2 x 2 contingency table *(as in this example)*, the Chi-square should not be used if more than 25% of the expected frequencies is less than 5. If such a situation arises, we may employ Fisher's exact test *(available in most statistical packages)* as an alternative to the chi-square test.
      - ✓ For larger tables, the Chi-square should not be used if any of the expected frequencies is less than 1 or more than 20% of the expected frequencies are less than 5. If such a situation arises, one may consider increasing the sample size or pooling some of the rows and/or columns *(although, pooling categories after the data are seen may affect*

the random nature of the sample). A preferred alternative is to employ an *exact test* for tables larger than 2 x 2 *(available in most statistical packages)*.

c. Each participant's response appears just once thereby ensuring that the number of participants in each cell is independent.

2. *State the null hypothesis and alternative hypothesis*

H_0: $p_{\text{World cup}} = p_{\text{Copa America}} = p_{\text{European Championships}}$

H_1: $p_{\text{World cup}}$, $p_{\text{Copa America}}$, and $p_{\text{European Championships}}$ are not all equal

or

H_0: The distribution of successes/failures is the same for the 3 populations

H_1: The distribution of successes/failures is not the same for the 3 populations

3. *State the statistical decision rule for a selected level of significance*

a. Appropriate test statistic is the Chi-square *contingency table* test
b. The level of significance for this test: $\alpha = 0.05$ *(right tail area in the diagram below)*
c. Identify the critical value *(A segment of the χ^2 tables is included here)*

Identifying 5.991 in the diagram below requires 0.05 to be allocated to the right tail @ (rows – 1) x (columns – 1) degrees of freedom

d. Reject the null hypothesis *(H_o)* when the calculated test statistic *(χ^2)* from part 4 below > Critical value *(5.991)*

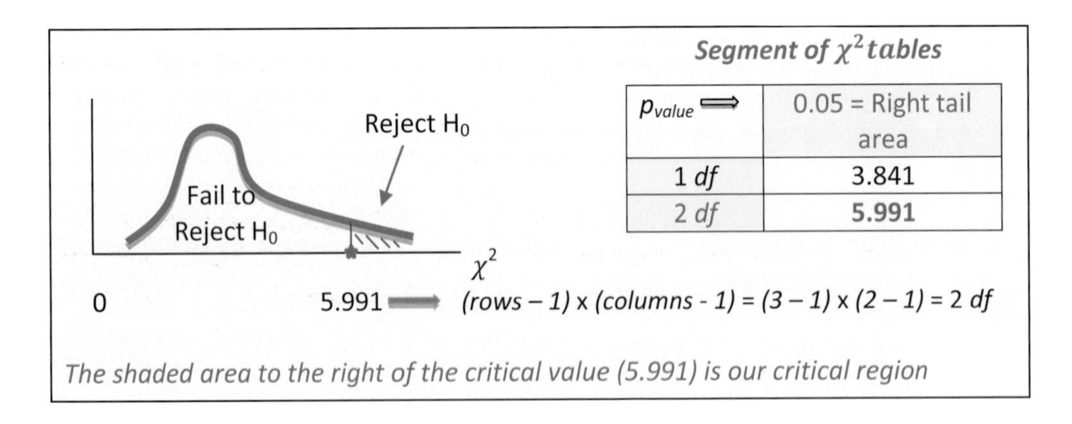

Segment of χ^2 tables

p_{value} ⟹	0.05 = Right tail area
1 *df*	3.841
2 *df*	**5.991**

The shaded area to the right of the critical value (5.991) is our critical region

4. *Select and calculate the appropriate test statistic*

How to calculate expected frequencies:

$$\mathbf{E} = \frac{Row\ total\ x\ column\ total}{overall\ total}$$

$\mathbf{E_1} = \frac{153\ x\ 323}{409} = 120.83$ $\mathbf{E_2} = \frac{153\ x\ 86}{409} = 32.17$ $\mathbf{E_3} = \frac{133\ x\ 323}{409} = 105.03$

$\mathbf{E_4} = \frac{133\ x\ 86}{409} = 27.97$ $\mathbf{E_5} = \frac{123\ x\ 323}{409} = 97.14$ $\mathbf{E_6} = \frac{123\ x\ 86}{409} = 25.86$

	Penalty				
	Success		*Failure*		Total
	Observed	*Expected*	*Observed*	*Expected*	
World Cup = Pop^n 1	**109 O_1**	120.83 $\mathbf{E_1}$	**44 O_2**	32.17 $\mathbf{E_2}$	153
Copa America = Pop^n 2	**110 O_3**	105.03 $\mathbf{E_3}$	**23 O_4**	27.97 $\mathbf{E_4}$	133
European championships = Pop^n 3	**104 O_5**	97.14 $\mathbf{E_5}$	**19 O_6**	25.86 $\mathbf{E_6}$	123
Total	323		86		409

Appropriate test statistic: Chi-Square Test (χ^2):

$$\chi^2 = \sum\frac{(O_i - E_i)^2}{E_i} = \frac{(O_1 - E_1)^2}{E_1} + \frac{(O_2 - E_2)^2}{E_2} + \cdots + \frac{(O_6 - E_6)^2}{E_6}$$

df = (r – 1) x (c – 1)

$$= \frac{(109 - 120.83)^2}{120.83} + \frac{(44 - 32.17)^2}{32.17} + \frac{(110 - 105.03)^2}{105.03}$$

$$= \frac{(23 - 27.97)^2}{27.97} + \frac{(104 - 97.14)^2}{97.14} + \frac{(19 - 25.86)^2}{25.86} = 8.929$$

df = (3 – 1) x (2 – 1) = 2 df

5. *Compare the calculated test statistic with the critical value*

The calculated χ^2 value of 8.929 falls *(to the right of 5.991)* where we reject H_0. In rejecting H_0, we are inferring that the proportion of successes is not the same at the three tournaments at the 0.05 level of significance and that there is sufficient evidence to support this.

6. *Derive or locate an approximate p value – Working with a segment of the χ^2 tables*

		➡	*0.05 and below*	
p values ⇨	0.10	0.05	0.025	0.01
1 *df*	2.705	3.841	5.023	6.634
2 *df*	4.605	5.991	7.377	9.210
.	......	......		

χ^2 = 8.929 lies between 7.377 and 9.210

Interpreting the p value

a. Traditional approach – explicit reference to a selected cut-off point of say α = 0.05:

   The *p* value which corresponds to the calculated χ^2 value *(8.929)* at 2 degrees of freedom lies between 0.025 and 0.01. Since the *p* value is below 0.05, we reject H_0 at the 0.05 level of significance. *(Applying the p value decision rule: If p value < 0.05 we reject H_0).*

b. Current approach – no explicit reference to a selected cut-off point of say α = 0.05. The cut-off point is implicitly assumed as a guide value. The current approach is to report an exact *p* value *(included in the output of all statistical software packages)*. Using tables will only give us approximations.

   The p value reveals the likelihood of being wrong if we reject H_0 (the p value appears to fall between 0.0.025 and 0.01 i.e. between 2.5 times and 1 time in 100).

Effect Size Procedure

How large or strong is the difference in proportion of successes for each tournament?

1. *Calculate Cramer's V for contingency tables of all sizes*

$$\text{Cramer's } V = \sqrt{\frac{\chi^2}{n\ x\ min(r-1,c-1)}}$$

Use r or c whichever is the smaller of the two

$$\text{Cramer's } V = \sqrt{\frac{8.929}{409(2-1)}} = 0.148$$

2. *Convert Cramer's V to effect size w (Cowen, 1988)*

$$w = V\sqrt{q-1} \longrightarrow w = 0.148\sqrt{2-1} = 0.148$$

$w = V\sqrt{q-1}$ *(Adapted from Cohen, 1988)* where *w* = effect size *w*,

V = Cramer's *V*, and *q* = the number of rows or columns *(whichever is the smaller of the two)*

3. *State your inferences - Guidelines proposed by Cohen (1988).*

Effect size w	*Interpretation*
If w < .1	Negligible Effect
If w ≥.1 but <.3	Small Effect
If w ≥.3 but <.5	Medium / Moderate Effect
If w ≥.5	Large Effect

This effect size value *(w = 0.148)* suggests a small effect. This suggests that magnitude of difference in the proportion of successes for each tournament is small.

Reported results using the current approach (implicit cut-off guide point of α = 0.05):

The χ^2 value of 8.929 *(df = 2)* has an associated probability value between 0.025 and 0.01 which reveals that the likelihood of being wrong if we reject H_0 is between 1 and 2.5 times in 100. However, the magnitude of difference in the proportion of successes for each tournament is small *(Cramer's V = 0.148).*

Power of the statistical test procedure using *G*power 3* software = 78.5%

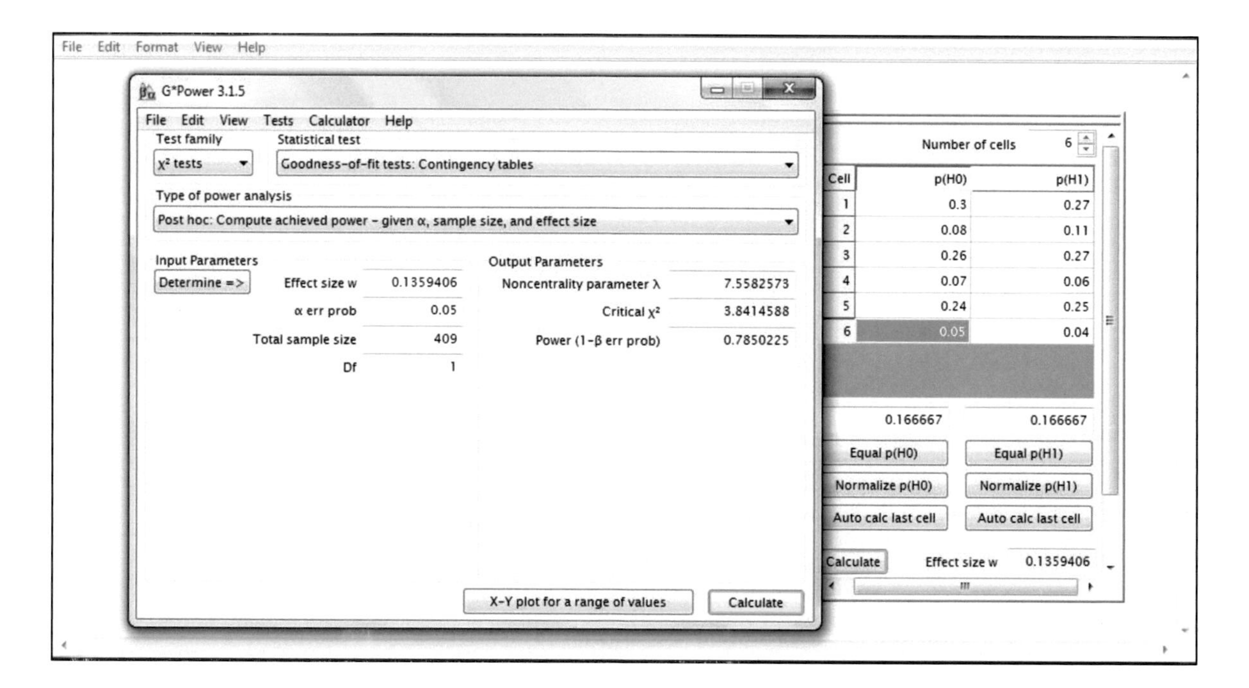

8.6 A note on effect size

In the traditional null hypothesis significance testing, you start with a null hypothesis *(which is assumed to be true unless collected sample evidence suggests otherwise)* and an alternative hypothesis. The application of an appropriate statistical test procedure then produces a *p* value which allows you to reject or fail to reject the null hypothesis.

A *statistically significant* result *(i.e. where we reject the null hypothesis)* simply indicates that your collected sample evidence contradicts the null hypothesis and that this contradictory evidence is very unlikely to have arisen in error. But it is unwise for the researcher to interpret more from a *statistically significant p* value i.e. to go beyond its actual meaning. The *p* value is not an index of effect size (*e.g. effect size indicates magnitude or size of association for Chi-square test for independence*). A statistically significant result must not be confused with implying a practical or meaningful significance.

A naive researcher might conclude from a piece of research that *the result was highly significant ($p < 0.001$)* and present this as evidence of practical or meaningful significance. As we have seen in this chapter *(example 3)*, a larger sample size can lead to a *statistically significant p* value with a negligible effect size. A *statistically significant* result must therefore be followed by an effect size procedure. This is the point where a non-statistical judgement must be made to judge whether the calculated *effect size value* is evidence of practical or meaningful significance.

The *'Effect size w' (Cohen, 1988)* is the benchmark measure that we use in this text. Cohen *(1988)* presented general guidelines for the interpretation of *'Effect size w'* which are intended to be used *only* when context-specific guidelines are unavailable in the researcher's particular research area. The guidelines are as follows:

Effect size w	*Interpretation*
If $w < .1$	Negligible Effect
If $w \geq .1$ but $< .3$	Small Effect
If $w \geq .3$ but $< .5$	Medium / Moderate Effect
If $w \geq .5$	Large Effect

The following table is a useful guide to the variety of effect size measure available.

Effect Size Measures	***Contingency Table Size***	***Effect Size Formulas***	***Conversion to Effect size w***	***Range***
Effect size w	*1 x c*	$w = \sqrt{\frac{\chi^2}{n}}$	$w = \sqrt{\frac{\chi^2}{n}}$	*0 to >1*
Phi (ϕ)[1]	*2 x 2*	$Phi\ (\phi) = \sqrt{\frac{\chi^2}{n}}$	*w = Phi (ϕ)*	*0 to >1*
Cramer's V[2]	*All matrix sizes*	$C_V = \sqrt{\frac{\chi^2}{n\ x\ min(r-1,c-1)}}$	$w = V\sqrt{q-1}$	*0 to 1*
Contingency[3] *Coefficient*	*All matrix sizes*	$C = \sqrt{\frac{\chi^2}{n + \chi^2}}$	$w = \sqrt{\frac{C^2}{1+C^2}}$	*0 to C_{max}*

Notes to table:

1. *In the case of a 2 x 2 table, Effect size w will equal the value of the Phi (ϕ). The Phi(ϕ) coefficient is a special case of the Pearson product moment correlation coefficient, computed by representing the classes as numbers. Therefore, in the case of a 2 x 2 table (and only in the case of a 2 x 2 table), the squared value of the Phi(ϕ) coefficient) can be interpreted as a proportion of the variance accounted for or the coefficient of determination, Volker (2006).*
2. $w = V\sqrt{q-1}$ *(Adapted from Cohen, 1988) where w = effect size w, V = Cramer's V and q = the number of rows or columns (whichever is the smaller of the two). Cramer's V is 'scale invariant' in that if the scale of your study increases, the effect size stays constant as long as you maintain the cell proportions in accordance with the smaller contingency table, Conover (1999). Given that Cramer's V is an extension of the Phi(ϕ) coefficient, the calculations for Effect Size w, Phi(ϕ) coefficient and Cramer's V will yield the same result for a 2 x 2 contingency table. In addition, when one variable has more than two categories and the other remains dichotomous (i.e. 2 x 3, 2 x 4, 2 x 5, etc.), the calculation for Cramer's V will always equal Effect Size w.*
3. *0 to* $C_{max} = \sqrt{\frac{min(r-1,c-1)-1}{min(r-1,c-1)}}$

Whilst *Cramer's V* and *Contingency Coefficient* are standardised effect size measures in their own right and can be reported in place of *Effect size w (see tables below)*, the advantage of using *Effect size w* is its greater generality in characterising Chi-square relationships, Volker (2006). To interpret *Cramer's V*, we refer to *(Cohen's Guidelines, 1988)*:

df = 1	$0.10 < V < 0.30$	Small effect
	$0.30 < V < 0.50$	Medium effect
	$V > 0.50$	Large effect
df = 2	$0.07 < V < 0.21$	Small effect
	$0.21 < V < 0.35$	Medium effect
	$V > 0.35$	Large effect
df = 3	$0.06 < V < 0.17$	Small effect
	$0.17 < V < 0.29$	Medium effect
	$V > 0.29$	Large effect

To interpret *Contingency Coefficient*, we refer to Cohen's *(Guidelines, 1988)*:

Contingency coefficient	*Interpretation*
If $C < .1$	Negligible Effect
If $C \geq 0.1$ but < 0.287	Small Effect
If $C \geq 0.287$ but < 0.447	Medium / Moderate Effect
If $C \geq 0.447$	Large Effect

8.7 MCQs and Solutions

1. Consider the following table:

	Do Smoke	Do Not Smoke	Total
Do Drink	50	15	65
Do not Drink	20	25	45
Total	70	40	110

This table is called a:

(a) 2 x 2 contingency table with 1 degree of freedom
(b) 2 x 2 contingency table with 2 degrees of freedom
(c) 3 x 3 contingency table with 1 degree of freedom
(d) 3 x 3 contingency table with 2 degree of freedom

2. Consider the following SPSS output for the data presented in 1 above.

	Value	df	Asymp.Sig (2-sided)	Exact Sig (2-sided)	Exact Sig (2-sided)
Pearson Chi-Square	12.121	1	.000		
Continuity Correction[a]	10.759	1	.001		
Fisher's Exact Test				.001	.001

a. Computed only for a 2 x 2 table = Yates Correction for Continuity
b. 0 cells (.0%) have expected count less than 5

		Value	Approx.Sig.
Nominal by Nominal	Phi	.332	.000
	Cramer's V	.332	.000

Which of the following is a correct interpretation of this output?

(a) The statistically significant 2 x 2 chi-square, $\chi^2(df = 1, n = 110) = 12.121, p < 0.001$, has a moderate effect according to Cohen's (1988) general standards, $w = 0.332$
(b) A non-significant 2 x 2 chi-square, $\chi^2(df = 1, n = 110) = 12.121, p < 0.001$, has a moderate effect according to Cohen's (1988) general standards, $w = 0.332$
(c) The statistically significant 2 x 2 chi-square, $\chi^2(df = 1, n = 110) = 12.121, p < 0.001$, has a small effect according to Cohen's (1988) general standards, $w = 0.332$
(d) A non-significant 2 x 2 chi-square, $\chi^2(df = 1, n = 110) = 12.121, p < 0.001$, has a small effect according to Cohen's (1988) general standards, $w = 0.332$

3. Which of the following is untrue?

(a) In a contingency table, when all the expected frequencies equal the observed frequencies, the calculated Chi-square statistic equals zero
(b) When conducting the Chi-square goodness of fit test , the rejection of the null hypothesis indicates that at least one of the multinomial probabilities is not equal to its corresponding value as stated in the null hypothesis
(c) When conducting a chi-square goodness of fit test, the smaller the value of the Chi-square test value, the more likely it is that we will reject the null hypothesis
(d) The expected frequencies in a goodness of fit test are the number of observations that should fall into each class in a frequency distribution in accordance with our claimed expected frequencies pattern

4. Assume that an educational psychologist has categorised the 45 identified spectrum-related cases from a study undertaken in ten primary schools in the south east.

k =3 categories	Autistic Disorder	Aspergers disorder	Development Disorder *(other)*
Observed frequencies	25	6	14

$\chi^2(df = 2, n = 45) = 12.13, p < 0.01, w = 0.52$

A Chi-square procedure *(goodness of fit)* was conducted for this set of three categories, testing the null hypothesis of equal frequencies across the disorders. Which of the following is a correct interpretation of this output?

(a) A statistically significant Chi-square, $\chi^2(df = 2, n = 45) = 12.13, p < 0.01$, with a moderate effect according to Cohen's (1988) general standards, $w = 0.52$
(b) A statistically significant Chi-square, $\chi^2(df = 2, n = 45) = 12.13, p < 0.01$, with a large effect according to Cohen's (1988) general standards, $w = 0.52$
(c) A non-significant Chi-square, $\chi^2(df = 2, n = 45) = 12.13, p < 0.01$, with a moderate effect according to Cohen's (1988) general standards, $w = 0.52$
(d) A non-statistically significant Chi-square, $\chi^2(df = 2, n = 45) = 12.13, p < 0.01$, with a large effect according to Cohen's (1988) general standards, $w = 0.52$

5. The Chi-square test *(goodness of fit test)* in 4 above has the following degrees of freedom:

(a) $k - 1$
(b) $k - 3$
(c) $(r - 1)(c - 1)$
(d) $k - 1 - m$

6. 290 people indicate their preference between five brands of energy drink.

$k = 5$	Booster	Hypedog	Trigger	Rocket	Turbo
Observed frequencies	67	83	77	6	57

What value will represent the equal expected frequencies for the cells?

(a) 57
(b) 58
(c) 290
(d) None of the above

Questions 7 to 9 relate to the following output:

Consider the following contingency table *(derived from the British Board of Trade report on the sinking of the Titanic in the North Atlantic Ocean on 15 April 1912)*. The following data related to adult male and female passengers of all classes.

Gender * Survival

		Lost	*Survived*	Total
Men	Count	**659**	**146**	805
	Expected Count	510.2	294.8	
	% within gender	81.9%	18.1%	
Women	Count	**106**	**296**	402
	Expected Count	254.8	147.2	
	% within gender	26.4%	73.6%	
Total	Count	765	442	1207

Pearson Chi-Square = 355.79 $df = 1$ $p < 0.001$
Continuity Correction = 355.41 $df = 1$ $p < 0.001$

Phi(ϕ) = 0.543
Cramer's V = 0.543

7. Which of the following is a correct interpretation of this output?

(a) The association between gender and survival is not statistically significant
(b) Survival was independent of gender
(c) The relationship between gender and survival is statistically significant
(d) We cannot determine if an association between gender and survival exists

8. Which of the following is incorrect?

   (a) *Phi*(ϕ) = *Cramer's V* = *Effect Size w* in this example
   (b) The magnitude of the relationship between gender and survival is large according to Cohen's 1988 guidelines
   (c) Surviving the *Titanic* is associated with the gender of a passenger
   (d) The effect size measures enable us to determine if the association between gender and survival is statistically significant.

9. Which of the following is incorrect?

   (a) The χ^2 value is 355.79
   (b) The number of people in this study is 1207
   (c) 81.9% of adult male passengers perished against 26.4% of adult female passengers
   (d) *Phi*(ϕ) will equal *Cramer's V* for contingency tables of all sizes

Questions 10 to 12 relate to the following output:

Consider the following contingency table (derived from the British Board of Trade report on the sinking of the *Titanic* in the North Atlantic Ocean on 15 April 1912). The following data related to adult male and female passengers of all classes.

Social class * Survival

		Lost	*Survived*	Total
Upper	Count	**122**	**197**	319
	Expected Count	202.18	116.82	
	% within gender	38.24%	61.76%	
Middle	Count	**167**	**94**	261
	Expected Count	165.42	95.58	
	% within gender	63.98%	36.02%	
Lower	Count	**476**	**151**	627
	Expected Count	397.39	229.61	
	% within gender	75.92%	24.08%	
Total		765	442	1207

Pearson Chi-Square = 129.34   *df* = 2 $p < 0.001$

Cramer's V = 0.327

10. Which of the following is a correct interpretation of this output?

(a) The association between social class and survival is not significant
(b) Survival was independent of social class
(c) The relationship between social class and survival is significant
(d) We cannot determine if an association between social class and survival exists

11. Which of the following is incorrect?

(a) *Cramer's V = Effect Size w* in this example
(b) The magnitude of the relationship between social class and survival is moderate according to Cohen's 1988 guidelines
(c) Surviving the *Titanic* was moderately associated with the social class of a passenger
(d) A significant finding will automatically suggest a moderate to large effect size *(in accordance with Cohen's guidelines 1988)*

12. Which of the following is incorrect?

(a) More than half the upper class passengers survived whilst less than one quarter of lower class passengers survived
(b) More than half of middle class passengers were lost whilst less than 40% of upper class passengers were lost
(c) Social class, whilst an important determinant of survival *(as measured by effect size)*, was less so than gender *(as measured by effect size)*
(d) The association between social class and survival was not statistically significant whilst the association between gender and survival was statistically significant.

13. Which of the following is incorrect?

(a) The Chi-square is a non-parametric test procedure
(b) A larger sample size, whilst maintaining the cell proportions in a contingency table, may result in a statistically significant association even though the effect size remains unchanged
(c) To declare dependence between two variables in a contingency table is to suggest that the two variables are not associated with each other
(d) To declare independence between two variables in a contingency table is to suggest that the two variables are not associated with each other

14. Which of the following is incorrect?

    (a) Yates's Continuity Correction is strongly recommended for a 2 x 2 contingency table, particularly when the sample size is small
    (b) In a Chi-square test for independence, we are sampling from one population at the outset of our study and our interest is in two variables X and Y, and especially in whether random observations of X and Y are independent
    (c) In a Chi-square test for equality of proportions, we are sampling from two populations at the outset of our study and our interest is in one variable Y that is considered on ≥ 2 populations
    (d) It is inappropriate to use a Chi-square test procedure *(goodness of fit test)*, which is a non-parametric test procedure, to test the assumption that a random sample is drawn from a normal distribution, in order to validate a parametric test procedure

15. If you wish to test the hypothesis that students prefer to be assessed with a 'multiple choice questions' format above the following formats, essay style questions, interview with the teacher, which sort of analysis would be most appropriate?

    (a) Chi-square test procedure *(goodness of fit)*
    (b) Chi-square test procedure *(test of independence)*
    (c) Fishers exact test
    (d) Yates's Continuity Correction

16. Which of the following is true?

    (a) In a chi-square test procedure, each sampled individual must contribute to every cell
    (b) In a chi-square test procedure, each cell must have an equal number of sampled individuals
    (c) In a chi-square test procedure, each sampled individual can appear in more than one cell
    (d) None of the above is true.

17. The following represents the distribution of preferences for a random sample of 33 students. The students were to select one from four available elective modules.

k = 4 categories	Sociology	Behavioural Science	Psychology	Statistics
Observed frequencies	10	8	11	4
	$\chi^2 = 3.48$ $df = 3$ $p = 0.32$ $w = 0.325$			

    Which of the following is a correct interpretation of this output?

(a) Because the $p > 0.05$ we can infer that preference for particular subjects is statistically significant
(b) There are no preferences for particular subjects and that the Chi-square value = 3.48 is likely to have arisen from sampling error
(c) There are preferences for particular subjects at the 0.05 level of significance since our p value > 0.05
(d) We are constrained from making inferences since both Yates's Continuity correction and Fishers' exact test are missing

18. Consider the following contingency table:

		Smoking		
		Do Smoke	*Do not Smoke*	*Total*
Drinking	*Do Drink*	70	32	32
	Do Not Drink	7	1	50
	Total	77	33	82

Chi-square value = 1.26 $df = 1$ $p = 0.26$ $w = 0.124$

Which of the following is a correct interpretation of this output?

(a) Because the *Effect size w* is small we can infer that there is no statistically significant relationship/association between drinking and smoking
(b) There is a statistically significant relationship/association between drinking and smoking at the 0.05 level of significance
(c) There is no statistically significant relationship/association between drinking and smoking at the 0.05 level of significance. The observed relationship between drinking and smoking may be due to sampling error
(d) We are constrained from making inferences since both Yates's Continuity correction and Fishers' exact test are missing.

Questions 19 to 20 relate to the research construct:

Consider the following questions and determine the appropriate statistical analysis assuming all statistical prerequisites *(random sample conducted etc.)* have been met. You have sampled from one population and dichotomised with respect to 'gender' and 'opinion'

Question – Are you

1. *Male*
2. *Female*

Question – 'The lecturer explains things very clearly' (Strike off your preferred choice)

Strongly Disagree	*Disagree*	*Neutral*	*Agree*	*Strongly Agree*
1	*2*	*3*	*4*	*5*

19. Which of the following is correct?

(a) The two questions will yield two qualitative data variables. I favour a Chi-square test procedure *(Test for independence)*
(b) The two questions will yield two quantitative data variables. I favour a Chi-square test procedure *(Test for independence)*
(c) The two questions will yield two qualitative data variables. I favour a Chi-square test procedure *(Test for equality of proportions)*
(d) The two questions will yield two quantitative data variables. I favour a Chi-square test procedure *(Test for equality of proportions)*

20. Which of the following is incorrect:

(a) The contingency table constructed will be a 2 x 5 matrix
(b) The *Effect size w* will yield an identical value as *Cramer's V*
(c) I may consider increasing the sample size if more than 20% of the expected frequencies is <5 or if any of the expected frequencies is <1 or I may conduct an *exact test* procedure "available in most statistical packages"
(d) In effect, I will be testing whether the distribution of opinion is the same for both the population of males and the population of females

MCQ Solutions

1. (a)	6. (b)	11. (d)	16. (d)
2. (a)	7. (c)	12. (d)	17. (b)
3. (c)	8. (d)	13. (c)	18. (c)
4. (b)	9. (d)	14. (d)	19. (a)
5. (a)	10. (c)	15. (a)	20. (d)

n	*Gender*	*Smoking Behaviour*	*SU doing good job*	*n*	*Gender*	*Smoking Behaviour*	*SU doing good job*
	Male = 1 Female = 2	*Do Smoke = 1 Do Not Smoke = 2*	*Yes = 1 No = 2*		*Male = 1 Female = 2*	*Do Smoke = 1 Do Not Smoke = 2*	*Yes = 1 No = 2*
1	1	2	1	31	2	1	1
2	1	2	1	32	2	1	1
3	1	2	1	33	2	1	1
4	1	2	1	34	2	1	1
5	1	2	1	35	2	1	1
6	1	1	1	36	2	1	1
7	1	1	1	37	2	1	1
8	1	1	1	38	2	1	1
9	1	1	1	39	2	1	1
10	1	1	1	40	2	1	1
11	1	1	1	41	2	1	1
12	1	1	1	42	2	2	1
13	1	1	1	43	2	2	1
14	1	1	1	44	2	2	1
15	1	2	1	45	2	1	1
16	1	2	1	46	2	1	1
17	1	2	1	47	2	1	1
18	1	2	1	48	2	1	1
19	1	2	1	49	2	1	1
20	1	2	1	50	2	1	1
21	1	1	2	51	2	1	1
22	1	1	2	52	2	1	1
23	1	1	2	53	2	1	1
24	1	1	2	54	2	1	2
25	1	1	2	55	2	1	2
26	1	1	2	56	2	2	2
27	1	1	2	57	2	2	2
28	1	1	2	58	2	2	2
29	1	1	2	59	2	2	2
30	1	1	2	60	2	2	2

A random sample of 60 first year students was selected from the population of 600 first year students. No consideration was given to appropriate sample size.

The researchers' task is to test the following:

1. *Is there an association between gender and smoking behaviour at the 0.05 level of significance?*

2. *Is there an association between gender and opinion on the Students union at the 0.05 level of significance?*

3. *Use G*Power to calculate the 'post hoc' power for the Chi-square test procedure, using the following information:*

    a. *$\alpha = 0.05$*
    b. *Actual effect size d*
    c. *Degrees of freedom = 1*
    d. *Sample size = 60*

IBM SPSS Statistics 20 Instructions

Step 1 – Open *IBM SPSS Statistics 20* select *Type in data* and click *OK*. Click *Variable View* at the bottom left corner and enter the variables.

Variable View Editor

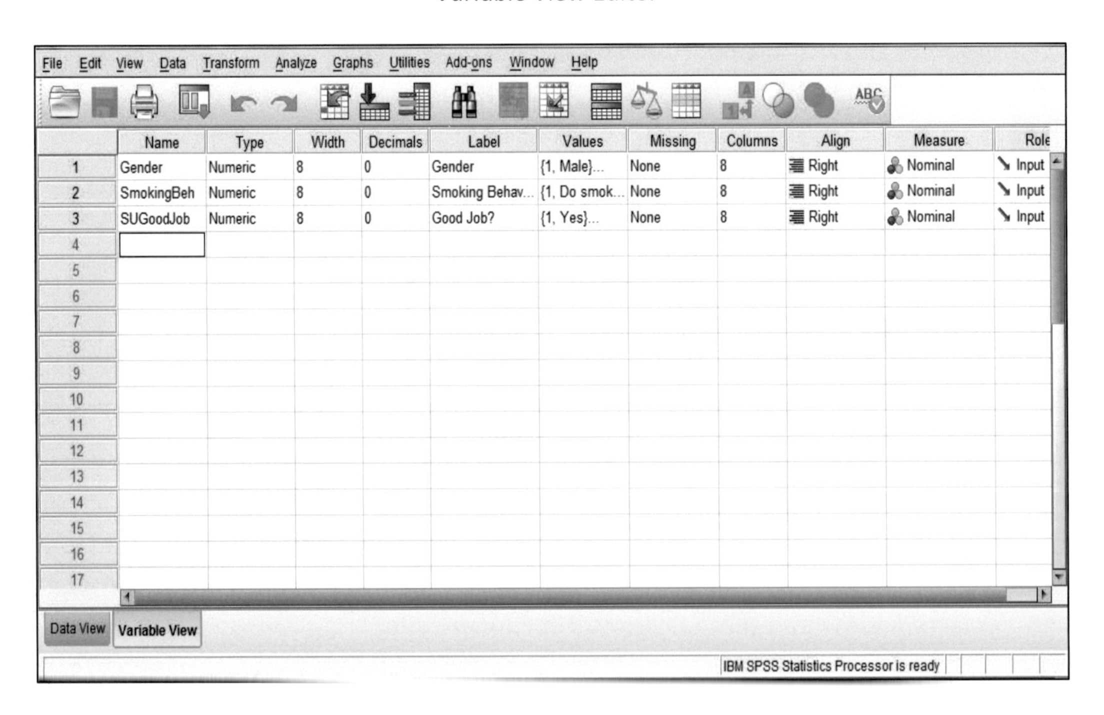

	Name	Type	Width	Decimals	Label	Values	Missing	Columns	Align	Measure	Role
1	Gender	Numeric	8	0	Gender	{1, Male}...	None	8	Right	Nominal	Input
2	SmokingBeh	Numeric	8	0	Smoking Behav...	{1, Do smok...	None	8	Right	Nominal	Input
3	SUGoodJob	Numeric	8	0	Good Job?	{1, Yes}...	None	8	Right	Nominal	Input

Step 2 – Click *Data View* at the bottom left corner and enter the data.

Data View Editor

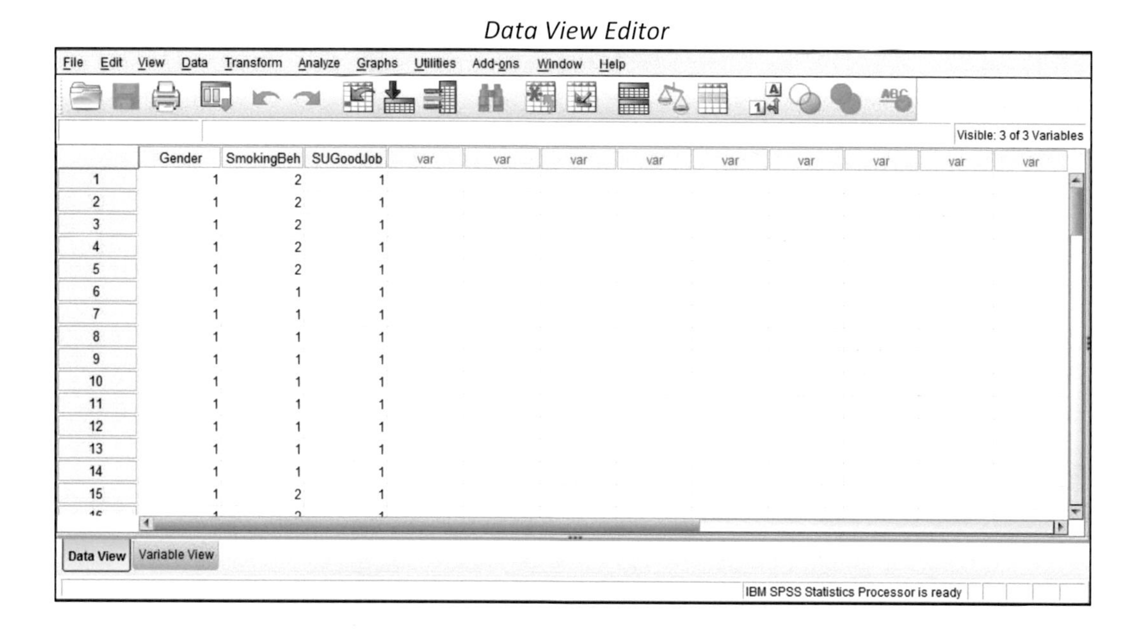

Step 3 – Click *Analyse* and select *Descriptive Statistics* and then select *Crosstabs.*

Data View Editor

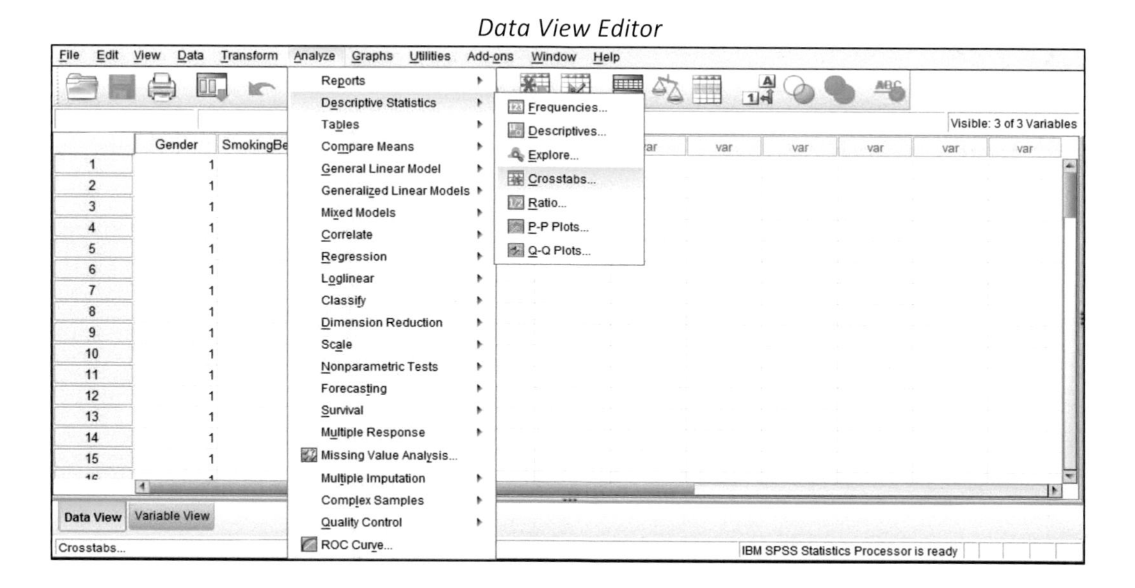

Step 4 – Move *Gender* into *Row(s)* and move *Smoking Behaviour* into *Column(s)*.

Data View Editor

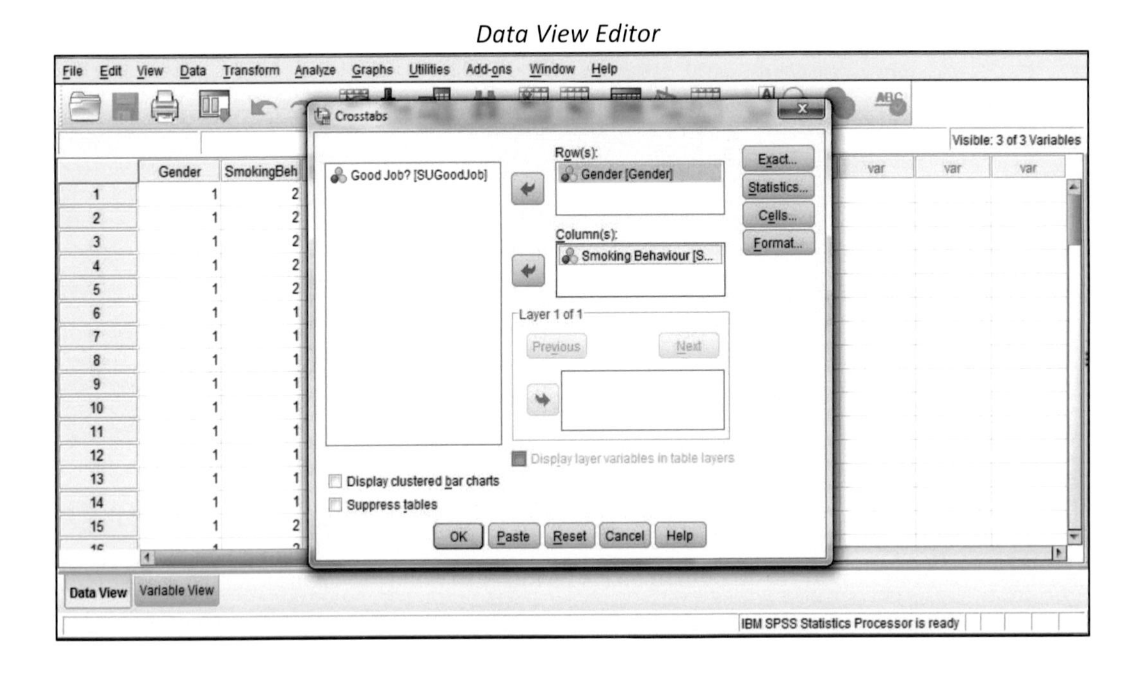

Step 5 – Click *Statistics* and tick *Chi-square* and *Contingency Coefficient* and *Phi and Cramer's V* and click *Continue*.

Data View Editor

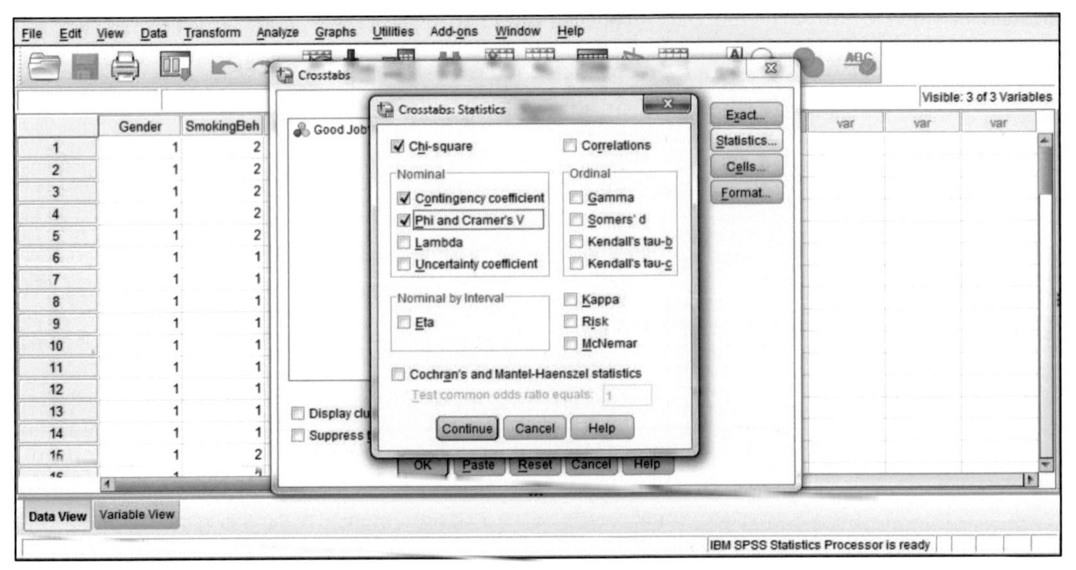

Step 6 – Click *Cells* and tick *Expected and Row* and click *Continue* and *OK*.

Data View Editor

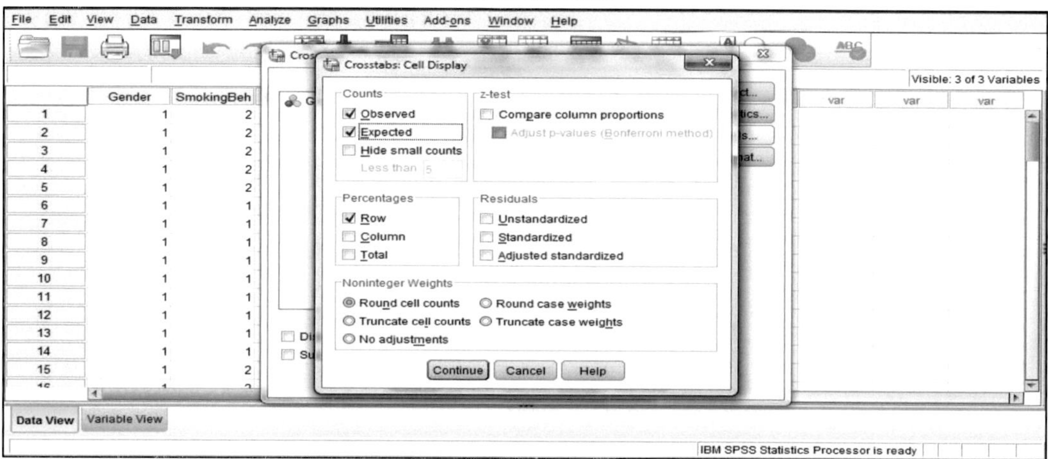

IBM SPSS Statistics 20 Output

Smoking Behaviour by Gender

			Smoking Behaviour		
			Do Smoke	Do Not Smoke	Total
Gender	Male	Count	19	11	30
		Expected Count	20.5	9.5	30
		% Within Gender	63.3%	36.7%	100%
	Female	Count	22	8	30
		Expected Count	20.5	9.5	30
		% Within Gender	73.3	26.7%	100%
Total			41	19	60

Chi-Square Tests

	Value	df	Asymp. Sig. (2-sided)	Exact Sig. (2-sided)	Exact Sig. (1-sided
Pearson Chi-Square	0.693[a]	1	0.405		
Continuity Correction[b]	0.308	1	0.579		
Fisher's Exact Test				0.580	0.290

a. *0 cells (0.0%) have expected count less than 5. The minimum expected count is 9.5*

b. *Computed only for a 2x2 table*

Symmetric Measures

		Value	*Approx. Sig.*
Nominal By Nominal	*Phi*	*-0.107*	*0.405*
	Cramer's V	*0.107*	*0.405*
	Contingency Coefficient	*0.107*	*0.405*

Power of the test using *G*Power 3*= 8.37%

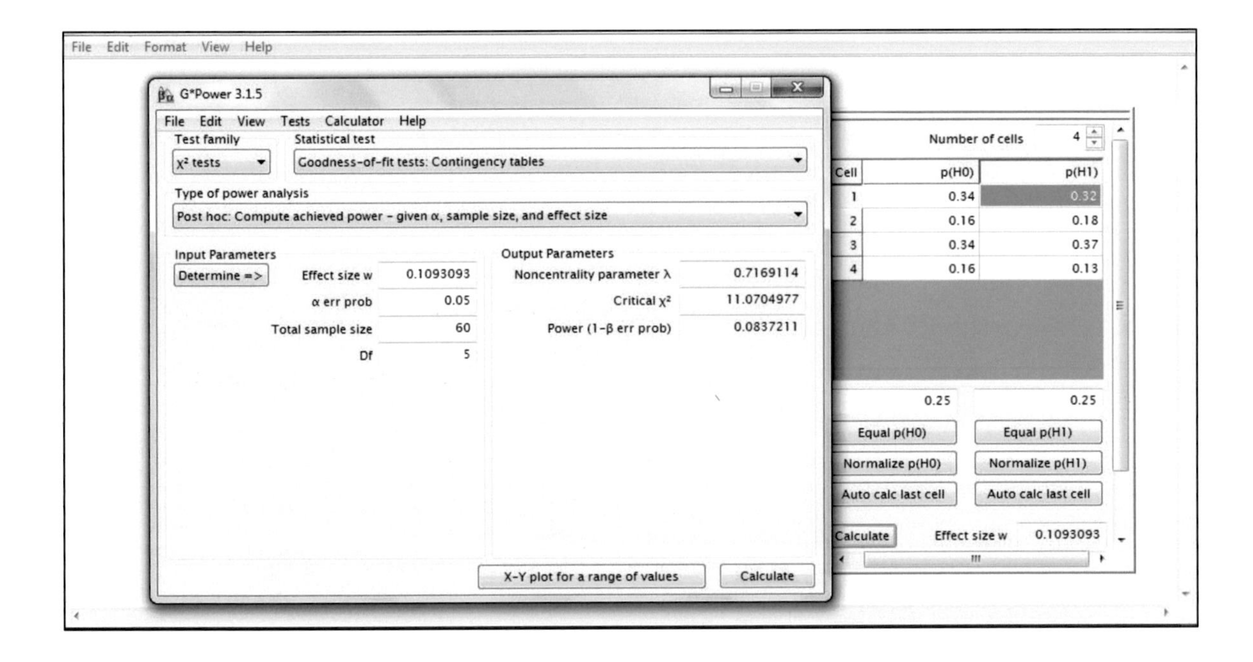

Chapter 9 – Inferential Procedures for Correlation and Regression

'I am sorry for the length of my letter, but I had not the time to write a short one.'

Blaise Pascal (1623–1662)

9.1 Schematic Chart – *Tests for Association/Relationship/Correlation*

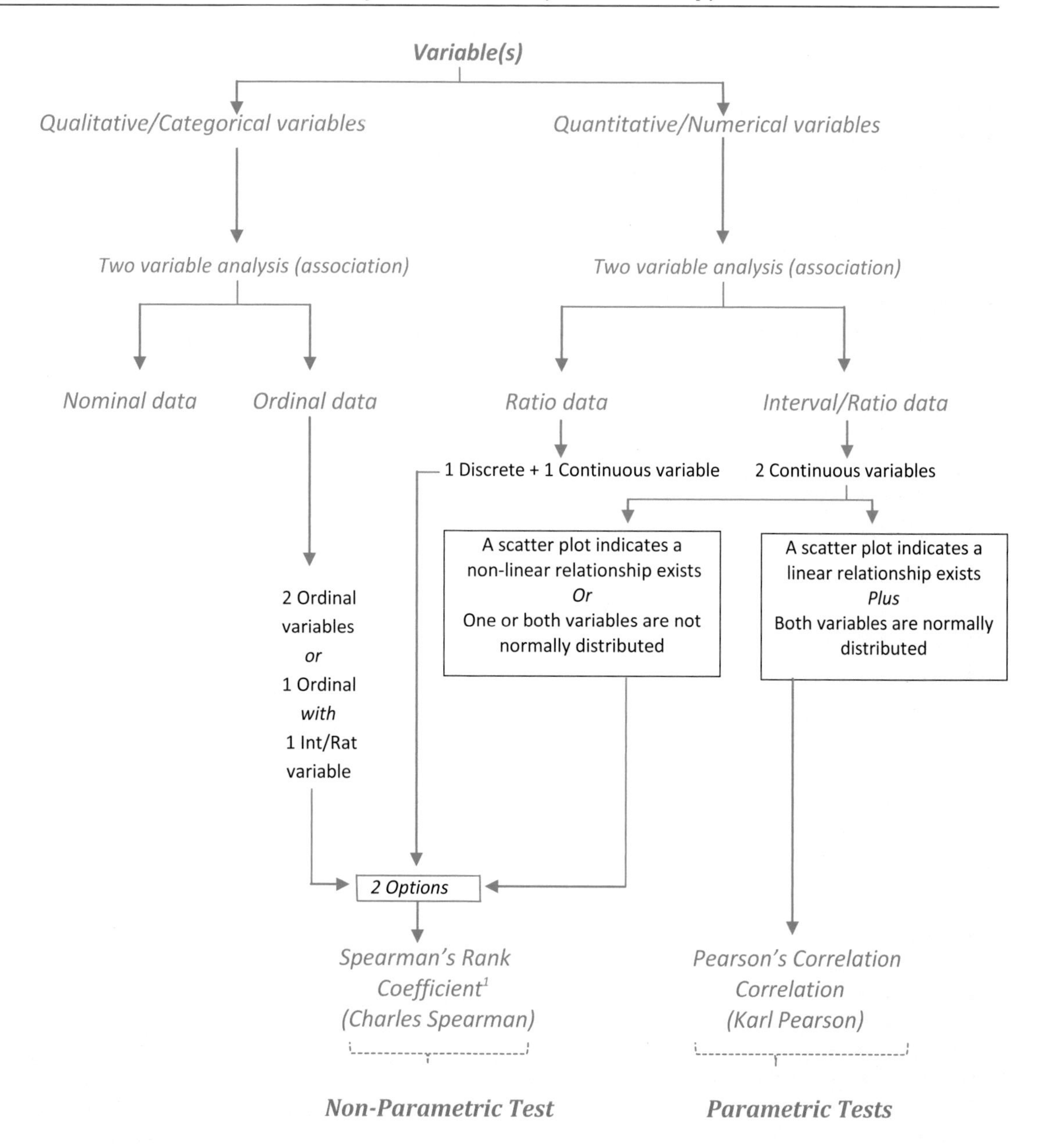

Notes:

1. *Prior to conducting the Spearman's Rank Correlation, both variables must be expressed as ranks*

9.2 Introductory Comments

There is little dispute regarding the relationship between smoking and cancer. A rise in smoking is associated with a rise in the incidence of cancer. Whilst we can observe that variables *co-vary*: a rise in one is matched by a rise in the other, it is inappropriate to automatically assume that causation can be inferred from such an observation. It is also inappropriate to infer that an apparently weak *co-variation* between two variables is evidence of little or no causation. To establish the presence and extent of causation between two variables, the researcher must go beyond the simple exercise of observing *(scatter plots)* and measuring the strength/magnitude of *co-variation* between two variables *(Pearson and Spearman correlation coefficients)*. When we observe and measure the relationship between two variables, it is with a strict understanding that no attempt is made to derive a causational inference from an apparently moderate to strong correlation between two variables. Observing an association or correlation between two variables can be considered a *necessary* but not *sufficient* condition to the task of establishing causation. To infer causation the researcher must conduct an experiment in which one variable *(referred to as the independent variable)* is systematically manipulated by the researcher and observations are recorded on the effects of these manipulations on another variable *(referred to as the dependent or criterion variable)*. A correlation design *(merely observing and measuring the strength of association between two variables)* lacks the essential requirement of independent manipulation.

Spurious correlations are commonplace, for example, whilst one can observe a strong *inverse relationship* between the fall in the population of sheep and a rise in the number of accounting graduates. Whilst we can observe and measure a definite relationship between the two variables, we cannot infer that a change in one causes a change in the other. Therefore, the researcher must understand that observing a pattern/relationship *(scatter plot),* measuring the strength/magnitude *(Pearson and Spearman correlation coefficients)* and establishing a *statistically significant* relationship *(i.e. an effect or a non-zero correlation via a statistical test procedure)* between two variables must incorporate the possibility that such a relationship is not *real* or *spurious*.

Correlation analysis between two variables *(i.e. bivariate analysis)* will enable the researcher to:

1. *Indicate the directional pattern of an association between two variables*

    a. *Positive – high scores on one variable will be associated with high scores on the other variable and vice versa*
    b. *Negative or inverse – high scores on one variable will be associated with low scores on the other variable and vice versa*
    c. *Zero – no association or discernible pattern is observed*

2. *Indicates the strength/magnitude of the relationship between two variables*

    a. *Zero to perfect positive linear correlation*
    b. *Zero to perfect negative linear correlation*

3. *Indicates whether the observed relationship is statistically significant*

9.3 Correlation

In correlation analysis no distinction is made between an *independent variable* and a *dependent variable*. The primary concern in correlation is to derive a measure *(a proportion or percentage)* which represents how well two variables move together in a *straight-line* fashion. We are interested in deriving a measure of the *linear relationship* between two variables. Intuitively, the measure that we derive represents how well a *straight line of best fit* best 'fits' the given set of data points *(see scatter plots below).*

Suppose that the researcher wishes to undertake a *correlation analysis* between two variables, a decision must be made on whether to employ:

1. *Pearson product-moment correlation coefficient (r)*
2. *Spearman rank correlation coefficient (r_s) or Spearman's Rho ρ*

The researcher will make the selection decision based on whichever of the following sets of assumptions best fits his sample data.

Pearson product-moment correlation coefficient *(r)*

Assumptions to validate the employment of Pearson's r

a. The sample must be randomly selected from the general population
b. Each person is included only once
c. Both variables are quantitative continuous variables
d. Both variables are derived from a normally distributed population
e. A scatterplot indicates that a linear relationship exists
f. Outliers should be removed or manipulated (either move must be justified)
g. There should be an even variation of points along the line (homoscedasticity)

Spearman rank correlation coefficient *(r_s)* or Spearman's Rho ρ

Assumptions to validate the employment of Spearman's Rho ρ

a. The sample must be randomly selected from the general population
b. Each person is included only once
c. Both variables are at least measured at the ordinal level

Interpreting Pearson's and Spearman's coefficients

The follow tables will assist the researcher interpret both the *Pearson's and Spearman's correlation coefficients*:

Interpreting Pearson's (r) or Spearman's rho (ρ)

Positive r or ρ	*Interpretation*	*Negative value r or ρ*
0.00	No linear correlation/ association	0.00
0.1 to 0.39	Weak or small linear correlation/association	-0.1 to -0.39
0.4 to 0.69	Modest or Moderate linear correlation/association	-0.4 to -0.69
0.7 to 0.99	Very strong linear correlation/association	-0.7 to -0.99
1.00	Perfect linear correlation/association	-1.00

Interpreting Pearson's coefficient and coefficient of determination

1. An additional measure, the *coefficient of determination* r^2 can easily be derived from the *Pearson's coefficient* r. The following table can be used to interpret the *coefficient of determination* r^2:

Interpreting the coefficient of determination r^2

Pearson's correlation coefficient = r	r^2	*Interpretation of* r^2 *% of variation of Y explained by X*
0.00	0.00	*0%*
0.10	0.01	*1%*
0.20	0.04	*4%*
.	.	.
0.80	0.64	*64%*
0.90	0.81	*81%*
1.00	1.00	*100%*

2. The following scatter plots depict varying degrees and directions of association between two quantitative *continuous* variables. Correlation analysis makes no distinction between the *independent variable* and the *dependent* variable; therefore, the correlation between any two variables *X* and *Y* is the same as the correlation between *Y* and *X*. However, traditionally the *dependent variable* is placed on the vertical axis and the *independent variable* is placed in the horizontal axis. Included in each diagram is a *Pearson's coefficient* r.

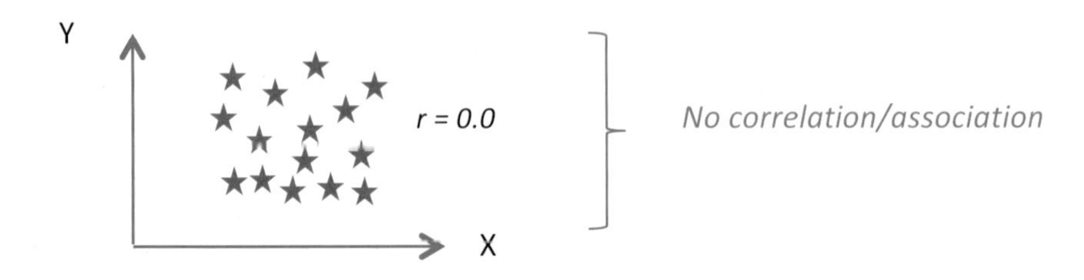

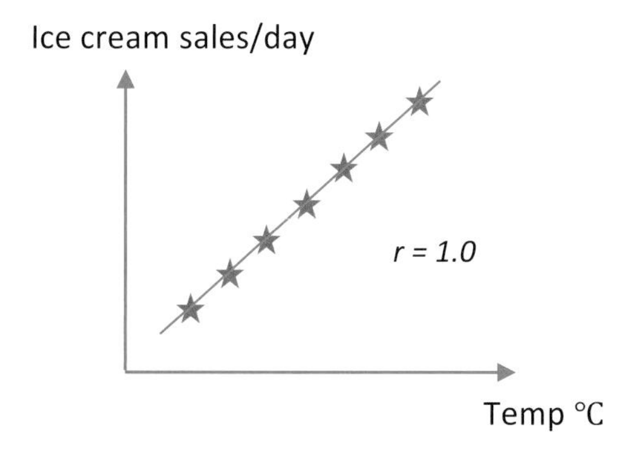

Perfect positive linear correlation

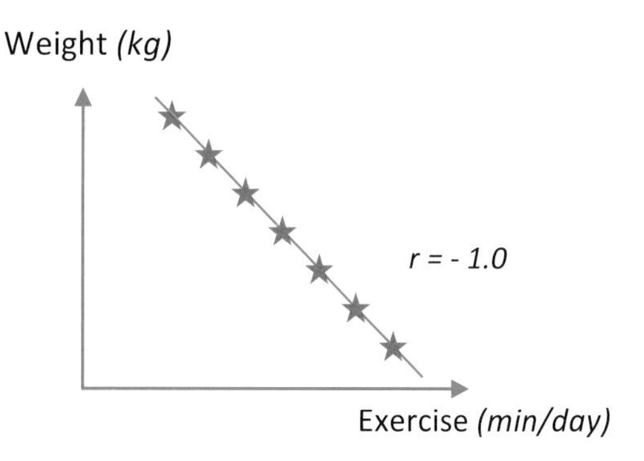

Perfect negative linear correlation

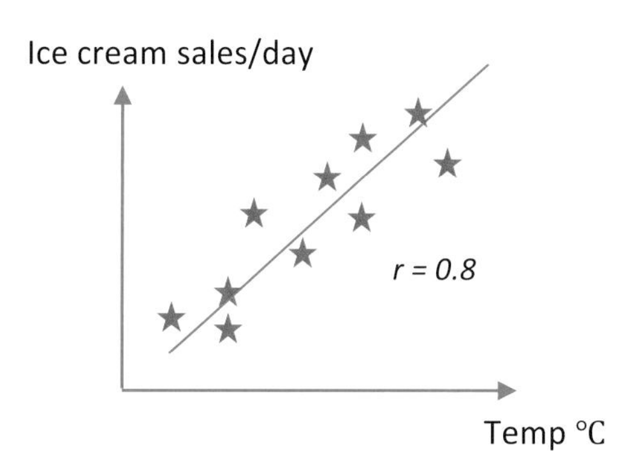

Very strong positive linear correlation

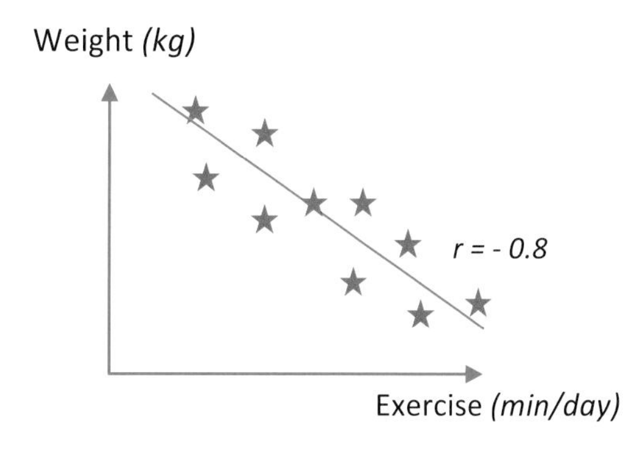

Very strong negative linear correlation

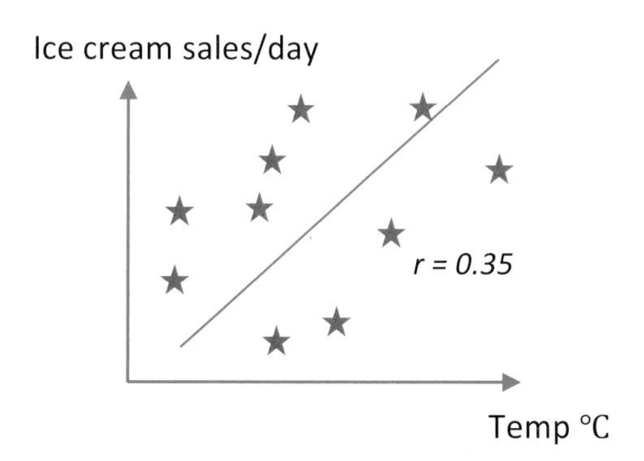

Weak positive linear correlation

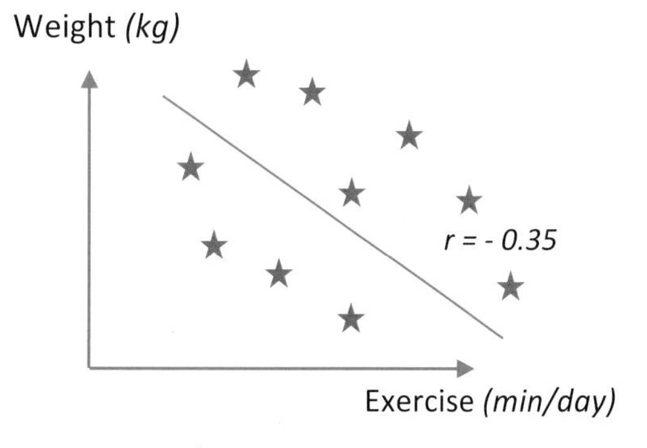

Weak negative linear correlation

3. The absence of linear correlation does not always imply the absence of association between variables. In fact, a more complex relationship may well be lurking in the data such as a curved *(non-linear)* relationship.

4. Once a non-zero measure of correlation is derived, then two variables can be judged to *share variance.* Consider the two variables *Weight (kg)* and *Exercise (min/day)* and suppose

that *Pearson's correlation coefficient* r = 0.80. By squaring this value, we derive the *coefficient of determination* r^2 *= 0.64*. This reveals that the two variables *share variance* to the tune of 64%. This can be interpreted as:

> *64% of the variation in the random sample of Weight (kg) values can be explained by the variation in the random sample of Exercise (min/day) values and vice versa.*

In other words, the samples of *weights* collected are different or varied and 64% of this variation is explained by the variation observed in the collected *exercise times* and vice versa. This also means that 36% of the variation observed in weights is left unexplained. The unexplained variation or the difference observed in weights which is not explained by the varying exercise regimes, is explained by other factors, such as age, genetics and environmental factors.

5. A correlation coefficient of 0.8 is not twice as strong as a correlation of 0.4. A correlation coefficient of 0.8 means that 64% of the variation is explained, whereas a correlation of 0.4 means that 16% of the variation is explained. Therefore a correlation coefficient of 0. 8 is four times as strong as a correlation of 0.4.

6. The correlation coefficient serves as an indicator of *Effect Size* assuming that the correlation has been declared *statistically significant*.

7. When you are examining the relationship or association between two variables, without consideration for others, then this is referred to as *zero-order correlation.* Once again, consider the two variables *Weight (kg)* and *Exercise (min/day)* and assuming that *Pearson's correlation coefficient* r = 0.80. One might suspect that *age* might be correlated with each of these variables. However, if you wish to investigate the association between *Weight (kg)* and *Exercise (min/day)* minus the effect of *age*, then this *partialling out of age* or holding the effect of *age* constant will reduce the coefficient of correlation between *Weight (kg)* and *Exercise (min/day).* This is referred to as *partial correlation.* If the coefficient of correlation between *Weight (kg)* and *Exercise (min/day)* is not reduced, then this would indicate that the association between *Weight (kg)* and *Exercise (min/day)* is not affected by *age*. The partialling out of age in this example is known as *first-order correlation*. If we decided to partial out two variables then this is known as *second-order correlation*.

9.4 Statistical Inference: *Pearson product-moment correlation coefficient (r)*

Consider the following simple data

Example 1

Ten students are given an aptitude test prior to the commencement of a special task. The students are then required to undertake the task and their performance is assessed.

These are the results:

Student	Aptitude Score *(0 – 100)*	Performance score *(0 – 100)*
1	38	26
2	59	57
3	68	34
4	40	42
5	14	23
6	33	57
7	87	83
8	71	97
9	62	72
10	81	74

Example 1

1. *Represent the results on a scatter plot*
2. *Comment on the relationship between the two variables*
3. *Calculate Pearson's correlation coefficient*
4. *Interpret its meaning*
5. *What is the coefficient of determination*
6. *Interpret its meaning*
7. *Test the hypothesis that a linear relationship exists between the two scores at the 0.05 level of significance*
8. *Use G*power 3 to calculate the post hoc power of the statistical test*

Solutions 1

1.

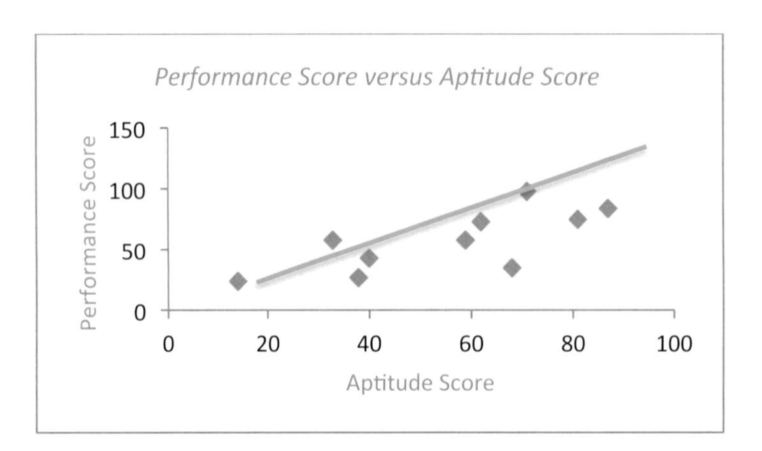

2. The relationship is a positive one *(as the value of one variable rises then so too does the value of the other, and vice versa)*. There does not appear to be any outliers and a line drawn through the data suggests that the data follows a linear pattern. There appears to be a strong linear association or correlation between the two variables.

3. The key to calculating the *Pearson's correlation coefficient (r)* is allow the formula to guide the expansion of the following table.

Student	*X*	*Y*	*XY*	X^2	Y^2
1	38	26	988	1444	676
2	59	57	3363	3481	3249
3	68	34	2312	4624	1156
4	40	42	1680	1600	1764
5	14	23	322	196	529
6	33	57	1881	1089	3249
7	87	83	7221	7569	6889
8	71	97	6887	5041	9409
9	62	72	4464	3844	5184
10	81	74	5994	6561	5476
n = 10	$\sum X = 553$	$\sum Y = 565$	$\sum XY = 35112$	$\sum X^2 = 35449$	$\sum Y^2 = 37581$

$$(r) = \frac{n \sum XY - \sum X \sum Y}{\sqrt{(n \sum X^2 \quad [\sum X]^2)(n \sum Y^2 \quad [\sum Y]^2)}}$$

$$r = \frac{n \sum XY - \sum X \sum Y}{\sqrt{(n \sum X^2 - [\sum X]^2)(n \sum Y^2 - [\sum Y]^2)}}$$

$$r = \frac{10\ x\ 35112 - 553\ x\ 565}{\sqrt{(10\ x\ 35449 - [553]^2)\ (10\ x\ 37581 - [565]^2)}}$$

$$r = \frac{38675}{\sqrt{(48681)\ (56585)}} = \frac{38675}{52484} = \mathbf{0.74}$$

4. The value r = 0.74 indicates a very strong positive linear association. If a line is superimposed onto the scatter plot such that this line best represents the data, *(line of best fit)*, then we can say that this line represents the data points to the tune of 75%. If all the data points lay along the line then the line would represent the data points to the tune of 100%. There is 75% agreement or association between the two continuous variables.

5. The coefficient of determination = $r^2 = 0.74^2 = 0.55$.

6. When two variables are associated or correlated with each other, then we are certain that they are not independent of each other and that the variation in the values of one variable explains a certain percentage of the variation in the values of the other variable. In this example 55% of the variation in performance scores is explained by the variation in aptitude scores and vice versa.

7. Test the hypothesis that the association between the variables *is different from* zero *(that the association between the two variables is real or does exist in the population)* at the 0.05 level of significance.

   Whilst the scatter diagram does reveal a strong positive linear association between the two *continuous* variables, this finding represent the observed association from a random sample. However, can we generalise this finding to the entire population or is this observed association due to sampling error *(due to chance)*.

   Step 1

   To undertake this test for *statistical significance*, the assumption of normal distributions for the two variables is required.

   Step 2

   H_0: The correlation in the population is zero
   H_1: The correlation in the population is not zero
   or
   H_0: An association between the two variables does not exist in the population
   H_1: An association between the two variables does exist in the population

   Since the alternative hypothesis does not refer to either a positive or negative association, this is a two tailed test.

Step 3

a. The level of significance for this test: $\alpha = 0.05$

b. The critical values with reference to the appropriate tables

Segment of the t tables

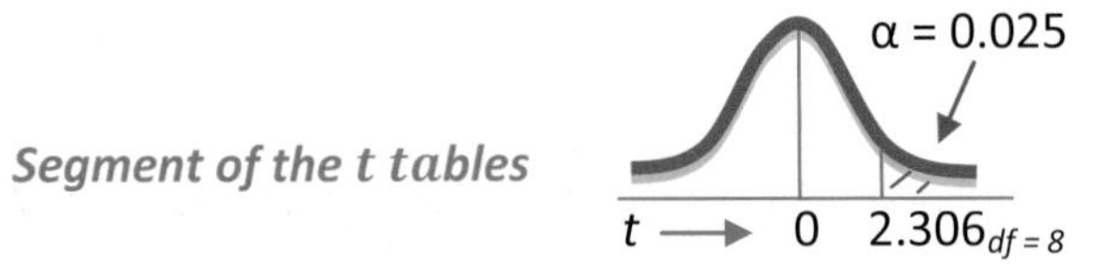

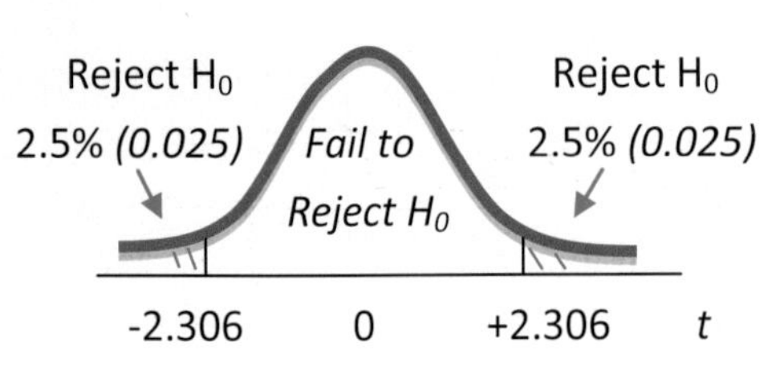

p_{val} 1-tail	$t_{0.100}$	$t_{0.050}$	$t_{0.025}$
p_{val} 2-tail	$t_{0.200}$	$t_{0.100}$	$t_{0.050}$
df = 7	.	.	.
df = 8	.	.	**2.306**

Degrees of freedom = n -2 = 10 - 2 = 8

Step 4

t test statistic for the coefficient of correlation

$$t = \frac{r\sqrt{n-2}}{\sqrt{1-r^2}} = \frac{0.74\sqrt{10-2}}{\sqrt{1-0.55}} = \mathbf{3.12}$$

Step 5

Since 3.12 falls into the critical region, we reject H_0 and infer that an association between the two variables does exist in the population at the 0.05 level of significance.

8. *Using G*power 3, the post hoc power of the statistical test is 86.33%.*

*G*power 3*

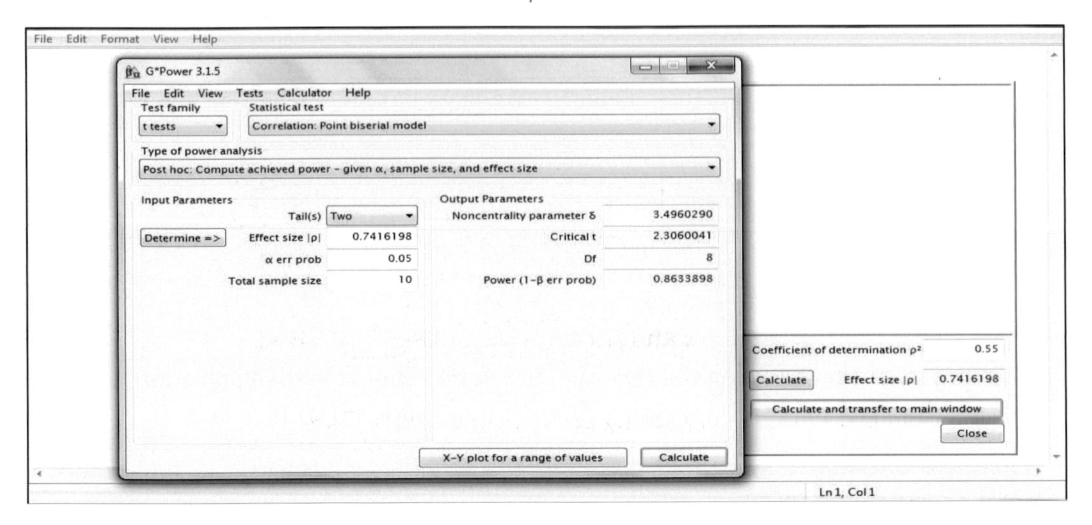

9.5 Statistical Inference: *Spearman rank correlation coefficient (r_s)*

Consider the following simple dataset which includes two variables measured at the ordinal level.

Example 2

The top eight ranking tennis professionals and their finishing positions at a recent 'major' are as follows:

Tennis Professional	World ranking	Placing at recent major
1	1	3
2	2	5
3	3	1
4	4	2
5	5	4
6	6	6
7	7	8
8	8	7

Calculate Spearman's correlation coefficient and interpret its meaning

Person	World ranking	Recent Placing	Difference = d	d^2
1	1	3	-2	4
2	2	5	-3	9
3	3	1	2	4
4	4	2	2	4
5	5	4	1	1
6	6	6	0	0
7	7	8	-1	1
8	8	7	1	1
				$\sum d^2 = 24$

$$\textbf{Spearman's Rho } \rho = 1 - \frac{6\ x \sum d^2}{n\ (n^2-1)} = 1 - \frac{6\ x\ 24}{8\ (64-1)} = \mathbf{0.71}$$

The value of ρ = 0.71 indicates a very strong positive linear association.

9.6 Simple Linear Regression – *An introduction*

Simple Linear Regression *(SLR)* provides a mathematical equation that specifically locates the line that best fits the data on a scatterplot. This *line of best fit* is also referred to the regression equation. This regression equation enables us to predict *normal* population values for normally distributed variables, given a selected value from another normally distributed population variable.

The regression equation predicts the mean Y value for any observed X value

For a simple linear regression the *line of best fit*, that is the regression line through the data points on a scatter plot, is described by the following equation:

$$\mathbf{Y = a + bX}$$

Example 3

When the *line of best fit* predicts with 100% accuracy *(using data which is perfectly linear)*

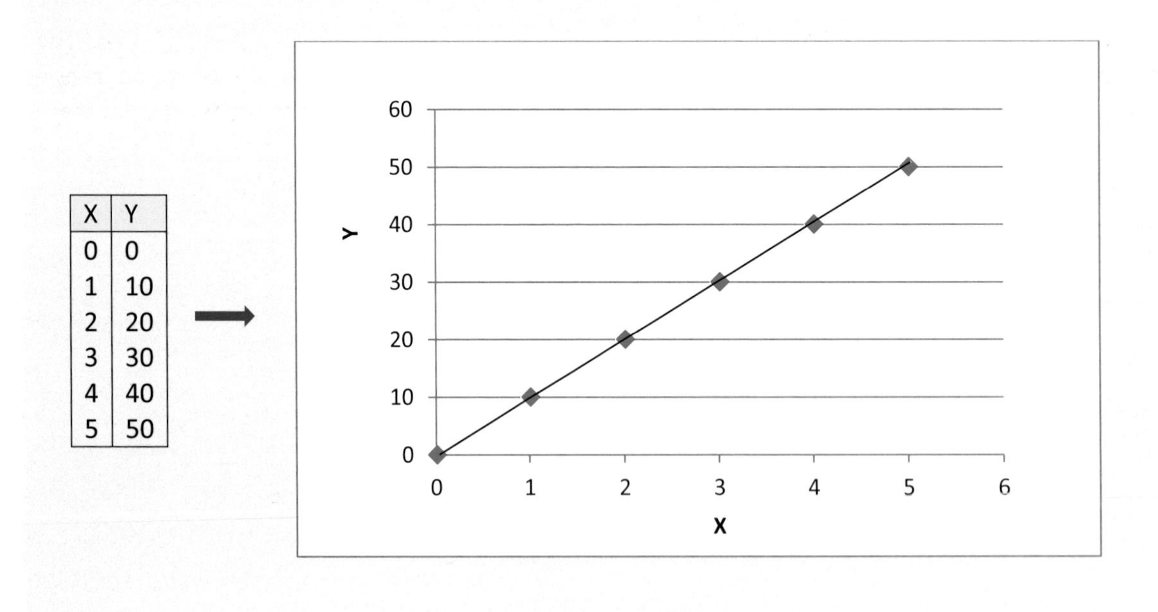

X	Y
0	0
1	10
2	20
3	30
4	40
5	50

To calculate the *Pearson's correlation coefficient* the following table is prepared:

X	Y	XY	X^2	Y^2
0	0	0	0	0
1	10	10	1	100
2	20	40	4	400
3	30	90	9	900
4	40	160	16	1600
5	50	250	25	2500
$\sum X = 15$	$\sum Y = 150$	$\sum XY = 550$	$\sum X^2 = 55$	$\sum Y^2 = 5500$
$\bar{X} = 2.5$	$\bar{Y} = 25$			

$$r = \frac{n \sum XY - \sum X \sum Y}{\sqrt{(n \sum X^2 - [\sum X]^2)\,(n \sum Y^2 - [\sum Y]^2)}}$$

$$= \frac{(5 \times 550) - (15 \times 150)}{\sqrt{(5 \times 55 - [15]^2)\,(5 \times 5500 - [150]^2)}} = \mathbf{1.00}$$

$$r^2 = 1^2 = 1$$

As we would expect, there is a perfect positive linear association between the variables. The regression line is not only the *line of best fit*, it is the *line of perfect fit*. All of the variation in one variable is explained by the variation in the other variable. The two variables share 100% variance.

To estimate the *line of best fit*, we must find the values for *a* and *b* in Y = a + bX

$$\mathbf{b} = \frac{n \sum XY - \sum X \sum Y}{n \sum X^2 - (\sum X)^2} = \frac{(5 \times 550) - (15 \times 150)}{(5 \times 55) - (225)} = \mathbf{10}$$

$$\mathbf{a} = \bar{\mathbf{Y}} - \mathbf{b}\bar{\mathbf{X}} \text{ or } \mathbf{a} = \frac{\sum Y - b \sum X}{n} = \mathbf{25 - 10(2.5) = 0}$$

therefore

Y = 0 + 10X

The regression equation Y = 0 + 10X *Where Y = dependent/response variable*

Where X = Independent/explanatory variable

Intercept of the line = where the line begins

Slope of the line = How steep the line is

The estimated regression equation *(Y = 0 + 10 X)* tells us that as X increases by 1 then Y increases by 10. If a person scores 0 for X then they score 0 on Y also. This can also be interpreted from the estimated regression equation.

Prediction using the regression equation

If we place a score of 4 *(value for X)* into the regression equation, then the predicted value for Y will be 40. This can also be derived by inspection of the graph and the table. The equation in this instance predicts with 100% accuracy. There will be no errors in our predictions. This is only true when there is a perfect linear association *(negative or positive)* between two variables.

The difference between the predicted scores and the actual scores is referred to as *residuals*. In this example, if I am absolutely certain that there is a perfect association between the two variables, then my predictions will equate to the actual scores.

Given value of X	Predicted Scores = $\hat{Y}$	Actual Score = Y	Residuals = Y - $\hat{Y}$
2	20	20	0
3	30	30	0
4	40	40	0

The regression line $Y = a + bX$ was estimated from a sampled range of values of X and Y. It is wise to use this model to make predictions using values for X which are within the range of values used to estimate the equation. This method of prediction is referred to as *interpolation.* Interpolation is reliable. If we are uncertain about how the variables associate outside the sample range, then it is unwise to use the model to make predictions using values outside the sampled range. If we take values for X which are outside the sample range, this method of prediction is *extrapolation*. Extrapolation is unreliable.

Example 4

When the *line of best fit* does not predict with 100% accuracy *(using data which is not perfectly linear).*

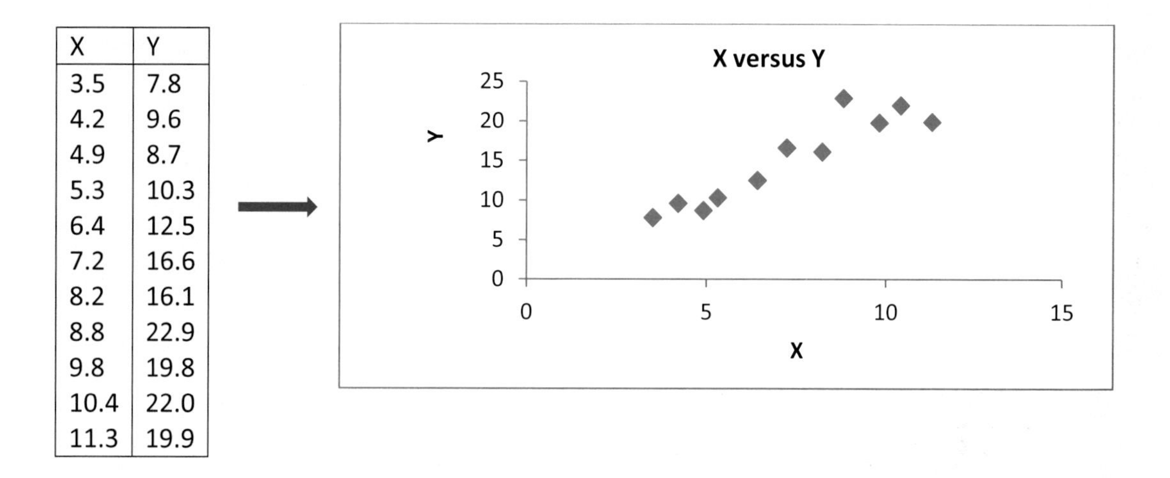

X	Y
3.5	7.8
4.2	9.6
4.9	8.7
5.3	10.3
6.4	12.5
7.2	16.6
8.2	16.1
8.8	22.9
9.8	19.8
10.4	22.0
11.3	19.9

To calculate the *Pearson's correlation coefficient* the following table is prepared:

X	Y	XY	X^2	Y^2
3.5	7.8	27.30	12.30	60.84
4.2	9.6	40.32	17.64	92.16
4.9	8.7	42.63	24.01	75.69
5.3	10.3	54.59	28.09	106.09
6.4	12.5	80.00	40.96	156.25
7.2	16.6	119.52	51.84	275.56
8.2	16.1	132.02	67.24	259.21
8.8	22.9	201.52	77.44	524.41
9.8	19.8	194.04	96.04	392.04
10.4	22.0	228.80	108.16	484.00
11.3	19.9	224.87	127.67	396.01
$\sum X = 80.00$	$\sum Y = 166.20$	$\sum XY = 1345.60$	$\sum X^2 = 651.40$	$\sum Y^2 = 2822.30$
$\bar{X} = 7.27$	$\bar{Y} = 15.11$			

$$r = \frac{n \sum XY - \sum X \sum Y}{\sqrt{(n \sum X^2 - [\sum X]^2)\,(n \sum Y^2 - [\sum Y]^2)}}$$

$$= \frac{(11\ x\ 1345.60) - (80.00\ x\ 166.20)}{\sqrt{(11\ x\ 651.40 - [80.00]^2)\,(11\ x\ 2822.30 - [166.20]^2)}}$$

$$r^2 = 0.93^2 = 0.86$$

There is a very strong positive linear association between the variables. 86% of the variation in one variable is explained by the variation in the other variable. The two variables share 86% variance.

To estimate the *line of best fit*, we must find the values for *a* and *b* in Y = a + bX

$$b = \frac{n\sum XY - \sum X \sum Y}{n\sum X^2 - (\sum X)^2} = \frac{(11 \; x \; 1345.60)-(80.00 \; x \; 166.20)}{(11 \; x \; 651.40)-(6400)} = \mathbf{1.97}$$

$$a = \bar{Y} - b\bar{X} \text{ or } a = \frac{\sum Y - b\sum X}{n} = \mathbf{15.11 - 1.97(7.27) = 0.79}$$

Therefore

Y = 0.79 + 1.97X

The regression equation Y = 0.79 + 1.97X

Where Y = dependent/response variable
Where X = Independent/explanatory variable

Intercept of the line = where the line begins

Slope of the line = How steep the line is

As X increases by 1 then Y increases by 1.97 and If X has a value of 0 then the value of Y is 0.79.

Prediction using the regression equation

If we place a value of 6 *(value for X)* in the regression equation, then the prediction for Y is 12.61.

Given value of X	Predicted Scores = $\hat{Y}$	Actual Score = Y	Residuals = Y - $\hat{Y}$
4.2	Y = 0.79 + 1.97(4.2) = 9.064	9.6	0.536
6.4	Y = 0.79 + 1.97(6.4) = 13.398	12.5	- 0.898
8.8	Y = 0.79 + 1.97(8.8) = 18.126	22.9	4.774

The relationship between X and Y is linear for values within the range of values used to estimate the regression line.

9.7 MCQs and Solutions

1. A correlation coefficient tells us:

(a) The slope of the equation through the data
(b) How well one variable predicts another
(c) How closely two variables are linearly related
(d) None of the above

2. The coefficient of determination indicates:

(a) How much of the variation in the scores of one variable is explained or accounted for by the variation in the scores of the other variable
(b) The strength of association between two variables
(c) How well one variable predicts another
(d) Whether the relationship is linear or non linear

3. If 81% of the variation in scores of variable A has been accounted for by the variation in the scores of variable B, how much of the variance is unexplained?
(a) 19%
(b) 81%
(c) 9%
(d) 91%

4. If two variables have no association between them, then the correlation coefficient is:

(a) +1
(b) -1
(c) Zero
(d) +0.1

5. List the strongest and weakest relationship respectively:

		Statistics grade	*P* value
Class attendance	Pearson Correlation	+ 0.75	0.01
Intelligence Quotient	Pearson Correlation	+ 0.65	0.04
Hours of study	Pearson Correlation	+ 0.70	0.02
Distance from college	Pearson Correlation	- 0.35	0.05

(a) Class attendance and distance from college
(b) Class attendance and Intelligence Quotient
(c) Class attendance and hours of study
(d) Intelligence Quotient and hours of study

6. If you have a correlation coefficient of 0.3, how much variance is left unexplained?

(a) 30%
(b) 70%
(c) 9%
(d) 91%

7. Which of the following is untrue:

(a) Correlation does not imply causation
(b) A positive relationship means that as scores on X rises, then scores on Y also rises
(c) A negative relationship means that as scores on X falls, then scores on Y also falls
(d) A perfect linear relationship is where all the points on the scatterplot fall on a straight line

8. 290 people indicate their preference between five brands of energy drink:

Booster	Hypedog	Trigger	Rocket	Turbo
67	83	77	6	57

What are the expected frequencies for the cells?
(a) 57
(b) 58
(c) 290
(d) None of the above

9. An association of – 0.60 has been observed between the height and weight of a group of school children. How much of the variation in weight can be explained by the variation in height (and vice versa)?

(a) 60%
(b) 40%
(c) 36%
(d) 64%

10. The line of best fit:

(a) Minimises the distance between the observations and the regression line
(b) Is the best of all possible lines
(c) Maximises the association between X and Y
(d) All of these

11. In a linear regression analysis, the residuals are:

(a) Actual scores minus the predicted scores
(b) Actual scores plus the predicted scores
(c) The correlation between the actual and predicted scores
(d) The difference between actual and predicted scores

12. The line of best fit:

(a) Minimises the distance between the observations and the regression line
(b) Is the best of all possible lines
(c) Maximises the association between X and Y
(d) All of these

Consider the following data for Q17 to:

X	4	5	8	10	11	12	14	15	17	19
Y	39	23	28	19	26	16	16	14	7	10

The following calculations were derived:
$\sum X = 115$ $\sum Y = 198$ $\sum X^2 = 1{,}541$ $\sum Y^2 = 4{,}728$ $\sum XY = 1{,}960$

13. The value Pearson's correlation coefficient is:

(a) – 0.79
(b) – 0.82
(c) – 0.85
(d) – 0.88

14. The slope of the calculated regression line is:

(a) – 0.80
(b) – 1.10
(c) – 1.40
(d) – 1.70

15. The intercept of the calculated regression line is:

(a) 39
(b) 41
(c) 0.43
(d) 45

16. The predicted value of Y for an X value of 14 is:

(a) 13
(b) 14
(c) 15
(d) 16

MCQ Solutions

1. (c)	6. (d)	11. (a)	16. (c)
2. (a)	7. (c)	12. (d)	
3. (a)	8. (b)	13. (d)	
4. (c)	9. (c)	14. (d)	
5. (a)	10. (d)	15. (a)	

9.8 IBM SPSS Statistics 20 Instructions

1. **Suppose that we wish to know the value of Pearson's correlation coefficient and the associated probability. Use the data from Example 1 in Chapter 9**

Step 1 – Open *IBM SPSS Statistics 20* select *Type in data* and click *OK*. Click *Variable View* at the bottom left corner and enter the variables *Aptitude Score* and *Performance Score (using the data from the first example in Chapter 9.* Click *Analyse* and then *Correlate* and select *Bivariate*.

Data Editor

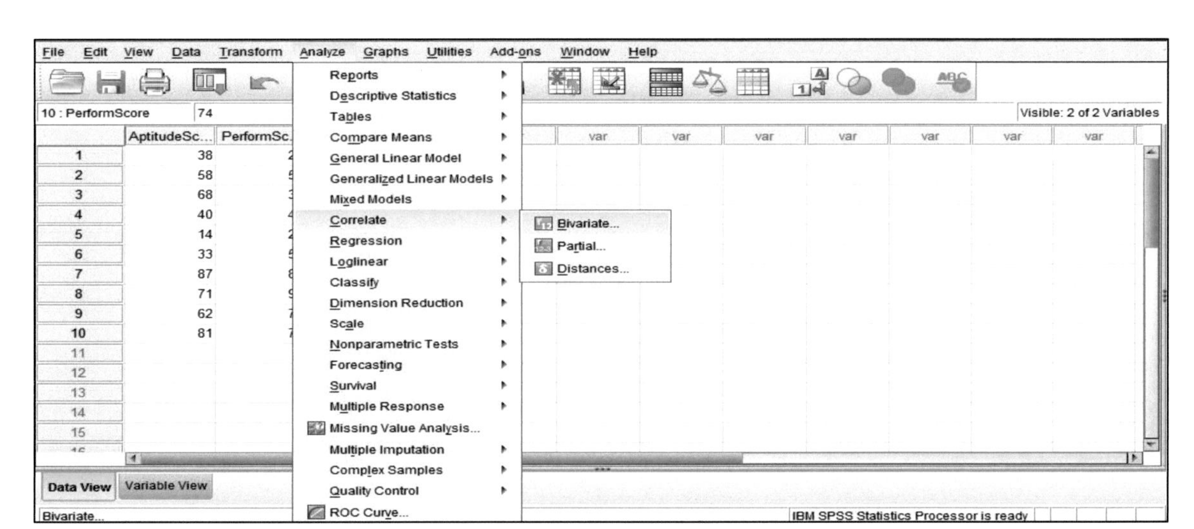

Step 2 – In the dialogue box *Bivariate Correlations*, place the two variables into the *Variables* box. Ensure that *Pearson and two tailed* is selected. Then click *OK*.

Data Editor

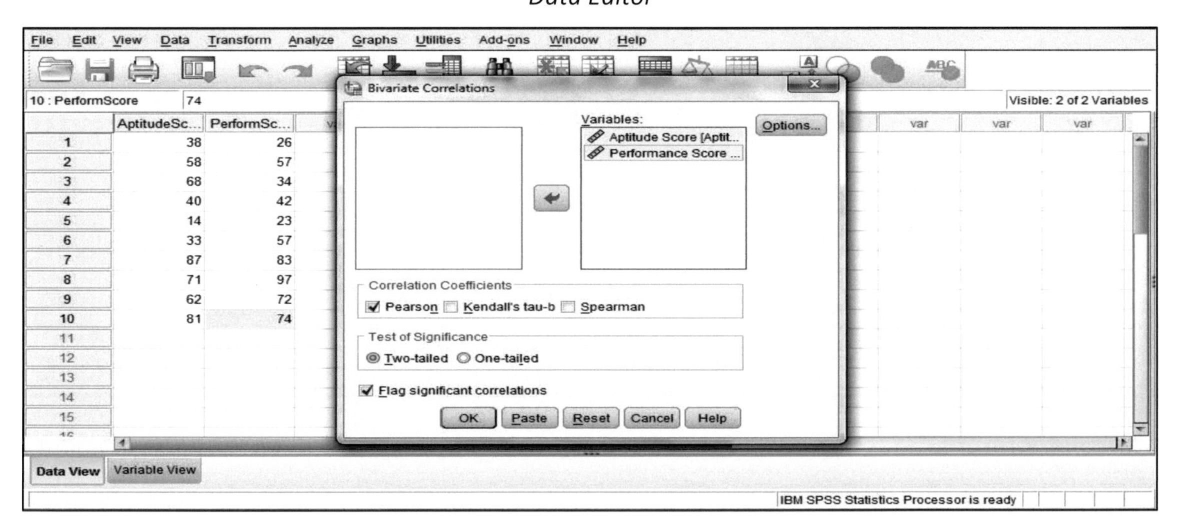

IBM SPSS Statistics 20 Output

Correlations

		Aptitude Score	Performance Score
Aptitude Score	Pearson Correlation	1	.737*
	Sig. (2-tailed)		.015
	N	10	10
Performance Score	Pearson Correlation	.737*	1
	Sig. (2-tailed)	.015	
	N	10	10

*. Correlation is significant at the 0.05 level (2-tailed).

2. **Suppose that we wish to know the value of Spearman's correlation coefficient and the associated probability. Use the data from Example 2 in Chapter 9.**

Step 1 – Open *IBM SPSS Statistics 20* select *Type in data* and click *OK*. Click *Variable View* at the bottom left corner and enter the variables *World Ranking* and *Placing at a recent major (using the data from the second example in Chapter 9.* Click *Analyse* and then *Correlate* and select *Bivariate*.

Data Editor

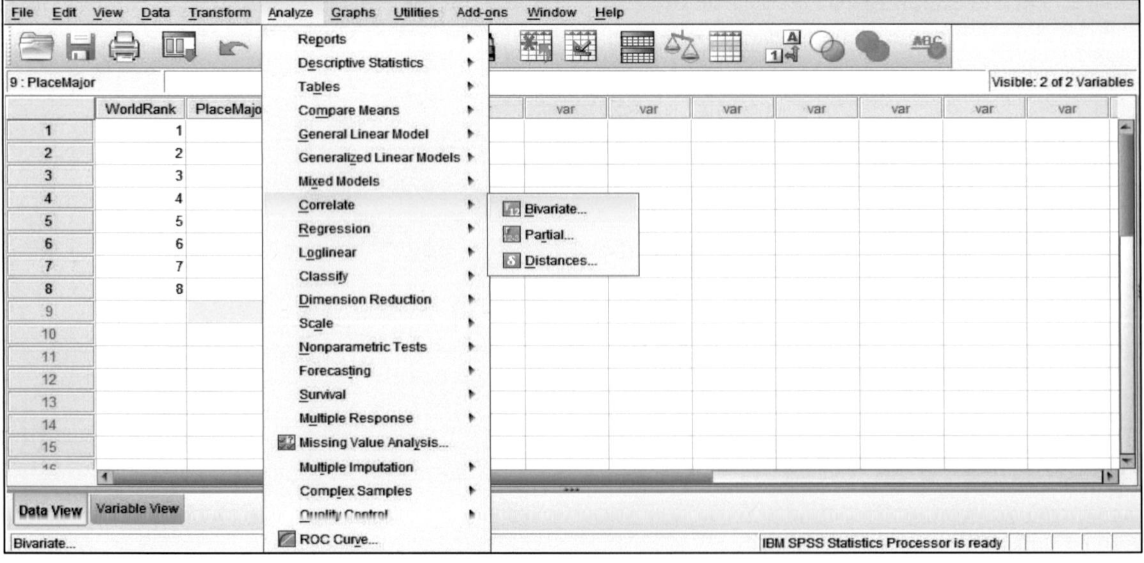

Step 2 – In the dialogue box *Bivariate Correlations*, place the two variables into the *Variables* box. Ensure that *Spearman and two tailed* is selected. Then click *OK*.

Data Editor

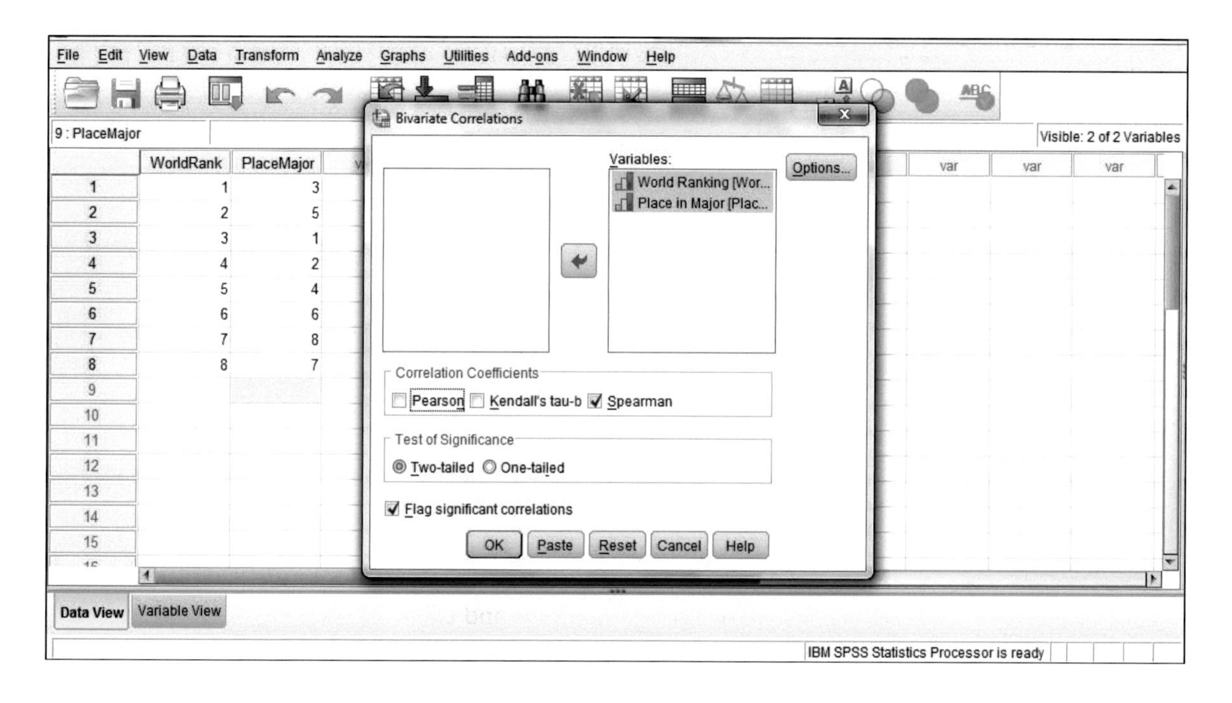

Correlations

			World Ranking	Place in Major
Spearman's rho	World Ranking	Correlation Coefficient	1.000	.714*
		Sig. (2-tailed)	.	.047
		N	8	8
	Place in Major	Correlation Coefficient	.714*	1.000
		Sig. (2-tailed)	.047	.
		N	8	8

*. Correlation is significant at the 0.05 level (2-tailed).

3. Derive the *line of best fit* for the data from Example 3 in Chapter 9

Step 1 – Open *IBM SPSS Statistics 20* select *Type in data* and click *OK*. Click *Variable View* at the bottom left corner and enter the variables *X* and *Y (using the data from the third example in Chapter 9.* Click *Graphs* and then *Legacy Dialogs* and then *ScatterDot*.

Data Editor

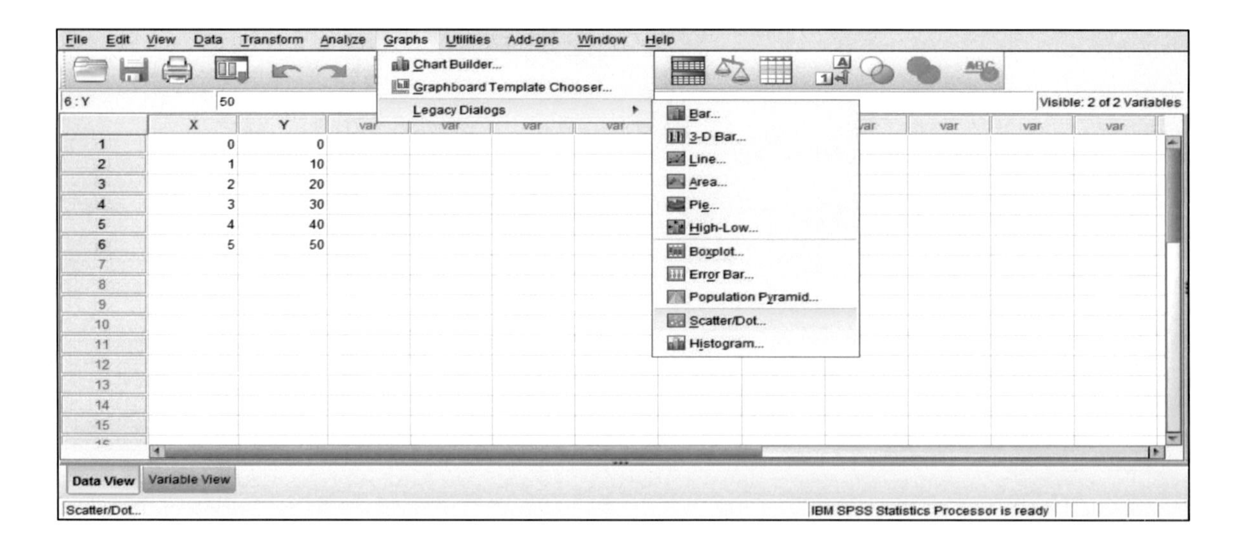

Step 2 – Ensure that *Simple Scatter* is highlighted, then click *Define*.

Data Editor

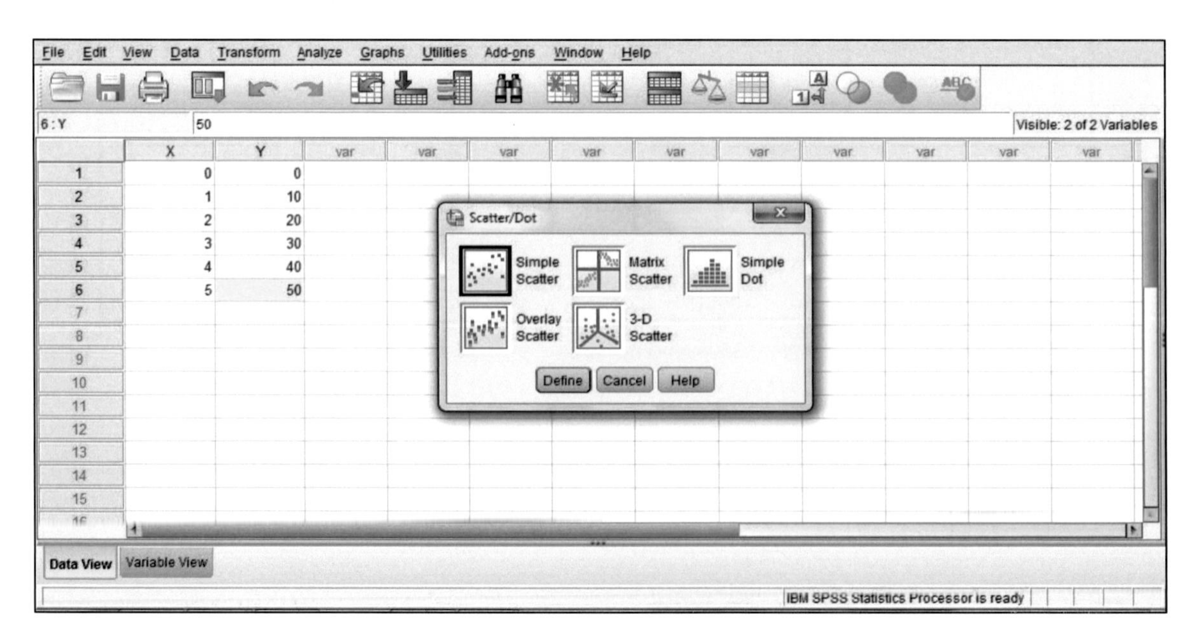

Step 3 – Move the variable X into the *X Axis* cell and move the variable Y into the *Y Axis* cell, then click *OK*

Data Editor

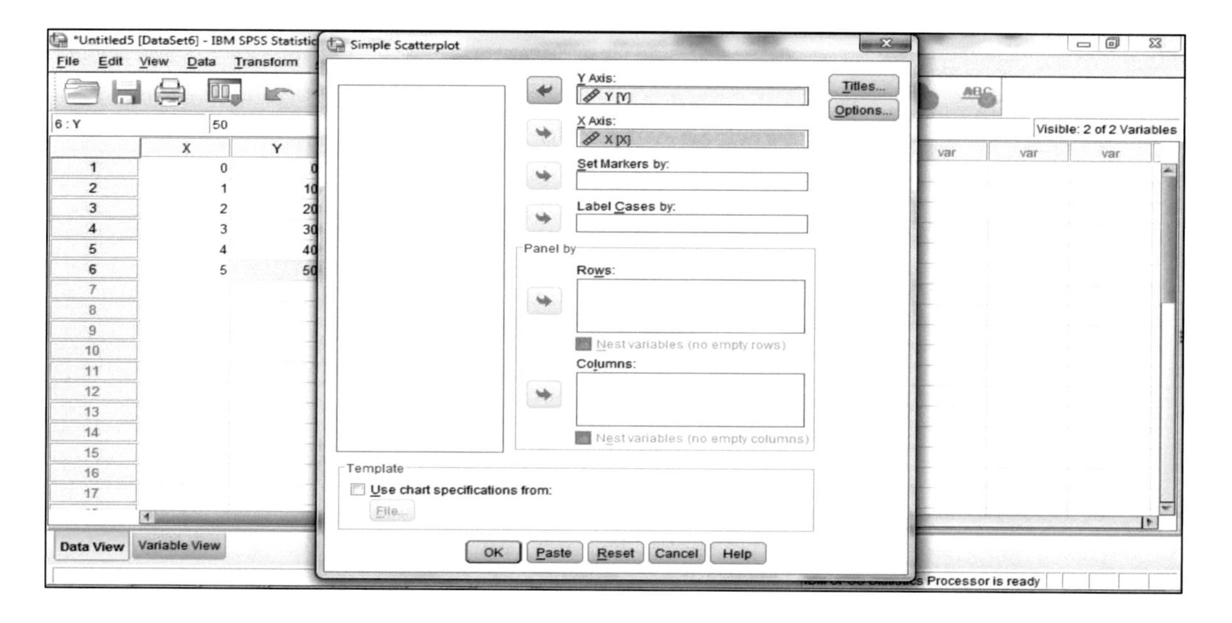

Step 4 – Double click on the scatter graph and select *Options* and then *Reference line from Equation.*

Data Editor

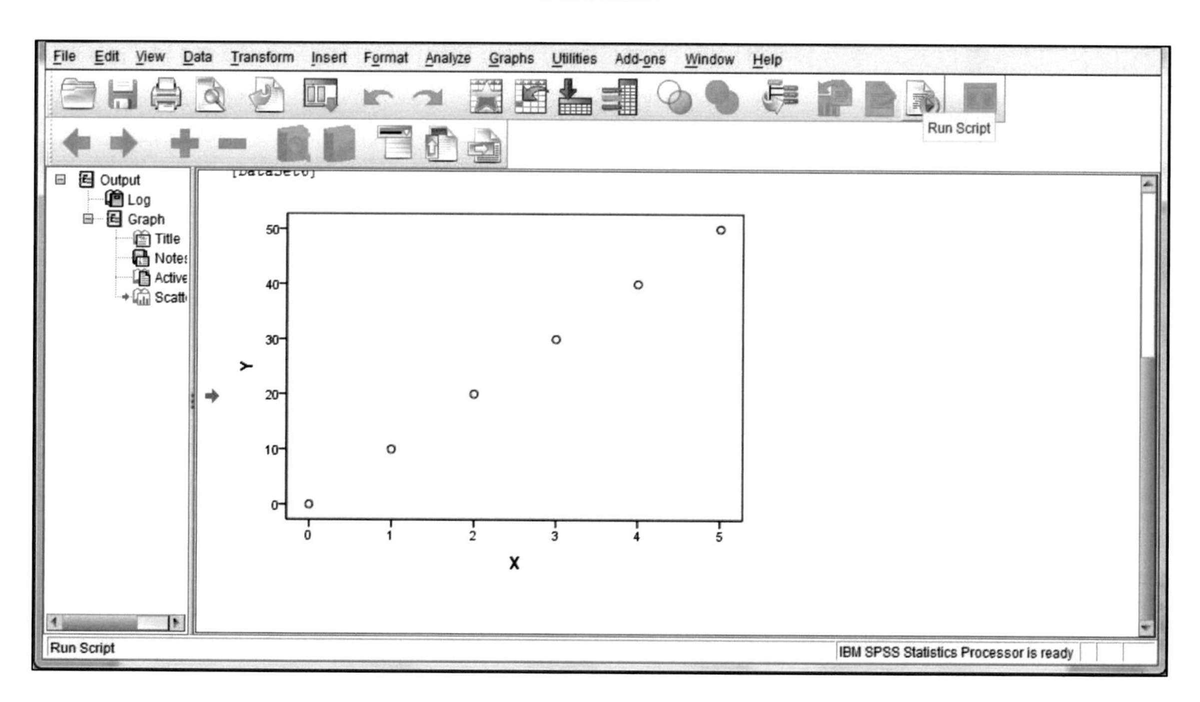

Data Editor

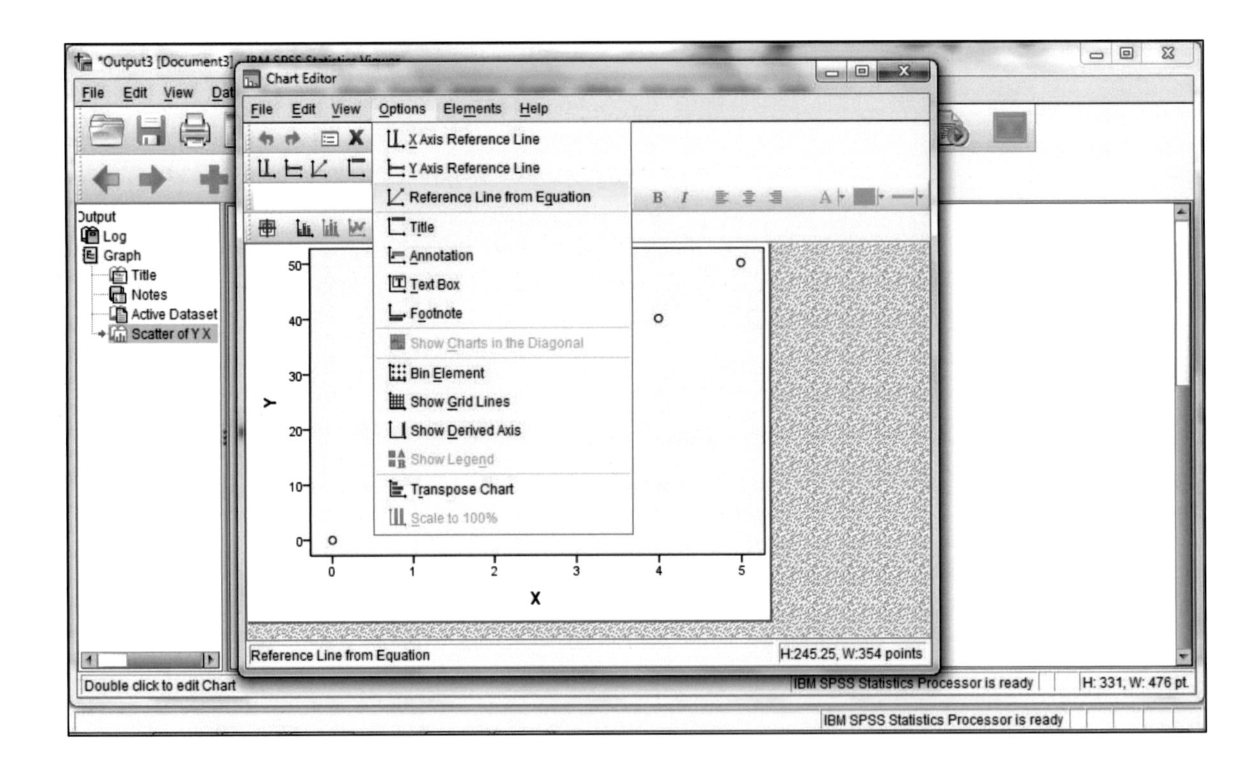

Data Editor

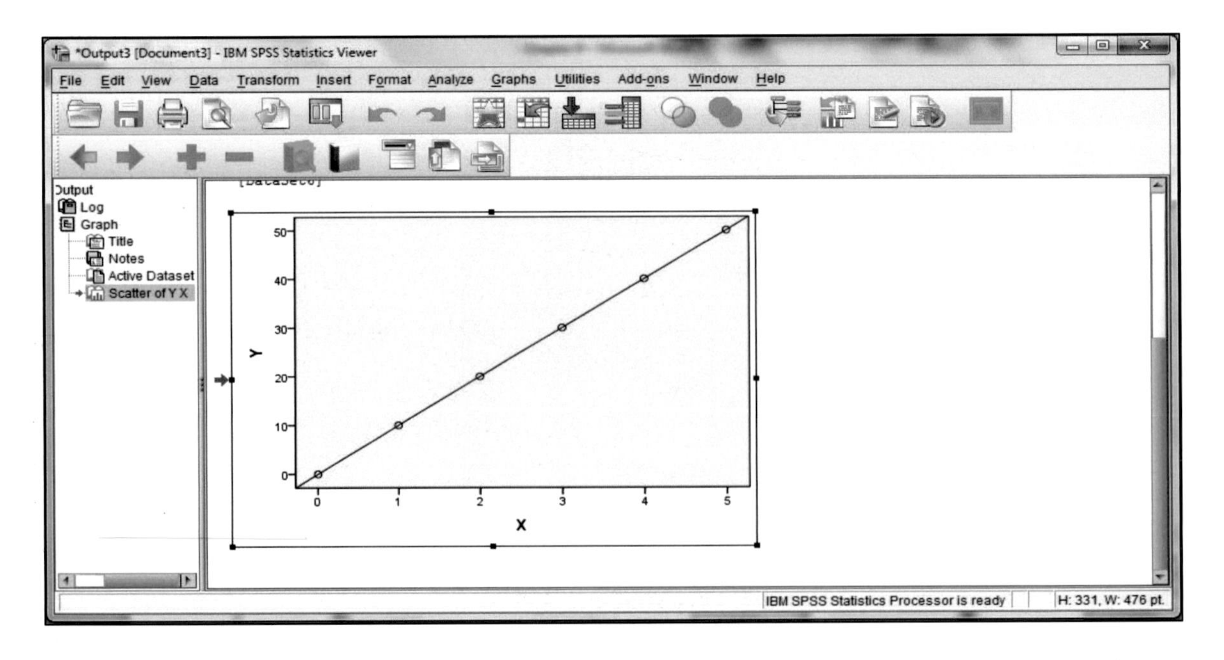

4. **Derive the values for *a* and *b* in the *line of best fit*. Use the data from Example 4 in Chapter 9**

Step 1 – Select *Analyse* then Regression and then *Linear*

Data Editor

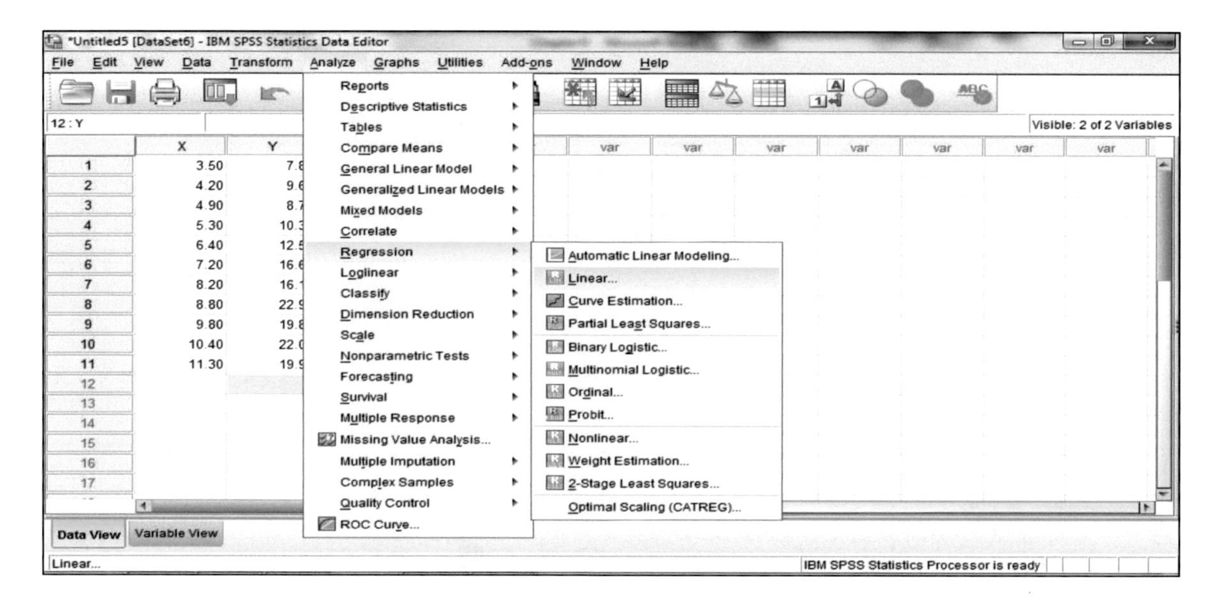

Step 2 – Place the variable X into the *Independent* cell and place the variable Y into the *Dependent* cell, then click *OK*

Data Editor

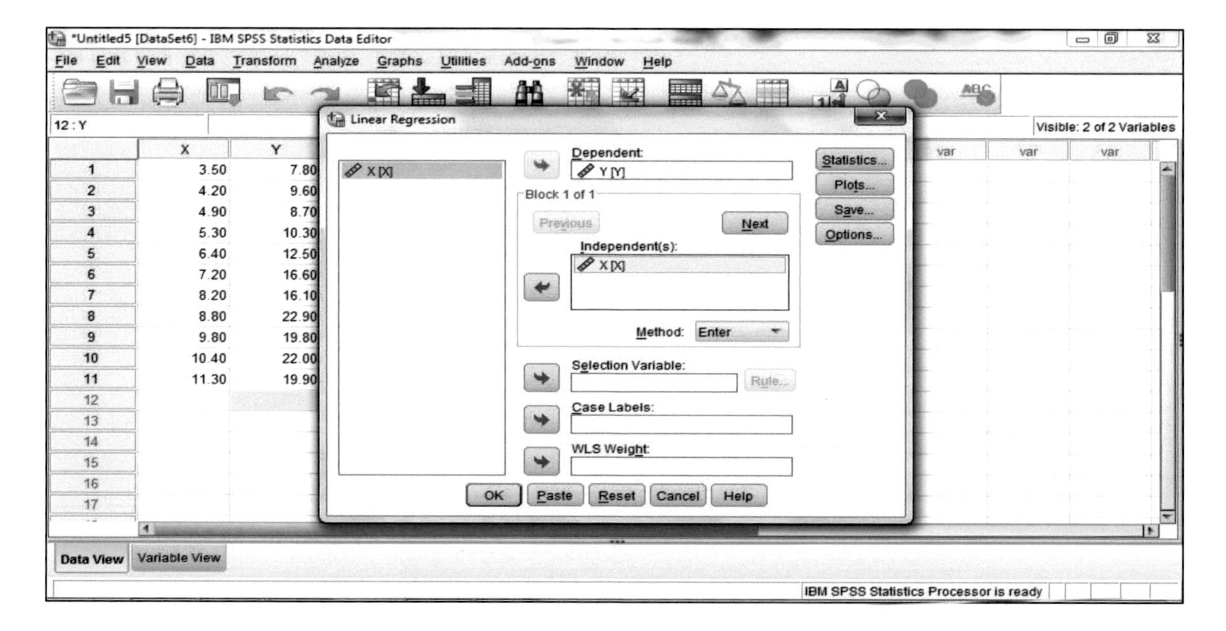

Model Summary

Model	R	R Square	Adjusted R Square	Std. Error of the Estimate
1	.931[a]	.866	.851	2.15241

a. Predictors: (Constant), X

ANOVA[a]

Model		Sum of Squares	df	Mean Square	F	Sig.
1	Regression	269.433	1	269.433	58.157	.000[b]
	Residual	41.696	9	4.633		
	Total	311.129	10			

a. Dependent Variable: Y

b. Predictors: (Constant), X

Coefficients[a]

Model		Unstandardized Coefficients		Standardized Coefficients	t	Sig.
		B	Std. Error	Beta		
1	(Constant)	.794	1.986		.400	.699
	X	1.968	.258	.931	7.626	.000

a. Dependent Variable: Y

Table 1 *Normal (z) Distribution (z tables)*

0.0250

z → 0 1.96

z	.00	.01	.02	.03	.04	.05	.06	.07	.08	.09
0.0	.5000	.4960	.4920	.4880	.4840	.4801	.4761	.4721	.4681	.4641
0.1	.4602	.4562	.4522	.4483	.4443	.4404	.4364	.4325	.4286	.4247
0.2	.4207	.4168	.4129	.4090	.4052	.4013	.3974	.3936	.3897	.3859
0.3	.3821	.3783	.3745	.3707	.3669	.3632	.3594	.3557	.3520	.3483
0.4	.3446	.3409	.3372	.3336	.3300	.3264	.3228	.3192	.3156	.3121
0.5	.3085	.3050	.3015	.2981	.2946	.2912	.2877	.2843	.2810	.2776
0.6	.2743	.2709	.2676	.2643	.2611	.2578	.2546	.2514	.2483	.2451
0.7	.2420	.2389	.2358	.2327	.2296	.2266	.2236	.2206	.2177	.2148
0.8	.2119	.2090	.2061	.2033	.2005	.1977	.1949	.1922	.1894	.1867
0.9	.1841	.1814	.1788	.1762	.1736	.1711	.1685	.1660	.1635	.1611
1.0	.1587	.1562	.1539	.1515	.1492	.1469	.1446	.1423	.1401	.1379
1.1	.1357	.1335	.1314	.1292	.1271	.1251	.1230	.1210	.1190	.1170
1.2	.1151	.1131	.1112	.1093	.1075	.1056	.1038	.1020	.1003	.0985
1.3	.0968	.0951	.0934	.0918	.0901	.0885	.0869	.0853	.0838	.0823
1.4	.0808	.0793	.0778	.0764	.0749	.0735	.0721	.0708	.0694	.0681
1.5	.0668	.0655	.0643	.0630	.0618	.0606	.0594	.0582	.0571	.0559
1.6	.0548	.0537	.0526	.0516	.0505	.0495	.0485	.0475	.0465	.0455
1.7	.0446	.0436	.0427	.0418	.0409	.0401	.0392	.0384	.0375	.0367
1.8	.0359	.0351	.0344	.0336	.0329	.0322	.0314	.0307	.0301	.0294
1.9	.0287	.0281	.0274	.0268	.0262	.0256	**.0250**	.0244	.0239	.0233
2.0	.0227	.0222	.0216	.0211	.0206	.0201	.0197	.0192	.0187	.0183
2.1	.0178	.0743	.0170	.0165	.0161	.0157	.0153	.0150	.0146	.0142
2.2	.0139	.0135	.0132	.0128	.0125	.0122	.0119	.0116	.0113	.0110
2.3	.0107	.0104	.0101	.0099	.0096	.0093	.0091	.0088	.0086	.0084
2.4	.0082	.0079	.0077	.0075	.0073	.0071	.0069	.0067	.0065	.0063
2.5	.0062	.0060	.0058	.0057	.0055	.0053	.0052	.0050	.0049	.0048

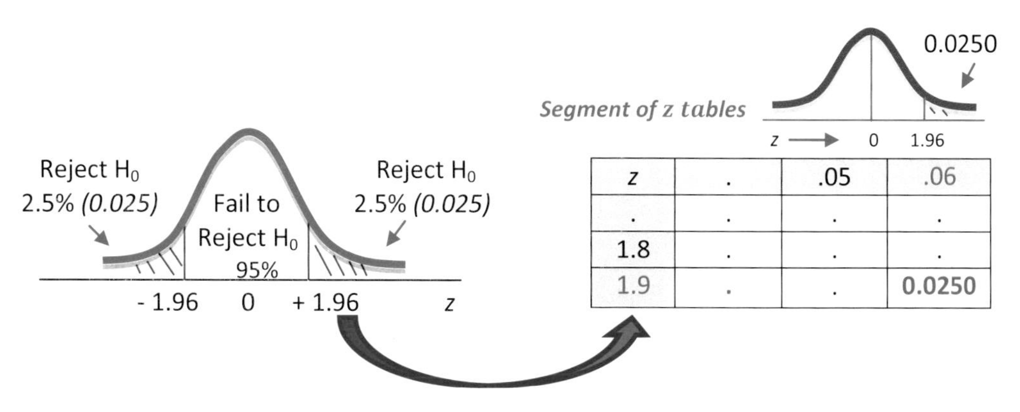

z	.	.05	.06
.	.	.	.
1.8	.	.	.
1.9	.	.	**0.0250**

Table 2 *Student's (t) Distribution (t tables)*

α = .025

t → 0 $2.101_{df=18}$

	Select test type (one or two tail) then select the level of significance (α): e.g. α = 0.05					
p_{values} *1-tail* →	0.10	0.05	0.025	0.01	0.005	0.0005
p_{values} *2-tail* →	0.20	0.10	**0.05**	0.02	0.01	0.001
1 *df*	3.078	6.314	12.706	31.821	63.657	636.619
2 *df*	1.886	2.920	4.303	6.965	9.925	31.599
3 *df*	1.638	2.353	3.182	4.541	5.841	12.924
4 *df*	1.533	2.132	2.776	3.747	4.604	8.610
5 *df*	1.476	2.015	2.571	3.365	4.032	6.869
6 *df*	1.440	1.943	2.447	3.143	3.707	5.959
7 *df*	1.415	1.895	2.365	2.896	3.355	5.041
8 *df*	1.397	1.860	2.306	2.896	3.355	5.041
9 *df*	1.383	1.833	2.262	2.821	3.250	4.781
10 *df*	1.372	1.812	2.228	2.764	3.169	4.587
11 *df*	1.363	1.796	2.201	2.718	3.106	4.437
12 *df*	1.356	1.782	2.179	2.681	3.055	4.318
13 *df*	1.350	1.771	2.160	2.650	3.012	4.221
14 *df*	1.345	1.761	2.145	2.624	2.977	4.140
15 *df*	1.341	1.753	2.131	2.602	2.947	4.073
16 *df*	1.337	1.746	2.120	2.583	2.921	4.015
17 *df*	1.333	1.740	2.110	2.567	2.898	3.965
18 *df*	1.330	1.734	**2.101**	2.552	2.878	3.922
19 *df*	1.328	1.729	2.093	2.539	2.861	3.883
20 *df*	1.325	1.725	2.086	2.528	2.845	3.850
21 *df*	1.323	1.721	2.080	2.518	2.831	3.819
22 *df*	1.321	1.717	2.074	2.508	2.819	3.792
23 *df*	1.319	1.714	2.069	2.500	2.807	3.768
24 *df*	1.318	1.711	2.064	2.492	2.797	3.745
25 *df*	1.316	1.708	2.060	2.485	2.787	3.725
26 *df*	1.315	1.706	2.056	2.479	2.779	3.707
27 *df*	1.314	1.703	2.052	2.473	2.771	3.690
28 *df*	1.313	1.701	2.048	2.467	2.763	3.674
29 *df*	1.311	1.699	2.045	2.462	2.756	3.659
30 *df*	1.310	1.697	2.042	2.457	2.750	3.646

Suppose the test is a two tailed test and the chosen level of significance for the test is 5% or α = 0.05 and the degrees of freedom is 18. The critical value for the test is 2.101.

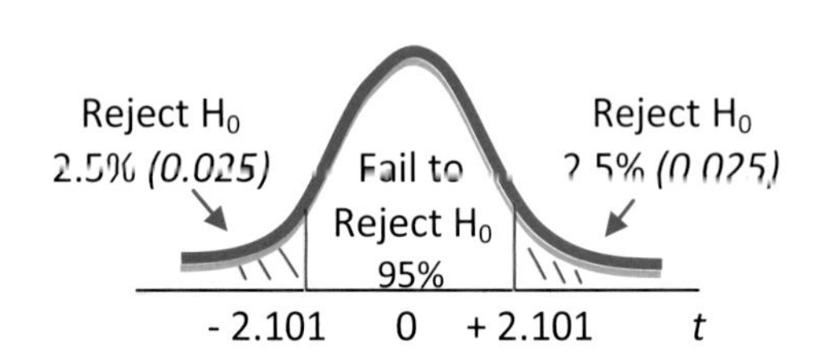

Segment of the t tables

α = .025

t → 0 $2.101_{df=18}$

p_{val} *1-tail*	$t_{0.100}$	$t_{0.050}$	$t_{0.025}$
p_{val} *2 tail*	$t_{0.200}$	$t_{0.100}$	$t_{0.050}$
df = 17	.	.	.
df = 18	.	1.734	**2.101**

Table 3 *Chi-square (χ^2) Distribution*

	Select one of these as a level of significance (α): e.g. α = 0.05									
p values ⟹	.	0.90	.	.		0.10	**0.05**	0.025	0.01	0.005
1 *df*	.	0.015	.	.		2.705	3.841	5.023	6.634	7.879
2 *df*	.	0.210	.	.		4.605	5.991	7.377	9.210	10.596
3 *df*	.	0.584	.	.		6.251	7.814	9.348	11.344	12.838
4 *df*	.	0.063	.	.		7.779	9.487	11.143	12.276	14.860
5 *df*	.	1.610	.	.		9.263	11.070	12.832	15.085	16.749
6 *df*	.	2.204	.	.		10.644	12.591	14.449	16.811	18.547

Suppose that the level of significance for the test is selected at 5% or α = 0.05 and the degrees of freedom (df) is 3, then the critical value will be 7.814.

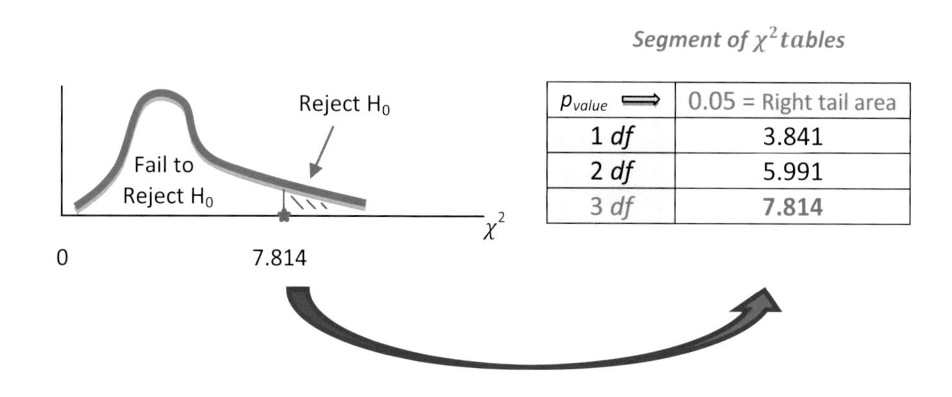

p_{value} ⟹	0.05 = Right tail area
1 *df*	3.841
2 *df*	5.991
3 *df*	**7.814**

Table 4 *Segments of the Binomial Distribution Table*

A multiple choice exam has five answers to each question (p = 0.20). If a student answers all questions randomly, what is the probability of getting four (x = 4) out of ten correct (n = 10)? Answer = .0881

a. *n = 10 repeated trials*

b. *You guess a correct answer (success) versus an incorrect answer (failure)*

c. *The probability of success on a single trial = p (success) =* $\frac{1}{5}$ *= 0.20 = p*

d. *Your choice in one trial is not influenced by a previous decision i.e. each trial is independent*

		p									
	X	.	.	.	.20	.25	.30	.35	.40	.45	.50
	0	.	.	.	.3277	.2373	.	.	.	.0503	.0313
	1	.	.	.	.4096	.3955	.	.	.	.2059	.1563
n = 5	2	.	.	.	.2048	.2637	.	.	.	.3369	.3125
	3	.	.	.	.0512	.0879	.	.	.	.2757	.3125
	4	.	.	.	.0064	.0146	.	.	.	.1128	.1563
	5	.	.	.	.0003	.0010	.	.	.	.0185	.0313

		p									
	X	.	.	.	.20	.25	.30	.35	.40	.45	.50
	0	.	.	.	.1074	.0563	.	.	.	.0025	.0010
	1	.	.	.	.2684	.1877	.	.	.	.0207	.0098
	2	.	.	.	.3020	.2816	.	.	.	.0763	.0439
	3	.	.	.	.2013	.2503	.	.	.	.1665	.1172
n = 10	4	.	.	.	.0881	.1460	.	.	.	.2384	.2051
	5	.	.	.	.0264	.0584	.	.	.	.2340	.2461
	6	-	.	.	.0055	.0162	.	.	.	.1596	.2051
	7	-	-	.	.0008	.0031	.	.	.	.0746	.1172
	8	-	-	-	.0001	.0004	.	.	.	.0229	.0439
	9	-	-	-	-	-	.	.	.	.0042	.0098
	10	-	-	-	-	-	-	-	.	.0003	.0010

		p									
	x	.	.	.	.20	.25	.30	.35	.40	.45	.50
	0	.	.	.	.0115	.0032	.	.	-	-	-
	1	.	.	.	.0576	.0211	.	.	.	.0001	-
	2	.	.	.	.1369	.0669	.	.	.	.0008	.0002
	3	.	.	.	.2054	.1339	.	.	.	.0040	.0011
	4	-	.	.	.2182	.1897	.	.	.	.0139	.0046
	5	-	.	.	.1746	.2023	.	.	.	.0365	.0148
	6	-	.	.	.1091	.1686	.	.	.	.0746	.0370
	7	-	-	.	.0545	.1124	.	.	.	.1221	.0739
	8	-	-	.	.0222	.0609	.	.	.	.1623	.1201
	9	-	-	.	.0074	.0271	.	.	.	.1771	.1602
n = 20	10	-	-	.	.0020	.0099	.	.	.	.1593	.1762
	11	-	-	-	.0005	.0030	.	.	.	.1185	.1602
	12	-	-	-	.0001	.0008	.	.	.	.0727	.1201
	13	-	-	-	-	.0002	.	.	.	.0366	.0739
	14	-	-	-	-	-	.	.	.	.0049	.0370
	15	-	-	-	-	-	-	.	.	.0013	.0148
	16	-	-	-	-	-	-	-	.	.0002	.0046
	17	-	-	-	-	-	-	-	-	-	.0011
	18	-	-	-	-	-	-	-	-	-	.0002
	19	-	-	-	-	-	-	-	-	-	-
	20	-	-	-	-	-	-	-	-	-	-

Table 5 ***A segment of Poisson Probabilities***

A business receives on average 3 complaints per day. What is the probability that the company will receive zero complaints tomorrow? = .0498

The probability that the company will receive zero complaints tomorrow i.e. p(X = 0). Since we have one day (one interval) then the mean = λ = 3. The mean = 3, the Interval = per day and the complaints are independent of each other.

	λ			
X	3	4	5	6
0	.0498	.0183	.0067	.0025
1	.1494	.0733	.0337	.0149
2	.2240	.1465	.0842	.0446
3	.2240	.1954	.1404	.0892
4	.1680	.1954	.1755	.1339
5	.1008	.1563	.1755	.1606
6	.0504	.1042	.1462	.1606
7	.0216	.0595	.1044	.1377
8	.0081	.0298	.0653	.1033
9	.0027	.0132	.0363	.0688
10	.0008	.0053	.0181	.0413
11	.0002	.0019	.0082	.0225
12	.0001	.0006	.0034	.0113
13	-	.0002	.0013	.0052
14	-	.0001	.0005	.0022
15	-	-	.0002	.0009
16	-	-	-	.0003
17	-	-	-	.0001

References

Chapter 1

Blaikie, N. (2003) *Analysing Quantitative Data.* London: SAGE Publications.
Bryman, A. (2004) *Social Research Methods (2nd ed.).* Oxford: Oxford University Press.
Clason, D. L., Dormody, T.J. (1994) Analysing Data Measured by Individual Likert-Type Items. *Journal of Agricultural Education, Volume 35,* No. 4.
Cohen, S., Kamarck, T., Mermelstein, R. (1983) A global measure of perceived stress. *Journal of Health and Social Behaviour, 24, No.4,* 385-396.
Cohen, L., Manion, L., Morrison, K. (2000) *Research Methods in Education (5th ed.).* London: RoutledgeFarmer.
Dancey, C.P., Reidy, J. (2004) *Statistics Without Maths for Psychology (3rd ed.).* Essex: Pearson Education Limited.
Goldstein, G., Hersen, M. (1984) *Handbook of Psychological Assessment.* New York: Pergamon Press.
Kinnear, P.R., Gray, C.D. (2011) *IBM SPSS Statistics 18 Made Simple (3rd ed.).* East Sussex: Psychology Press.
Huff, D. (1973) *How to lie with statistics.* Pelican Books.
Lind, D.A., Marchal, W.G., Mason, R.D. (2002) *Statistical Techniques in Business & Economics (11th ed.).* New York: McGraw-Hill Irwin.
Nieuwenhuis, G. (2009) *Statistical Methods for Business and Economics.* Berkshire: McGraw-Hill Education.
Runyon, R.P., Haber, A. (1976) *Fundamentals of Behavioural Statistics (3rd ed.).* USA: Addison-Wesley.

Chapter 2

Blaine, D. (2003) *Mysterious Stranger.* London: Pan Macmillan Ltd.
Cook, E. T. (1913) The life of Florence Nightingale. London: Macmillan
Groebner, D.F., Shannon, P.W. (1985) *Business Statistics: A Decision-Making Approach (2nd ed.).* Columbus OH: Merrill.
Kinnear, P.R., Gray, C.D. (2011) *IBM SPSS Statistics 18 Made Simple (3rd ed.).* East Sussex: Psychology Press.
Rehmeyer, J. (2008) Florence Nightingale: The passionate statistician. Available: http://www.sciencenews.org/view/generic/id/38937
Runyon, R.P., Haber, A. (1976) *Fundamentals of Behavioural Statistics (3rd ed.).* USA: Addison-Wesley.

Chapter 3

Balanda, K. P., MacGillivray. H. L. (1995) Measuring Skewness with Respect to the Mode. *The American Statistician, 49,* 34-38.
Conover, W.J. (1999) *Practical nonparametric statistics (3rd ed.).* John Wiley & Sons, Inc.
Doane, D.P., Seward. L.E. (2011) Measuring Skewness: A Forgotten Statistic?. *Journal of Statistics Education, Volume 19, Number 2.*
Dufour, J.M., Farhat. A., Gardiol. L., Khalaf. L. (1998) Simulation-based Finite Sample Normality Tests in Linear Regressions. *Econometrics Journal, Vol. 1,* 154-173.

Horswell, R. L., Looney. S.W. (1993) Diagnostic Limitations of Skewness Coefficients in Assessing Departures from Univariate and Multivariate Normality. *Communications in Statistics: Simulation and Computation, 22*, 437-459.
Keskin, S. (2006) Comparison of Several Univariate Normality Tests Regarding Type 1 Error Rate and Power of the Test in Simulation based Small Samples. *Journal of Applied science Research 2(5). 296-300.*
Mendes, M., Pala. A. (2003) Type 1 Error Rate and Power of Three Normality Tests. *Pakistan Journal of Information and Technology 2(2),* 135-139.
Pallant, Julie. (2005) *SPSS Survival Manual (2nd ed.).* Berkshire: Open University Press, McGraw-Hill Education.
Razali, N.M., Wah. (2011) Power comparisons of Shapiro-Wilk, Kolmogorov-Smirnov, Lilliefors and Anderson-Darling tests. *Journal of Statistical Modeling and Analytics. Vol.2 No. 1, 21-33.*
Tabachnick, B., Fidell, L.S. (2005) *Using Multivariate Statistics (5th ed.).* Boston: Allyn & Bacon (Pearson International Edition).

Chapter 5

Berry, G. (1986) Statistical Significance and Confidence intervals. *Medical Journal of Australia: 144;* 618 - 19.
Cohen, J. (1992) A Power Primer. *Available: http://www.idi.ntnu.no/grupper/su/publ/ese/cohen-powerprimer92.pdf. Washington D. C.: American Psychological Association*
Erdfelder, E., Faul, F., & Buchner, A. (1996). GPOWER: A general power analysis program. *Behaviour Research Methods, Instruments, and Computers, 28, 1 – 11.*
Faul, F., Erdfeldfer, E., Lang, A. G., and Buchner, A. (2007). G*Power 3: A flexible statistical power analysis program for the social, behavioural and biomedical sciences. *Behaviour Research Methods, 39, 175-91.*
Gardner, MJ, Altman. D.G. (1986) Confidence intervals rather than p values: estimation rather than hypothesis testing. *British Medical Journal; 292;* 746 – 750.
Peat, J. Barton, B. Elliot, E. (2008) *Statistics Workbook for Evidence – based Health Care.* John Wiley & Sons, Inc.
Wikipedia (2012) Silver Blaze, *Available:* http://en.wikipedia.org/wiki/Silver_Blaze *[Accessed 6 Jan 2013, 10h50]*

Chapter 7

Aczel, Amir, D. (2002) *Complete Business statistics (5th ed.)* McGrath-Hill Irwin.

Chapter 8

Cohen, J. (1988) *Statistical power analysis for the behavioural sciences (2nd ed.).* Hillsdale, NJ: Erlbaum.
Conover, W.J. (1999) *Practical nonparametric statistics (3rd ed.).* John Wiley & Sons, Inc.
Everitt, B.S. (1980) *The Analysis of Contingency Tables*. London: Chapman and Hall Ltd.
Howell, DC. (2007) *Statistical Methods for psychology (6th ed.).* Belmont, CA: Thomson/Wadsworth.
Peat, J. Barton, B. Elliot, E. (2008) *Statistics Workbook for Evidence – based Health Care.* John Wiley & Sons, Inc.
Streiner, D.L. (2002) Breaking up is hard to do: the heartbreak of dichotomizing continuous data. *Canadian Journal of Psychiatry, 47:* 262-6.
Volker, M.A. (2006) Psychology in the schools. *Vol. 43(6)*

Index

I

N

O

P

Q

R

S

T

V

Y

Z

For additional resources

www.essentialstatistics.com